PEARSON   ALWAYS LEARNING

Financial Risk Manager (FRM®) Exam Part I

Quantitative Analysis

Sixth Custom Edition for
Global Association of Risk Professionals
2016

GARP | Global Association of Risk Professionals

Excerpts taken from:

Introduction to Econometrics, Brief Edition by James H. Stock and Mark W. Watson

Options, Futures, and Other Derivatives, Ninth Edition by John C. Hull

Pearson Learning Solutions, 330 Hudson Street, New York, New York 10013
A Pearson Education Company
www.pearsoned.com

Printed in the United States of America

3 16

000200010272005412

AM/KE

ISBN 10: 1-323-30854-7
ISBN 13: 978-1-323-30854-7

Contents

Contents

CHAPTER 7 LINEAR REGRESSION WITH ONE REGRESSOR 83

CHAPTER 8 REGRESSION WITH A SINGLE REGRESSOR 101

2016 FRM Committee Members

Probabilities

Learning Objectives

Candidates, after completing this reading, should be able to:

- Describe and distinguish between continuous and discrete random variables.
- Define and distinguish between the probability density function, the cumulative distribution function, and the inverse cumulative distribution function.
- Calculate the probability of an event given a discrete probability function.

- Distinguish between independent and mutually exclusive events.
- Define joint probability, describe a probability matrix, and calculate joint probabilities using probability matrices.
- Define and calculate a conditional probability, and distinguish between conditional and unconditional probabilities.

Excerpt is Chapter 2 of Mathematics and Statistics for Financial Risk Management, *Second Edition, by Michael B. Miller.*

In this chapter we explore the application of probabilities to risk management. We also introduce basic terminology and notations that will be used throughout the rest of this book.

DISCRETE RANDOM VARIABLES

The concept of probability is central to risk management. Many concepts associated with probability are deceptively simple. The basics are easy, but there are many potential pitfalls.

In this chapter, we will be working with both discrete and continuous random variables. Discrete random variables can take on only a countable number of values—for example, a coin, which can be only heads or tails, or a bond, which can have only one of several letter ratings (AAA, AA, A, BBB, etc.). Assume we have a discrete random variable X, which can take various values, x_i. Further assume that the probability of any given x_i occurring is p_i. We write:

$$P[X = x_i] = p_i \text{ s.t. } x_i \in \{x_1, x_2, \dots, x_n\} \tag{1.1}$$

where $P[\cdot]$ is our probability operator.[1]

An important property of a random variable is that the sum of all the probabilities must equal one. In other words, the probability of any event occurring must equal one. Something has to happen. Using our current notation, we have:

$$\sum_{i=1}^{n} p_i = 1 \tag{1.2}$$

CONTINUOUS RANDOM VARIABLES

In contrast to a discrete random variable, a continuous random variable can take on any value within a given range. A good example of a continuous random variable is the return of a stock index. If the level of the index can be any real number between zero and infinity, then the return of the index can be any real number greater than −1.

Even if the range that the continuous variable occupies is finite, the number of values that it can take is infinite. For

this reason, for a continuous variable, the probability of any *specific* value occurring is zero.

Even though we cannot talk about the probability of a specific value occurring, we can talk about the probability of a variable being within a certain range. Take, for example, the return on a stock market index over the next year. We can talk about the probability of the index return being between 6% and 7%, but talking about the probability of the return being exactly 6.001% is meaningless. Between 6% and 7% there are an infinite number of possible values. The probability of anyone of those infinite values occurring is zero.

For a continuous random variable X, then, we can write:

$$P[r_1 < X < r_2] = p \tag{1.3}$$

which states that the probability of our random variable, X, being between r_1 and r_2 is equal to p.

Probability Density Functions

For a continuous random variable, the probability of a specific event occurring is not well defined, but some events are still more likely to occur than others. Using annual stock market returns as an example, if we look at 50 years of data, we might notice that there are more data points between 0% and 10% than there are between 10% and 20%. That is, the density of points between 0% and 10% is higher than the density of points between 10% and 20%.

For a continuous random variable we can define a probability density function (PDF), which tells us the likelihood of outcomes occurring between any two points. Given our random variable, X, with a probability p of being between r_1 and r_2, we can define our density function, $f(x)$, such that:

$$\int_{r_1}^{r_2} f(x)dx = p \tag{1.4}$$

The probability density function is often referred to as the probability distribution function. Both terms are correct, and, conveniently, both can be abbreviated PDF.

As with discrete random variables, the probability of any value occurring must be one:

$$\int_{r_{min}}^{r_{max}} f(x)dx = 1 \tag{1.5}$$

where r_{min} and r_{max} define the lower and upper bounds of $f(x)$.

---

[1] "s.t." is shorthand for "such that". The final term indicates that x_i is a member of a set that includes n possible values, $x_1, x_2, \dots, x_n$. You could read the full equation as: "The probability that X equals x_i is equal to p_i, such that x_i is a member of the set $x_1, x_2,$ to x_n."

Example 1.1

Question:

Define the probability density function for the price of a zero coupon bond with a notional value of $10 as:

$$f(x) = \frac{x}{50} \text{ s.t. } 0 \le x \le 10$$

where x is the price of the bond. What is the probability that the price of the bond is between $8 and $9?

Answer:

First, note that this is a legitimate probability function. By integrating the PDF from its minimum to its maximum, we can show that the probability of any value occurring is indeed one:

$$\int_0^{10} \frac{x}{50} dx = \frac{1}{50} \int_0^{10} x\, dx = \frac{1}{50} \left[\frac{1}{2} x^2 \right]_0^{10} = \frac{1}{100}(10^2 - 0^2) = 1$$

If we graph the function, as in Figure 1-1, we can also see that the area under the curve is one. Using simple geometry:

$$\text{Area of triangle} = \frac{1}{2} \cdot \text{Base} \cdot \text{Height} = \frac{1}{2} \cdot 10 \cdot 0.2 = 1$$

To answer the question, we simply integrate the probability density function between 8 and 9:

$$\int_8^9 \frac{x}{50} dx = \left[\frac{1}{100} x^2 \right]_8^9 = \frac{1}{100}(9^2 - 8^2) = \frac{17}{100} = 17\%$$

The probability of the price ending up between $8 and $9 is 17%.

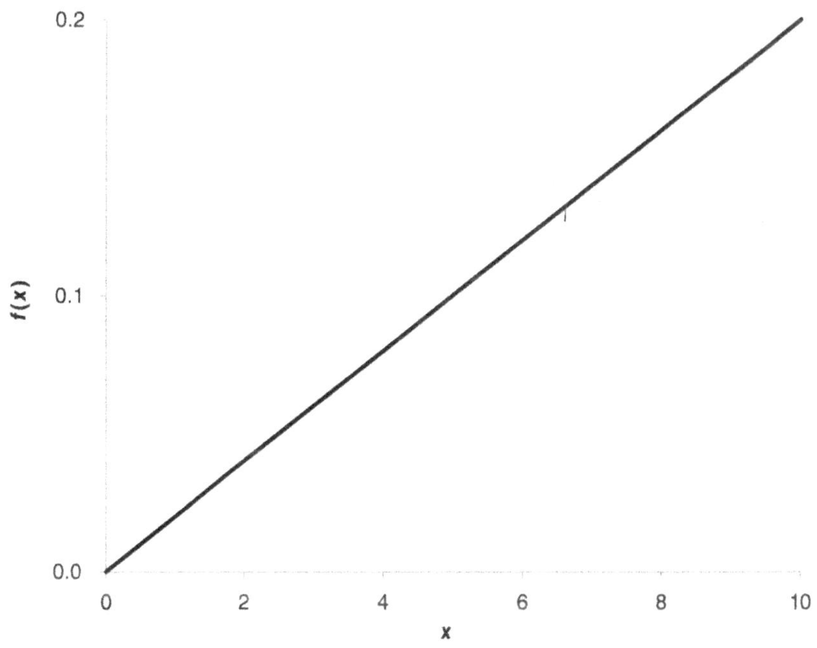

Cumulative Distribution Functions

Closely related to the concept of a probability density function is the concept of a cumulative distribution function or cumulative density function (both abbreviated CDF). A cumulative distribution function tells us the probability of a random variable being less than a certain value. The CDF can be found by integrating the probability density function from its lower bound. Traditionally, the cumulative distribution function is denoted by the capital letter of the corresponding density function. For a random variable X with a probability density function $f(x)$, then, the cumulative distribution function, $F(x)$, could be calculated as follows:

$$F(a) = \int_{-\infty}^{a} f(x)dx = P[X \le a] \tag{1.6}$$

As illustrated in Figure 1-2, the cumulative distribution function corresponds to the area under the probability density function, to the left of a.

By definition, the cumulative distribution function varies from 0 to 1 and is nondecreasing. At the minimum value of the probability density function, the CDF must be zero. There is no probability of the variable being less than the minimum. At the other end, all values are less than the maximum of the PDF. The probability is 100% (CDF = 1) that the random variable will be less than or equal to the maximum. In between, the function is nondecreasing. The reason that the CDF is nondecreasing is that, at a minimum, the probability of a random variable being between two points is zero. If the CDF of a random variable at 5 is 50%, then the lowest it could be at 6 is 50%, which would imply 0% probability of finding the variable between 5 and 6. There is no way the CDF at 6 could be less than the CDF at 5.

FIGURE 1-1 Probability density function.

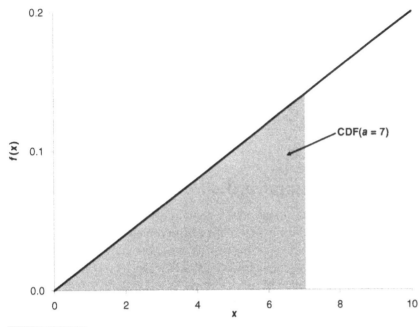

FIGURE 1-2 Relationship between cumulative distribution function and probability density.

Just as we can get the cumulative distribution from the probability density function by integrating, we can get the PDF from the CDF by taking the first derivative of the CDF:

$$f(x) = \frac{dF(x)}{dx} \qquad (1.7)$$

That the CDF is nondecreasing is another way of saying that the PDF cannot be negative.

If instead of wanting to know the probability that a random variable is less than a certain value, what if we want to know the probability that it is greater than a certain value, or between two values? We can handle both cases by adding and subtracting cumulative distribution functions. To find the probability that a variable is between two values, a and b, assuming b is greater than a, we subtract:

$$P[a < X \leq b] = \int_a^b f(x)dx = F(b) - F(a) \qquad (1.8)$$

To get the probability that a variable is greater than a certain value, we simply subtract from 1:

$$P[X > a] = 1 - F(a) \qquad (1.9)$$

This result can be obtained by substituting infinity for b in the previous equation, remembering that the CDF at infinity must be 1.

Example 1.2

Question:

Calculate the cumulative distribution function for the probability density function from the previous problem:

$$f(x) = \frac{x}{50} \text{ s.t. } 0 \leq x \leq 10 \qquad (1.10)$$

Then answer the previous problem: What is the probability that the price of the bond is between $8 and $9?

Answer:

The CDF can be found by integrating the PDF:

$$F(a) = \int_0^a f(x)dx = \int_0^a \frac{x}{50} dx$$

$$= \frac{1}{50} \int_0^a xdx = \frac{1}{50}\left[\frac{1}{2}x^2\right]_0^a = \frac{a^2}{100}$$

To get the answer to the question, we simply evaluate the CDF at $8 and $9 and subtract:

$$P[\$8 < x \leq \$9] = F(9) - F(8)$$

$$= \frac{9^2}{100} - \frac{8^2}{100} = \frac{81}{100} - \frac{64}{100} = \frac{17}{100} = 17\%$$

As before, the probability of the price ending up between $8 and $9 is 17%.

Inverse Cumulative Distribution Functions

The inverse of the cumulative distribution can also be useful. For example, we might want to know that there is a 5% probability that a given equity index will return less than −10.6%, or that there is a 1% probability of interest rates increasing by more than 2% over a month.

More formally, if $F(a)$ is a cumulative distribution function, then we define $F^{-1}(p)$, the inverse cumulative distribution, as follows:

$$F(a) = p \Leftrightarrow F^{-1}(p) = a \text{ s.t. } 0 \leq p \leq 1 \qquad (1.11)$$

As we will see in Chapter 3, while some popular distributions have very simple inverse cumulative distribution functions, for other distributions no explicit inverse exists.

Example 1.3

Question:

Given the cumulative distribution from the previous sample problem:

$$F(a) = \frac{a^2}{100} \text{ s.t. } 0 \le a \le 10$$

Calculate the inverse cumulative distribution function. Find the value of a such that 25% of the distribution is less than or equal to a.

Answer:

We have:

$$F(a) = p = \frac{a^2}{100}$$

Solving for p:

$$a = 10\sqrt{p}$$

Therefore, the inverse CDF is:

$$F^{-1}(p) = 10\sqrt{p}$$

We can quickly check that $p = 0$ and $p = 1$, return 0 and 10, the minimum and maximum of the distribution. For $p = 25\%$ we have:

$$F^{-1}(0.25) = 10\sqrt{0.25} = 10 \cdot 0.5 = 5$$

So 25% of the distribution is less than or equal to 5.

MUTUALLY EXCLUSIVE EVENTS

For a given random variable, the probability of any of two mutually exclusive events occurring is just the sum of their individual probabilities. In statistics notation, we can write:

$$P[A \cup B] = P[A] + P[B] \qquad \textbf{(1.12)}$$

where $[A \cup B]$ is the union of A and B. This is the probability of either *A or B* occurring. This is true only of mutually exclusive events.

This is a very simple rule, but, as mentioned at the beginning of the chapter, probability can be deceptively simple, and this property is easy to confuse. The confusion stems from the fact that *and* is synonymous with addition. If you say it this way, then the probability that *A or B* occurs is equal to the probability of *A and* the probability of *B*. It is not terribly difficult, but you can see where this could lead to a mistake.

This property of mutually exclusive events can be extended to any number of events. The probability that any of *n* mutually exclusive events occurs is simply the sum of the probabilities of those *n* events.

Example 1.4

Question:

Calculate the probability that a stock return is either below −10% or above 10%, given:

$$P[R < -10\%] = 14\%$$
$$P[R > +10\%] = 17\%$$

Answer:

Note that the two events are mutually exclusive; the return cannot be below −10% and above 10% at the same time. The answer is: 14% + 17% = 31 %.

INDEPENDENT EVENTS

In the preceding example, we were talking about one random variable and two mutually exclusive events, but what happens when we have more than one random variable? What is the probability that it rains tomorrow *and* the return on stock XYZ is greater than 5%? The answer depends crucially on whether the two random variables influence each other. If the outcome of one random variable is not influenced by the outcome of the other random variable, then we say those variables are independent. *If* stock market returns are independent of the weather, then the stock market should be just as likely to be up on rainy days as it is on sunny days.

Assuming that the stock market and the weather are independent random variables, then the probability of the market being up and rain is just the product of the probabilities of the two events occurring individually. We can write this as follows:

$$P[\text{rain and market up}] = P[\text{rain} \cap \text{market up}]$$
$$= P[\text{rain}] \cdot P[\text{market up}] \qquad \textbf{(1.13)}$$

We often refer to the probability of two events occurring together as their joint probability.

Example 1.5

Question:

According to the most recent weather forecast, there is a 20% chance of rain tomorrow. The probability that stock

XYZ returns more than 5% on any given day is 40%. The two events are independent. What is the probability that it rains and stock XYZ returns more than 5% tomorrow?

Answer:

Since the two events are independent, the probability that it rains and stock XYZ returns more than 5% is just the product of the two probabilities. The answer is: 20% x 40% = 8%.

PROBABILITY MATRICES

When dealing with the joint probabilities of two variables, it is often convenient to summarize the various probabilities in a probability matrix or probability table. For example, pretend we are investigating a company that has issued both bonds and stock. The bonds can be downgraded, upgraded, or have no change in rating. The stock can either outperform the market or underperform the market.

In Figure 1-3, the probability of both the company's stock outperforming the market and the bonds being upgraded is 15%. Similarly, the probability of the stock underperforming the market and the bonds having no change in rating is 25%. We can also see the unconditional probabilities, by adding across a row or down a column. The probability of the bonds being upgraded, irrespective of the stock's performance, is: 15% + 5% = 20%. Similarly, the probability of the equity outperforming the market is: 15% + 30% + 5% = 50%. Importantly, all of the joint probabilities add to 100%. Given all the possible events, one of them must happen.

Example 1.6

Question:

You are investigating a second company. As with our previous example, the company has issued both bonds and

		Stock		
		Outperform	**Underperform**	
Bonds	Upgrade	15%	5%	20%
	No Change	30%	25%	55%
	Downgrade	5%	20%	25%
		50%	50%	100%

FIGURE 1-3   Bonds versus stock matrix.

		Stock		
		Outperform	**Underperform**	
Bonds	Upgrade	5%	0%	5%
	No Change	40%	Y	Z
	Downgrade	X	30%	35%
		50%	50%	100%

FIGURE 1-4   Bonds versus stock matrix.

stock. The bonds can be downgraded, upgraded, or have no change in rating. The stock can either outperform the market or underperform the market. You are given the probability matrix shown in Figure 1-4, which is missing three probabilities, X, Y, and Z. Calculate values for the missing probabilities.

Answer:

All of the values in the first column must add to 50%, the probability of the stock outperforming the market; therefore, we have:

$$5\% + 40\% + X = 50\%$$
$$X = 5\%$$

We can check our answer for X by summing across the third row: 5% + 30% = 35%.

Looking down the second column, we see that Y is equal to 20%:

$$0\% + Y + 30\% = 50\%$$
$$Y = 20\%$$

Finally, knowing that $Y = 20\%$, we can sum across the second row to get Z:

$$40\% + Y = 40\% + 20\% = Z$$
$$Z = 60\%$$

CONDITIONAL PROBABILITY

The concept of independence is closely related to the concept of conditional probability. Rather than trying to determine the probability of the market being up *and* having rain, we can ask, "What is the probability that the stock market is up *given* that it is raining?" We can write this as a conditional probability:

$$P[\text{market up} \mid \text{rain}] = p \qquad (1.14)$$

The vertical bar signals that the probability of the first argument is conditional on the second. You would read Equation (1.14) as "The probability of 'market up' given 'rain' is equal to p."

Using the conditional probability, we can calculate the probability that it will rain *and* that the market will be up.

$$P[\text{market up and rain}] = P[\text{market up} \mid \text{rain}] \cdot P[\text{rain}] \quad \textbf{(1.15)}$$

For example, if there is a 10% probability that it will rain tomorrow and the probability that the market will be up *given* that it is raining is 40%, then the probability of rain and the market being up is 4%: 40% × 10% = 4%.

From a statistics standpoint, it is just as valid to calculate the probability that it will rain and that the market will be up as follows:

$$P[\text{market up and rain}] = P[\text{rain} \mid \text{market up}]$$
$$\cdot P[\text{market up}] \quad \textbf{(1.16)}$$

As we will see in Chapter 4 when we discuss Bayesian analysis, even though the right-hand sides of Equations (1.15) and (1.16) are mathematically equivalent, how we interpret them can often be different.

We can also use conditional probabilities to calculate unconditional probabilities. On any given day, either it rains or it does not rain. The probability that the market will be up, then, is simply the probability of the market being up when it is raining plus the probability of the market being up when it is not raining. We have:

$$P[\text{market up}] = P[\text{market up and rain}]$$
$$+ P[\text{market up and } \overline{\text{rain}}]$$

$$P[\text{market up}] = P[\text{market up} \mid \text{rain}] \cdot P[\text{rain}]$$
$$+ P[\text{market up} \mid \overline{\text{rain}}] \cdot P[\overline{\text{rain}}] \quad \textbf{(1.17)}$$

Here we have used a line over *rain* to signify logical negation; $\overline{\text{rain}}$ can be read as "not rain."

In general, if a random variable X has n possible values, $x_1, x_2, \ldots, x_n$, then the unconditional probability of Y can be calculated as:

$$P[Y] = \sum_{i=1}^{n} P[Y \mid x_i]P[x_i] \quad \textbf{(1.18)}$$

If the probability of the market being up on a rainy day is the same as the probability of the market being up on a day with no rain, then we say that the market is conditionally independent of rain. If the market is conditionally

independent of rain, then the probability that the market is up given that it is raining must be equal to the unconditional probability of the market being up. To see why this is true, we replace the conditional probability of the market being up given no rain with the conditional probability of the market being up given rain in Equation (1.17) (we can do this because we are assuming that these two conditional probabilities are equal).

$$P[\text{market up}] = P[\text{market up} \mid \text{rain}] \cdot P[\text{rain}]$$
$$+ P[\text{market up} \mid \text{rain}] \cdot P[\overline{\text{rain}}]$$

$$P[\text{market up}] = P[\text{market up} \mid \text{rain}] \cdot (P[\text{rain}] + P[\overline{\text{rain}}])$$

$$P[\text{market up}] = P[\text{market up} \mid \text{rain}] \quad \textbf{(1.19)}$$

In the last line of Equation (1.19), we rely on the fact that the probability of rain plus the probability of no rain is equal to one. Either it rains or it does not rain.

In Equation (1.19) we could just have easily replaced the conditional probability of the market being up given rain with the conditional probability of the market being up given no rain. If the market is conditionally independent of rain, then it is also true that the probability that the market is up given that it is not raining must be equal to the unconditional probability of the market being up:

$$P[\text{market up}] = P[\text{market up} \mid \overline{\text{rain}}] \quad \textbf{(1.20)}$$

In the previous section, we noted that if the market is independent of rain, then the probability that the market will be up and that it will rain must be equal to the probability of the market being up multiplied by the probability of rain. To see why this must be true, we simply substitute the last line of Equation (1.19) into Equation (1.15):

$$P[\text{market up and rain}] = P[\text{market up} \mid \text{rain}] \cdot P[\text{rain}]$$

$$P[\text{market up and rain}] = P[\text{market up}] \cdot P[\text{rain}] \quad \textbf{(1.21)}$$

Remember that Equation (1.21) is true only if the market being up and rain are independent. If the weather somehow affects the stock market, however, then the conditional probabilities might not be equal. We could have a situation where:

$$P[\text{market up} \mid \text{rain}] \neq P[\text{market up} \mid \overline{\text{rain}}] \quad \textbf{(1.22)}$$

In this case, the weather and the stock market are no longer independent. We can no longer multiply their probabilities together to get their joint probability.

Basic Statistics

2

Learning Objectives

Candidates, after completing this reading, should be able to:

- Interpret and apply the mean, standard deviation, and variance of a random variable.
- Calculate the mean, standard deviation, and variance of a discrete random variable.
- Interpret and calculate the expected value of a discrete random variable.
- Calculate and interpret the covariance and correlation between two random variables.
- Calculate the mean and variance of sums of variables.

- Describe the four central moments of a statistical variable or distribution: mean, variance, skewness, and kurtosis.
- Interpret the skewness and kurtosis of a statistical distribution, and interpret the concepts of coskewness and cokurtosis.
- Describe and interpret the best linear unbiased estimator.

Excerpt is Chapter 3 of Mathematics and Statistics for Financial Risk Management, *Second Edition, by Michael B. Miller.*

In this chapter we will learn how to describe a collection of data in precise statistical terms. Many of the concepts will be familiar, but the notation and terminology might be new.

AVERAGES

Everybody knows what an average is. We come across averages every day, whether they are earned run averages in baseball or grade point averages in school. In statistics there are actually three different types of averages: means, modes, and medians. By far the most commonly used average in risk management is the mean.

Population and Sample Data

If you wanted to know the mean age of people working in your firm, you would simply ask every person in the firm his or her age, add the ages together, and divide by the number of people in the firm. Assuming there are n employees and a_i is the age of the ith employee, then the mean, μ is simply:

$$\mu = \frac{1}{n}\sum_{i=1}^{n} a_i = \frac{1}{n}(a_1 + a_2 + \cdots + a_{n-1} + a_n) \qquad (2.1)$$

It is important at this stage to differentiate between population statistics and sample statistics. In this example, μ is the population mean. Assuming nobody lied about his or her age, and forgetting about rounding errors and other trivial details, we know the mean age of the people in your firm *exactly*. We have a complete data set of everybody in your firm; we've surveyed the entire population.

This state of absolute certainty is, unfortunately, quite rare in finance. More often, we are faced with a situation such as this: estimate the mean return of stock ABC, given the most recent year of daily returns. In a situation like this, we assume there is some underlying data-generating process, whose statistical properties are constant over time. The underlying process has a true mean, but we cannot observe it directly. We can only estimate the true mean based on our limited data sample. In our example, assuming n returns, we estimate the mean using the same formula as before:

$$\hat{\mu} = \frac{1}{n}\sum_{i=1}^{n} r_i = \frac{1}{n}(r_1 + r_2 + \cdots + r_{n-1} + r_n) \qquad (2.2)$$

where $\hat{\mu}$ (pronounced "mu hat") is our *estimate* of the true mean, based on our sample of n returns. We call this the sample mean.

The median and mode are also types of averages. They are used less frequently in finance, but both can be useful. The median represents the center of a group of data; within the group, half the data points will be less than the median, and half will be greater. The mode is the value that occurs most frequently.

Example 2.1

Question:

Calculate the mean, median, and mode of the following data set:

$$-20\%, -10\%, -5\%, -5\%, 0\%, 10\%, 10\%, 10\%, 19\%$$

Answer:

Mean: $= \frac{1}{9}(-20\% -10\% -5\% -5\% + 0\% + 10\% + 10\%$
$\qquad\qquad + 10\% + 19\%)$
$\qquad = 1\%$

Mode = 10%

Median = 0%

If there is an even number of data points, the median is found by averaging the two centermost points. In the following series:

$$5\%, 10\%, 20\%, 25\%$$

the median is 15%. The median can be useful for summarizing data that is asymmetrical or contains significant outliers.

A data set can also have more than one mode. If the maximum frequency is shared by two or more values, all of those values are considered modes. In the following example, the modes are 10% and 20%:

$$5\%, 10\%, 10\%, 10\%, 14\%, 16\%, 20\%, 20\%, 20\%, 24\%$$

In calculating the mean in Equation (2.1) and Equation (2.2), each data point was counted exactly once. In certain situations, we might want to give more or less weight to certain data points. In calculating the average return of stocks in an equity index, we might want to give more weight to larger firms, perhaps weighting their returns in proportion to their market capitalizations. Given n data points, $x_i = x_1, x_2, \ldots, x_n$ with corresponding weights, w_i, we can define the weighted mean, μ_w, as:

$$\mu_w = \frac{\sum_{i=1}^{n} w_i x_i}{\sum_{i=1}^{n} w_i} \qquad \text{(2.3)}$$

The standard mean from Equation (2.1) can be viewed as a special case of the weighted mean, where all the values have equal weight.

Discrete Random Variables

For a discrete random variable, we can also calculate the mean, median, and mode. For a random variable, X, with possible values, x_i, and corresponding probabilities, p_i, we define the mean, μ, as:

$$\mu = \sum_{i=1}^{n} p_i x_i \qquad \text{(2.4)}$$

The equation for the mean of a discrete random variable is a special case of the weighted mean, where the outcomes are weighted by their probabilities, and the sum of the weights is equal to one.

The median of a discrete random variable is the value such that the probability that a value is less than or equal to the median is equal to 50%. Working from the other end of the distribution, we can also define the median such that 50% of the values are greater than or equal to the median. For a random variable, X, if we denote the median as m, we have:

$$P[X \geq m] = P[X \leq m] = 0.50 \qquad \text{(2.5)}$$

For a discrete random variable, the mode is the value associated with the highest probability. As with population and sample data sets, the mode of a discrete random variable need not be unique.

Example 2.2

Question:

At the start of the year, a bond portfolio consists of two bonds, each worth $100. At the end of the year, if a bond defaults, it will be worth $20. If it does not default, the bond will be worth $100. The probability that both bonds default is 20%. The probability that neither bond defaults is 45%. What are the mean, median, and mode of the year-end portfolio value?

Answer:

We are given the probability for two outcomes:

$$P[V = \$40] = 20\%$$
$$P[V = \$200] = 45\%$$

At year-end, the value of the portfolio, V, can have only one of three values, and the sum of all the probabilities must sum to 100%. This allows us to calculate the final probability:

$$P[V = \$120] = 100\% - 20\% - 45\% = 35\%$$

The mean of V is then $140:

$$\mu = 0.20 \cdot \$40 + 0.35 \cdot \$120 + 0.45 \cdot \$200 = \$140$$

The mode of the distribution is $200; this is the most likely single outcome. The median of the distribution is $120; half of the outcomes are less than or equal to $120.

Continuous Random Variables

We can also define the mean, median, and mode for a continuous random variable. To find the mean of a continuous random variable, we simply integrate the product of the variable and its probability density function (PDF). In the limit, this is equivalent to our approach to calculating the mean of a discrete random variable. For a continuous random variable, X, with a PDF, $f(x)$, the mean, μ, is then:

$$\mu = \int_{x_{min}}^{x_{max}} x f(x) dx \qquad \text{(2.6)}$$

The median of a continuous random variable is defined exactly as it is for a discrete random variable, such that there is a 50% probability that values are less than or equal to, or greater than or equal to, the median. If we define the median as m, then:

$$\int_{x_{min}}^{m} f(x) dx = \int_{m}^{x_{max}} f(x) dx = 0.50 \qquad \text{(2.7)}$$

Alternatively, we can define the median in terms of the cumulative distribution function. Given the cumulative distribution function, $F(x)$, and the median, m, we have:

$$F(m) = 0.50 \qquad \text{(2.8)}$$

The mode of a continuous random variable corresponds to the maximum of the density function. As before, the mode need not be unique.

Example 2.3

Question:

Using the now-familiar probability density function from Chapter 1,

$$f(x) = \frac{x}{50} \text{ s.t. } 0 \leq x \leq 10$$

what are the mean, median, and mode of x?

Answer:

As we saw in a previous example, this probability density function is a triangle, between $x = 0$ and $x = 10$, and zero everywhere else. See Figure 2-1.

For a continuous distribution, the mode corresponds to the maximum of the PDF. By inspection of the graph, we can see that the mode of $f(x)$ is equal to 10.

To calculate the median, we need to find m, such that the integral of $f(x)$ from the lower bound of $f(x)$, zero, to m is equal to 0.50. That is, we need to find:

$$\int_0^m \frac{x}{50} \, dx = 0.50$$

First we solve the left-hand side of the equation:

$$\int_0^m \frac{1}{50} \, dx = \frac{1}{50} \int_0^m x \, dx = \frac{x}{50} \left[\frac{1}{2} x^2 \right]_0^m = \frac{1}{100}(m^2 - 0) = \frac{m^2}{100}$$

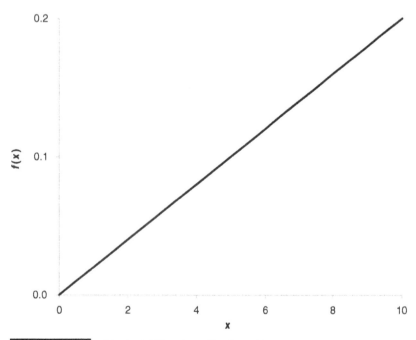

FIGURE 2-1 Probability density function.

Setting this result equal to 0.50 and solving for m, we obtain our final answer:

$$\frac{m^2}{100} = 0.50$$
$$m^2 = 50$$
$$m = \sqrt{50} = 7.07$$

In the last step we can ignore the negative root. If we hadn't calculated the median, looking at the graph it might be tempting to guess that the median is 5, the midpoint of the range of the distribution. This is a common mistake. Because lower values have less weight, the median ends up being greater than 5.

The mean is approximately 6.67:

$$\mu = \int_0^{10} x \frac{x}{50} \, dx = \frac{1}{50} \int_0^{10} x^2 dx = \frac{1}{50} \left[\frac{1}{3} x^3 \right]_0^{10} = \frac{1,000}{150} = \frac{20}{3} = 6.67$$

As with the median, it is a common mistake, based on inspection of the PDF, to guess that the mean is 5. However, what the PDF is telling us is that outcomes between 5 and 10 are much more likely than values between 0 and 5 (the PDF is higher between 5 and 10 than between 0 and 5). This is why the mean is greater than 5.

EXPECTATIONS

On January 15, 2005, the Huygens space probe landed on the surface of Titan, the largest moon of Saturn. This was the culmination of a seven-year-long mission. During its descent and for over an hour after touching down on the surface, Huygens sent back detailed images, scientific readings, and even sounds from a strange world. There are liquid oceans on Titan, the landing site was littered with "rocks" composed of water ice, and weather on the moon includes methane rain. The Huygens probe was named after Christiaan Huygens, a Dutch polymath who first discovered Titan in 1655. In addition to astronomy and physics, Huygens had more prosaic interests, including probability theory. Originally published in Latin in 1657, *De Ratiociniis in Ludo Aleae,* or *On the Logic of Games of Chance,* was one of the first texts to formally explore one of the most important concepts in probability theory, namely expectations.

Like many of his contemporaries, Huygens was interested in games of chance. As he described it, if a game has a 50% probability of paying $3 and a 50% probability of paying $7, then this is, in a way, equivalent to having $5 with certainty. This is because we *expect,* on average, to win $5 in this game:

$$50\% \cdot \$3 + 50\% \cdot \$7 = \$5 \qquad \textbf{(2.9)}$$

As one can already see, the concepts of expectations and averages are very closely linked. In the current example, if we play the game only once, there is no chance of winning exactly $5; we can win only $3 or $7. Still, even if we play the game only once, we say that the expected value of the game is $5. That we are talking about the mean of all the potential payouts is understood.

We can express the concept of expectations more formally using the expectation operator. We could state that the random variable, X, has an expected value of $5 as follows:

$$E[X] = 0.50 \cdot \$3 + 0.50 \cdot \$7 = \$5 \qquad \textbf{(2.10)}$$

where $E[\cdot]$ is the expectation operator.[1]

In this example, the mean and the expected value have the same numeric value, $5. The same is true for discrete and continuous random variables. The expected value of a random variable is equal to the mean of the random variable.

While the value of the mean and the expected value may be the same in many situations, the two concepts are not exactly the same. In many situations in finance and risk management, the terms can be used interchangeably. The difference is often subtle.

As the name suggests, expectations are often thought of as being forward looking. Pretend we have a financial asset for which next year's mean annual return is known and equal to 15%. This is not an estimate; in this hypothetical scenario, we actually know that the mean *is* 15%. We say that the expected value of the return next year is 15%. We expect the return to be 15%, because the probability-weighted mean of all the possible outcomes is 15%.

Now pretend that we don't actually *know* what the mean return of the asset is, but we have 10 years' worth of historical data for which the mean is 15%. In this case the expected value may or may not be 15%. *If* we decide that the expected value is equal to 15%, based on the data, then we are making two assumptions: first, we are assuming that the returns in our sample were generated by the same random process over the entire sample period; second, we are assuming that the returns will continue to be generated by this same process in the future. These are very strong assumptions. *If* we have other information that leads us to believe that one or both of these assumptions are false, then we may decide that the expected value is something other than 15%. In finance and risk management, we often assume that the data we are interested in are being generated by a consistent, unchanging process. Testing the validity of this assumption can be an important part of risk management in practice.

The concept of expectations is also a much more general concept than the concept of the mean. Using the expectation operator, we can derive the expected value of functions of random variables. As we will see in subsequent sections, the concept of expectations underpins the definitions of other population statistics (variance, skewness, kurtosis), and is important in understanding regression analysis and time series analysis. In these cases, even when we could use the mean to describe a calculation, in practice we tend to talk exclusively in terms of expectations.

Example 2.4

Question:

At the start of the year, you are asked to price a newly issued zero coupon bond. The bond has a notional of $100. You believe there is a 20% chance that the bond will default, in which case it will be worth $40 at the end of the year. There is also a 30% chance that the bond will be downgraded, in which case it will be worth $90 in a year's time. If the bond does not default and is not downgraded, it will be worth $100. Use a continuous interest rate of 5% to determine the current price of the bond.

Answer:

We first need to determine the expected future value of the bond—that is, the expected value of the bond in one year's time. We are given the following:

$$P[V_{t+1} = \$40] = 0.20$$
$$P[V_{t+1} = \$90] = 0.30$$

---

[1] Those of you with a background in physics might be more familiar with the term *expectation value* and the notation $\langle X \rangle$ rather than $E[X]$. This is a matter of convention. Throughout this book we use the term *expected value* and $E[\ ]$, which are currently more popular in finance and econometrics. Risk managers should be familiar with both conventions.

Because there are only three possible outcomes, the probability of no downgrade and no default must be 50%:

$$P[V_{t+1} = \$100] = 1 - 0.20 - 0.30 = 0.50$$

The expected value of the bond in one year is then:

$$E[V_{t+1}] = 0.20 \cdot \$40 + 0.30 \cdot \$90 + 0.50 \cdot \$100 = \$85$$

To get the current price of the bond we then discount this expected future value:

$$E[V_t] = e^{-0.05} E[V_{t+1}] = e^{-0.05}\$85 = \$80.85$$

The current price of the bond, in this case $80.85, is often referred to as the present value or fair value of the bond. The price is considered fair because the discounted expected value of the bond is the price that a risk-neutral investor would pay for the bond.

The expectation operator is linear. That is, for two random variables, X and Y, and a constant, c, the following two equations are true:

$$E[X + Y] = E[X] + E[Y]$$

$$E[cX] = cE[X] \tag{2.11}$$

If the expected value of one option, A, is $10, and the expected value of option B is $20, then the expected value of a portfolio containing A and B is $30, and the expected value of a portfolio containing five contracts of option A is $50.

Be very careful, though; the expectation operator is not multiplicative. The expected value of the product of two random variables is not necessarily the same as the product of their expected values:

$$E[XY] \neq E[X]E[Y] \tag{2.12}$$

Imagine we have two binary options. Each pays either $100 or nothing, depending on the value of some underlying asset at expiration. The probability of receiving $100 is 50% for both options. Further, assume that it is always the case that if the first option pays $100, the second pays $0, and vice versa. The expected value of each option separately is clearly $50. If we denote the payout of the first option as X and the payout of the second as Y, we have:

$$E[X] = E[Y] = 0.50 \cdot \$100 + 0.50 \cdot \$0 = \$50 \tag{2.13}$$

It follows that $E[X]E[Y] = \$50 \times \$50 = \$2,500$. In each scenario, though, one option is valued at zero, so the product of the payouts is always zero: $100 · $0 = $0 · $100 = $0. The expected value of the product of the two option payouts is:

$$E[XY] = 0.50 \cdot \$100 \cdot \$0 + 0.50 \cdot \$0 \cdot \$100 = \$0 \tag{2.14}$$

In this case, the product of the expected values and the expected value of the product are clearly not equal. In the special case where $E[XY] = E[X]E[Y]$, we say that X and Y are independent.

If the expected value of the product of two variables does not necessarily equal the product of the expectations of those variables, it follows that the expected value of the product of a variable with itself does not necessarily equal the product of the expectation of that variable with itself; that is:

$$E[X^2] \neq E[X]^2 \tag{2.15}$$

Imagine we have a fair coin. Assign heads a value of +1 and tails a value of −1. We can write the probabilities of the outcomes as follows:

$$P[X = +1] = P[X = -1] = 0.50 \tag{2.16}$$

The expected value of any coin flip is zero, but the expected value of X^2 is +1, not zero:

$$E[X] = 0.50 \cdot (+1) + 0.50 \cdot (-1) = 0$$

$$E[X]^2 = 0^2 = 0$$

$$E[X^2] = 0.50 \cdot (+1^2) + 0.50 \cdot (-1^2) = 1 \tag{2.17}$$

As simple as this example is, this distinction is very important. As we will see, the difference between $E[X^2]$ and $E[X]^2$ is central to our definition of variance and standard deviation.

Example 2.5

Question:

Given the following equation,

$$y = (x + 5)^3 + x^2 + 10x$$

what is the expected value of y? Assume the following:

$$E[x] = 4$$

$$E[X^2] = 9$$

$$E[X^3] = 12$$

Answer:

Note that $E[x^2]$ and $E[x^3]$ cannot be derived from knowledge of $E[x]$. In this problem, $E[x^2] \neq E[x]^2$ and $E[x^3] \neq E[x]^3$.

To find the expected value of y, then, we first expand the term $(x + 5)^3$ within the expectation operator:

$$E[y] = E[(x + 5)^3 + x^2 + 10x] = E[x^3 + 16x^2 + 85x + 125]$$

Because the expectation operator is linear, we can separate the terms in the summation and move the constants outside the expectation operator:

$$E[y] = E[x^3] + E[16x^2] + E[85x] + E[125]$$

$$= E[x^3] + 16E[x^2] + 85E[x] + 125$$

At this point, we can substitute in the values for $E[x]$, $E[x^2]$, and $E[x^3]$, which were given at the start of the exercise:

$$E[y] = 12 + 16 \cdot 9 + 85 \cdot 4 + 125 = 621$$

This gives us the final answer, 621.

VARIANCE AND STANDARD DEVIATION

The variance of a random variable measures how noisy or unpredictable that random variable is. Variance is defined as the expected value of the difference between the variable and its mean squared:

$\sqrt{\sigma^2} = SD$

$$\sigma^2 = E[(X - \mu)^2] \qquad (2.18)$$

variance

where σ^2 is the variance of the random variable X with mean μ.

The square root of variance, typically denoted by σ, is called standard deviation. In finance we often refer to standard deviation as volatility. This is analogous to referring to the mean as the average. Standard deviation is a mathematically precise term, whereas volatility is a more general concept.

Example 2.6

Question:

A derivative has a 50/50 chance of being worth either +10 or −10 at expiry. What is the standard deviation of the derivative's value?

Answer:

$$\mu = 0.50 \cdot 10 + 0.50 \cdot (-10) = 0$$

$$\sigma^2 = 0.50 \cdot (10 - 0)^2 + 0.50 \cdot (-10 - 0)^2$$

$$= 0.5 \cdot 100 + 0.5 \cdot 100 = 100$$

$$\sigma = 10$$

In the previous example, we were calculating the population variance and standard deviation. *All* of the possible outcomes for the derivative were known.

To calculate the sample variance of a random variable X based on n observations, $x_1, x_2, \ldots, x_n$ we can use the following formula:

if means are unknown

$$\hat{\sigma}_x^2 = \frac{1}{n-1} \sum_{i=1}^{n} (x_i - \hat{\mu}_x)^2$$

$$E[\hat{\sigma}_x^2] = \sigma^2_x \qquad (2.19)$$

where $\hat{\mu}_x$ is the sample mean as in Equation (2.2). Given that we have n data points, it might seem odd that we are dividing the sum by $(n - 1)$ and not n. The reason has to do with the fact that $\hat{\mu}_x$ itself is an estimate of the true mean, which also contains a fraction of each x_i. It turns out that dividing by $(n - 1)$, not n, produces an unbiased estimate of σ^2. If the mean is known or we are calculating the population variance, then we divide by n. If instead the mean is also being estimated, then we divide by $n - 1$.

Equation (2.18) can easily be rearranged as follows (the proof of this equation is also left as an exercise):

$$\sigma^2 = E[X^2] - \mu^2 = E[X^2] - E[X]^2 \qquad (2.20)$$

Note that variance can be nonzero only if $E[X^2] \neq E[X]^2$.

When writing computer programs, this last version of the variance formula is often useful, since it allows us to calculate the mean and the variance in the same loop.

In finance it is often convenient to assume that the mean of a random variable is equal to zero. For example, based on theory, we might expect the spread between two equity indexes to have a mean of zero in the long run. In this case, the variance is simply the mean of the squared returns.

Example 2.7

Question:

Assume that the mean of daily Standard & Poor's (S&P) 500 Index returns is zero. You observe the following returns over the course of 10 days:

7%	−4%	11%	8%	3%	9%	−21%	10%	−9%	−1%

Estimate the standard deviation of daily S&P 500 Index returns.

Answer:

The sample mean is not exactly zero, but we are told to assume that the population mean *is* zero; therefore:

$$\hat{\sigma}_r^2 = \frac{1}{n}\sum_{i=1}^{n}(r_i^2 - 0^2) = \frac{1}{n}\sum_{i=1}^{n}r_i^2$$

$$\hat{\sigma}_r^2 = \frac{1}{10}\,0.0963 = 0.00963$$

$$\hat{\sigma}_r = 9.8\%$$

Note, because we were told to assume the mean was known, we divide by $n = 10$, not $(n - 1) = 9$.

As with the mean, for a continuous random variable we can calculate the variance by integrating with the probability density function. For a continuous random variable, X, with a probability density function, $f(x)$, the variance can be calculated as:

$$\sigma^2 = \int_{x_{min}}^{x_{max}} (x - \mu)^2 f(x)\,dx \qquad \textbf{(2.21)}$$

It is not difficult to prove that, for either a discrete or a continuous random variable, multiplying by a constant will increase the standard deviation by the same factor:

$$\sigma[cX] = c\sigma[X] \qquad \textbf{(2.22)}$$

In other words, if you own \$10 of an equity with a standard deviation of \$2, then \$100 of the same equity will have a standard deviation of \$20.

Adding a constant to a random variable, however, does not alter the standard deviation or the variance:

$$\sigma[X + c] = \sigma[X] \qquad \textbf{(2.23)}$$

This is because the impact of c on the mean is the same as the impact of c on any draw of the random variable, leaving the deviation from the mean for any draw unchanged. In theory, a risk-free asset should have zero variance and standard deviation. If you own a portfolio with a standard deviation of \$20, and then you add \$1,000 of cash to that portfolio, the standard deviation of the portfolio should still be \$20.

STANDARDIZED VARIABLES

It is often convenient to work with variables where the mean is zero and the standard deviation is one. From the preceding section it is not difficult to prove that, given a random variable X with mean μ and standard deviation σ, we can define a second random variable Y:

$$Y = \frac{X - \mu}{\sigma} \qquad \textbf{(2.24)}$$

such that Y will have a mean of zero and a standard deviation of one. We say that X has been standardized, or that Y is a standard random variable. In practice, if we have a data set and we want to standardize it, we first compute the sample mean and the standard deviation. Then, for each data point, we subtract the mean and divide by the standard deviation.

The inverse transformation can also be very useful when it comes to creating computer simulations. Simulations often begin with standardized variables, which need to be transformed into variables with a specific mean and standard deviation. In this case, we simply take the output from the standardized variable, multiply by the desired standard deviation, and then add the desired mean. The order is important. Adding a constant to a random variable will not change the standard deviation, but multiplying a non-mean-zero variable by a constant will change the mean.

Example 2.8

Question:

Assume that a random variable Y has a mean of zero and a standard deviation of one. Given two constants, μ and σ, calculate the expected values of X_1 and X_2, where X_1 and X_2 are defined as:

$$X_1 = \sigma Y + \mu$$
$$X_2 = \sigma(Y + \mu)$$

Answer:

The expected value of X_1 is μ:

$$E[X_1] = E[\sigma Y + \mu] = \sigma E[Y] + E[\mu] = \sigma \cdot 0 + \mu = \mu$$

The expected value of X_2 is $\sigma\mu$:

$$E[X_2] = E[\sigma(Y + \mu)] = E[\sigma Y + \sigma\mu]$$
$$= \sigma E[Y] + \sigma\mu = \sigma \cdot 0 + \sigma\mu = \sigma\mu$$

As warned in the previous section, multiplying a standard normal variable by a constant and then adding another constant produces a different result than if we first add and then multiply.

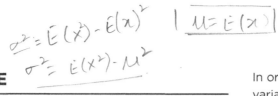

$$\sigma^2 = E(\hat{X}) - E(x)^2 \qquad \mu = E(x)$$
$$\sigma^2 = E(x^2) - \mu^2$$

COVARIANCE

Up until now we have mostly been looking at statistics that summarize one variable. In risk management, we often want to describe the relationship between two random variables. For example, is there a relationship between the returns of an equity and the returns of a market index?

Covariance is analogous to variance, but instead of looking at the deviation from the mean of one variable, we are going to look at the relationship between the deviations of two variables:

$$\sigma_{XY} = E[(X - \mu_X)(Y - \mu_Y)] \qquad \textbf{(2.25)}$$

where σ_{XY} is the covariance between two random variables, X and Y, with means μ_X and μ_Y, respectively. As you can see from the definition, variance is just a special case of covariance. Variance is the covariance of a variable with itself.

If X tends to be above μ_X when Y is above μ_Y (both deviations are positive) and X tends to be below μ_X when Y is below μ_Y (both deviations are negative), then the covariance will be positive (a positive number multiplied by a positive number is positive; likewise, for two negative numbers). If the opposite is true and the deviations tend to be of opposite sign, then the covariance will be negative. If the deviations have no discernible relationship, then the covariance will be zero.

Earlier in this chapter, we cautioned that the expectation operator is not generally multiplicative. This fact turns out to be closely related to the concept of covariance. Just as we rewrote our variance equation earlier, we can rewrite Equation (2.25) as follows:

$$\sigma_{XY} = E[(X - \mu_X)(Y - \mu_Y)] = E[XY] - \mu_X\mu_Y$$
$$\sigma_{xy} = E[XY] - E[X]E[Y] \qquad \textbf{(2.26)}$$

In the special case where the covariance between X and Y is zero, the expected value of XY is equal to the expected value of X multiplied by the expected value of Y:

$$\sigma_{XY} = 0 \Rightarrow E[XY] = E[X]E[Y] \qquad \textbf{(2.27)}$$

If the covariance is anything other than zero, then the two sides of this equation cannot be equal. Unless we know that the covariance between two variables is zero, we cannot assume that the expectation operator is multiplicative.

In order to calculate the covariance between two random variables, X and Y, assuming the means of both variables are known, we can use the following formula:

$$\hat{\sigma}_{x,y} = \frac{1}{n}\sum_{i=1}^{n}(x_i - \mu_x)(y_i - \mu_Y) \qquad \textbf{(2.28)}$$

If the means are unknown and must also be estimated, we replace n with $(n - 1)$:

$$\hat{\sigma}_{x,y} = \frac{1}{n-1}\sum_{i=1}^{n}(x_i - \hat{\mu}_x)(y_i - \hat{\mu}_Y) \qquad \textbf{(2.29)}$$

If we replaced y_i in these formulas with x_i, calculating the covariance of X with itself, the resulting equations would be the same as the equations for calculating variance from the previous section.

CORRELATION

Closely related to the concept of covariance is correlation. To get the correlation of two variables, we simply divide their covariance by their respective standard deviations:

$$\rho_{XY} = \frac{\sigma_{XY}}{\sigma_x\sigma_Y} \qquad \textbf{(2.30)}$$

Correlation has the nice property that it varies between −1 and +1. If two variables have a correlation of +1, then we say they are perfectly correlated. If the ratio of one variable to another is always the same and positive, then the two variables will be perfectly correlated.

If two variables are highly correlated, it is often the case that one variable *causes* the other variable, or that both variables share a common underlying driver. We will see in later chapters, though, that it is very easy for two random variables with no causal link to be highly correlated. *Correlation does not prove causation.* Similarly, if two variables are uncorrelated, it does not necessarily follow that they are unrelated. For example, a random variable that is symmetrical around zero and the square of that variable will have zero correlation.

Example 2.9

Question:

X is a random variable. X has an equal probability of being −1, 0, or +1. What is the correlation between X and Y if $Y = X^2$?

Answer:

We have:

$$P[X = -1] = P[X = 0] = P[X = 1] = \frac{1}{3}$$
$$Y = X^2$$

First, we calculate the mean of both variables:

$$E[X] = \frac{1}{3}(-1) + \frac{1}{3}(0) + \frac{1}{3}(1) = 0$$
$$E[Y] = \frac{1}{3}(-1^2) + \frac{1}{3}(0^2) + \frac{1}{3}(1^2) = \frac{1}{3}(1) + \frac{1}{3}(0) + \frac{1}{3}(1) = \frac{2}{3}$$

The covariance can be found as:

$$\text{Cov}[X,Y] = E[(X - E[X])(Y - E[Y])]$$
$$\text{Cov}[X,Y] = \frac{1}{3}(-1 - 0)\left(1 - \frac{2}{3}\right) + \frac{1}{3}(0 - 0)\left(0 - \frac{2}{3}\right)$$
$$+ \frac{1}{3}(1 - 0)\left(1 - \frac{2}{3}\right) = 0$$

Because the covariance is zero, the correlation is also zero. There is no need to calculate the variances or standard deviations.

As forewarned, even though X and Y are clearly related, their correlation is zero.

APPLICATION: PORTFOLIO VARIANCE AND HEDGING

If we have a portfolio of securities and we wish to determine the variance of that portfolio, all we need to know is the variance of the underlying securities and their respective correlations.

For example, if we have two securities with random returns X_A and X_B, with means μ_A and μ_B and standard deviations σ_A and σ_B, respectively, we can calculate the variance of X_A plus X_B as follows:

$$\sigma_{A+B}^2 = \sigma_A^2 + \sigma_B^2 + 2\rho_{AB}\sigma_A\sigma_B \quad \textbf{(2.31)}$$

where ρ_{AB} is the correlation between X_A and X_B. The proof is left as an exercise. Notice that the last term can either increase or decrease the total variance. Both standard deviations must be positive; therefore, if the correlation is positive, the overall variance will be higher than in the case where the correlation is negative.

If the variance of both securities is equal, then Equation (2.31) simplifies to:

$$\sigma_{A+B}^2 = 2\sigma^2(1 + \rho_{AB}) \quad \text{where } \sigma_A^2 = \sigma_B^2 = \sigma^2 \quad \textbf{(2.32)}$$

We know that the correlation can vary between −1 and +1, so, substituting into our new equation, the portfolio variance must be bound by 0 and $4\sigma^2$. If we take the square root of both sides of the equation, we see that the standard deviation is bound by 0 and 2σ. Intuitively, this should make sense. If, on the one hand, we own one share of an equity with a standard deviation of $10 and then purchase another share of the *same* equity, then the standard deviation of our two-share portfolio must be $20 (trivially, the correlation of a random variable with itself must be one). On the other hand, if we own one share of this equity and then purchase another security that always generates the exact opposite return, the portfolio is perfectly balanced. The returns are always zero, which implies a standard deviation of zero.

In the special case where the correlation between the two securities is zero, we can further simplify our equation. For the standard deviation:

$$\rho_{AB} = 0 \Rightarrow \sigma_{A+B} = \sqrt{2}\sigma \quad \textbf{(2.33)}$$

We can extend Equation (2.31) to any number of variables:

$$Y = \sum_{i=1}^{n} X_i$$
$$\sigma_Y^2 = \sum_{i=1}^{n}\sum_{j=1}^{n} \rho_{ij}\sigma_i\sigma_j \quad \textbf{(2.34)}$$

In the case where all of the X_i's are uncorrelated and all the variances are equal to σ, Equation (2.32) simplifies to:

$$\sigma_Y = \sqrt{n}\sigma \quad \textit{iff} \quad \rho_{ij} = 0 \; \forall \; i \neq j \quad \textbf{(2.35)}$$

This is the famous square root rule for the addition of uncorrelated variables. There are many situations in statistics in which we come across collections of random variables that are independent and have the same statistical properties. We term these variables independent and identically distributed (i.i.d.). In risk management we might have a large portfolio of securities, which can be approximated as a collection of i.i.d. variables. As we will see in subsequent chapters, this i.i.d. assumption also plays an important role in estimating the uncertainty inherent in statistics derived from sampling, and in the analysis of time series. In each of these situations, we will come back to this square root rule.

By combining Equation (2.31) with Equation (2.22), we arrive at an equation for calculating the variance of a linear combination of variables. If Y is a linear combination of X_A and X_B, such that:

$$Y = aX_A + bX_B \qquad \textbf{(2.36)}$$

then, using our standard notation, we have:

$$\sigma_Y^2 = a^2\sigma_A^2 + b^2\sigma_B^2 + 2ab\rho_{AB}\sigma_A\sigma_B \qquad \textbf{(2.37)}$$

Correlation is central to the problem of hedging. Using the same notation as before, imagine we have $1 of Security A, and we wish to hedge it with $h of Security B (if h is positive, we are buying the security; if h is negative, we are shorting the security). In other words, h is the hedge ratio. We introduce the random variable P for our hedged portfolio. We can easily compute the variance of the hedged portfolio using Equation (2.37):

$$P = X_A + hX_B$$
$$\sigma_P^2 = \sigma_A^2 + h^2\sigma_B^2 + 2h\rho_{AB}\sigma_A\sigma_B \qquad \textbf{(2.38)}$$

As a risk manager, we might be interested to know what hedge ratio would achieve the portfolio with the least variance. To find this minimum variance hedge ratio, we simply take the derivative of our equation for the portfolio variance with respect to h, and set it equal to zero:

$$\frac{d\sigma_P^2}{dh} = 2h\sigma_B^2 + 2\rho_{AB}\sigma_A\sigma_B$$
$$h^* = -\rho_{AB}\frac{\sigma_A}{\sigma_B} \qquad \textbf{(2.39)}$$

You can check that this is indeed a minimum by calculating the second derivative.

Substituting h^* back into our original equation, we see that the smallest variance we can achieve is:

$$\min[\sigma_P^2] = \sigma_A^2(1 - \rho_{AB}^2) \qquad \textbf{(2.40)}$$

At the extremes, where ρ_{AB} equals −1 or +1, we can reduce the portfolio volatility to zero by buying or selling the hedge asset in proportion to the standard deviation of the assets. In between these two extremes we will always be left with some positive portfolio variance. This risk that we cannot hedge is referred to as idiosyncratic risk.

If the two securities in the portfolio are positively correlated, then selling $h of Security B will reduce the portfolio's variance to the minimum possible level. Sell any less and the portfolio will be underhedged. Sell any more and the portfolio will be over hedged. In risk management it is possible to have too much of a good thing. A common mistake made by portfolio managers is to over hedge with a low-correlation instrument.

Notice that when ρ_{AB} equals zero (i.e., when the two securities are uncorrelated), the optimal hedge ratio is zero. You cannot hedge one security with another security if they are uncorrelated. Adding an uncorrelated security to a portfolio will always increase its variance.

This last statement is not an argument against diversification. If your entire portfolio consists of $100 invested in Security A and you *add* any amount of an uncorrelated Security B to the portfolio, the dollar standard deviation of the portfolio will increase. Alternatively, if Security A and Security B are uncorrelated and have the same standard deviation, then *replacing* some of Security A with Security B will decrease the dollar standard deviation of the portfolio. For example, $80 of Security A plus $20 of Security B will have a lower standard deviation than $100 of Security A, but $100 of Security A *plus* $20 of Security B will have a higher standard deviation—again, assuming Security A and Security B are uncorrelated and have the same standard deviation.

MOMENTS

Previously, we defined the mean of a variable X as:

$$\mu = E[X]$$

It turns out that we can generalize this concept as follows:

$$m_k = E[X^k] \qquad \textbf{(2.41)}$$

We refer to m_k as the kth moment of X. The mean of X is also the first moment of X.

Similarly, we can generalize the concept of variance as follows:

$$\mu_k = E[(X - \mu)^k] \qquad \textbf{(2.42)}$$

We refer to μ_k as the *kth* central moment of X. We say that the moment is central because it is centered on the mean. Variance is simply the second central moment.

While we can easily calculate any central moment, in risk management it is very rare that we are interested in anything beyond the fourth central moment.

SKEWNESS

The second central moment, variance, tells us how spread out a random variable is around the mean. The third central moment tells us how symmetrical the distribution is around the mean. Rather than working with the third central moment directly, by convention we first standardize the statistic. This standardized third central moment is known as skewness:

$$\text{Skewness} = \frac{E[(X - \mu)^3]}{\sigma^3} \qquad \textbf{(2.43)}$$

where σ is the standard deviation of X, and μ is the mean of X.

By standardizing the central moment, it is much easier to compare two random variables. Multiplying a random variable by a constant will not change the skewness.

A random variable that is symmetrical about its mean will have zero skewness. If the skewness of the random variable is positive, we say that the random variable exhibits positive skew. Figures 2-2 and 2-3 show examples of positive and negative skewness.

Skewness is a very important concept in risk management. If the distributions of returns of two investments are the same in all respects, with the same mean and standard deviation, but different skews, then the investment with more negative skew is generally considered to be more risky. Historical data suggest that many financial assets exhibit negative skew.

As with variance, the equation for skewness differs depending on whether we are calculating the population

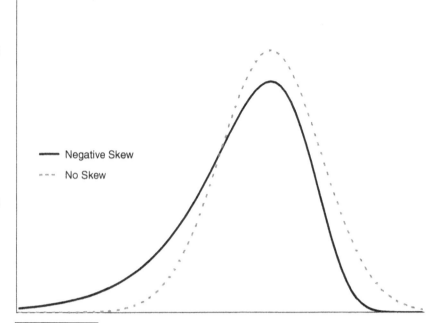

— Negative Skew
--- No Skew

FIGURE 2-3 Negative skew.

skewness or the sample skewness. For the population statistic, the skewness of a random variable X, based on n observations, $x_1, x_2, \ldots, x_m$ can be calculated as:

$$\hat{s} = \frac{1}{n}\sum_{i=1}^{n}\left(\frac{x_i - \mu}{\sigma}\right)^3 \qquad \textbf{(2.44)}$$

where μ is the population mean and σ is the population standard deviation. Similar to our calculation of sample variance, if we are calculating the sample skewness there is going to be an overlap with the calculation of the sample mean and sample standard deviation. We need to correct for that. The sample skewness can be calculated as:

$$\hat{s} = \frac{n}{(n-1)(n-2)}\sum_{i=1}^{n}\left(\frac{x_i - \hat{\mu}}{\hat{\sigma}}\right)^3 \qquad \textbf{(2.45)}$$

Based on Equation (2.20), for variance, it is tempting to guess that the formula for the third central moment can be written simply in terms of $E[X^3]$ and μ. Be careful, as the two sides of this equation are not equal:

$$E[(X + \mu)^k] \neq E[X^3] - \mu^3 \qquad \textbf{(2.46)}$$

The correct equation is:

$$E[(X - \mu)^3] = E[X^3] - 3\mu\sigma^2 - \mu^3 \qquad \textbf{(2.47)}$$

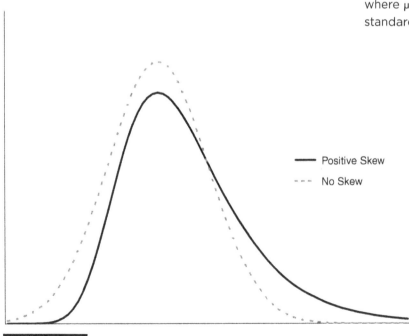

— Positive Skew
--- No Skew

FIGURE 2-2 Positive skew.

Example 2.10

Question:

Prove that the left-hand side of Equation (2.47) is indeed equal to the right-hand side of the equation.

Answer:

We start by multiplying out the terms inside the expectation. This is not too difficult to do, but, as a shortcut, we could use the binomial theorem:

$$E[(X - \mu)^3] = E[X^3 - 3\mu X^2 + 3\mu^2 X - \mu^3]$$

Next, we separate the terms inside the expectation operator and move any constants, namely μ, outside the operator:

$$E[(X^3 - 3\mu X^2 + 3\mu^2 X - \mu^3] = E[X^3] - 3\mu E[X^2] + 3\mu^2 E[X] - \mu^3$$

$E[X]$ is simply the mean, μ. For $E[X^2]$, we reorganize our equation for variance, Equation (2.20), as follows:

$$\sigma^2 = E[X^2] - \mu^2$$
$$E[X^2] = \sigma^2 + \mu^2$$

Substituting these results into our equation and collecting terms, we arrive at the final equation:

$$E[(X - \mu)^3] = E[X^3] - 3\mu(\sigma^2 + \mu^2) + 3\mu^2\mu - \mu^3$$
$$E[(X - \mu)^3] = E[X^3] - 3\mu\sigma^2 - \mu^3$$

For many symmetrical continuous distributions, the mean, median, and mode all have the same value. Many continuous distributions with negative skew have a mean that is less than the median, which is less than the mode. For example, it might be that a certain derivative is just as likely to produce positive returns as it is to produce negative returns (the median is zero), but there are more big negative returns than big positive returns (the distribution is skewed), so the mean is less than zero. As a risk manager, understanding the impact of skew on the mean relative to the median and mode can be useful. Be careful, though, as this rule of thumb does not always work. Many practitioners mistakenly believe that this rule of thumb is in fact always true. It is not, and it is very easy to produce a distribution that violates this rule.

KURTOSIS

The fourth central moment is similar to the second central moment, in that it tells us how spread out a random variable is, but it puts more weight on extreme points. As with skewness, rather than working with the central moment directly, we typically work with a standardized statistic. This standardized fourth central moment is known as kurtosis. For a random variable X, we can define the kurtosis as K, where:

$$K = \frac{E[(X - \mu)^4]}{\sigma^4} \tag{2.48}$$

where σ is the standard deviation of X, and μ is its mean.

By standardizing the central moment, it is much easier to compare two random variables. As with skewness, multiplying a random variable by a constant will not change the kurtosis.

The following two populations have the same mean, variance, and skewness. The second population has a higher kurtosis.

Population 1: $\{-17, -17, 17, 17\}$

Population 2: $\{-23, -7, 7, 23\}$

Notice, to balance out the variance, when we moved the outer two points out six units, we had to move the inner two points in 10 units. Because the random variable with higher kurtosis has points further from the mean, we often refer to distribution with high kurtosis as fat-tailed. Figures 2-4 and 2-5 show examples of continuous distributions with high and low kurtosis.

Like skewness, kurtosis is an important concept in risk management. Many financial assets exhibit high levels of kurtosis. If the distribution of returns of two assets have the same mean, variance, and skewness but different kurtosis, then the distribution with the higher kurtosis will tend to have more extreme points, and be considered more risky.

As with variance and skewness, the equation for kurtosis differs depending on whether we are calculating the population kurtosis or the sample kurtosis. For the population statistic, the kurtosis of a random variable X can be calculated as:

$$\hat{K} = \frac{1}{n}\sum_{i=1}^{n}\left(\frac{x_i - \mu}{\sigma}\right)^4 \tag{2.49}$$

$$\tilde{K} = \frac{n(n+1)}{(n-1)(n-2)(n-3)} \sum_{i=1}^{n} \left(\frac{x_i - \hat{\mu}}{\hat{\sigma}} \right)^4 \quad \textbf{(2.50)}$$

In the next chapter we will study the normal distribution, which has a kurtosis of 3. Because normal distributions are so common, many people refer to "excess kurtosis," which is simply the kurtosis minus 3.

$$K_{excess} = K - 3 \quad \textbf{(2.51)}$$

In this way, the normal distribution has an excess kurtosis of 0. Distributions with positive excess kurtosis are termed leptokurtotic. Distributions with negative excess kurtosis are termed platykurtotic. Be careful; by default, many applications calculate excess kurtosis, not kurtosis.

When we are also estimating the mean and variance, calculating the sample excess kurtosis is somewhat more complicated than just subtracting 3. If we have n points, then the correct formula is:

$$\tilde{K}_{excess} = \tilde{K} - 3 \frac{(n-1)^2}{(n-2)(n-3)} \quad \textbf{(2.52)}$$

where $\tilde{K}$ is the sample kurtosis from Equation (2.50). As n increases, the last term on the right-hand side converges to 3.

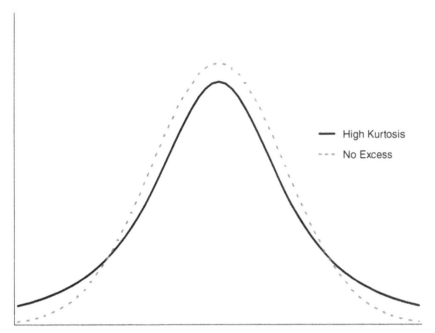

FIGURE 2-4 High kurtosis.

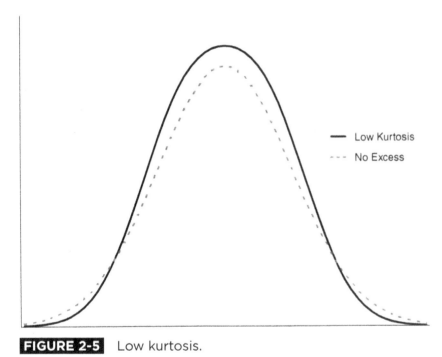

FIGURE 2-5 Low kurtosis.

where μ is the population mean and σ is the population standard deviation. Similar to our calculation of sample variance, if we are calculating the sample kurtosis there is going to be an overlap with the calculation of the sample mean and sample standard deviation. We need to correct for that. The sample kurtosis can be calculated as:

COSKEWNESS AND COKURTOSIS

Just as we generalized the concept of mean and variance to moments and central moments, we can generalize the concept of covariance to cross central moments. The third and fourth standardized cross central moments are referred to as coskewness and cokurtosis, respectively. Though used less frequently, higher-order cross moments can be very important in risk management.

As an example of how higher-order cross moments can impact risk assessment, take the series of returns shown in Figure 2-6 for four fund managers, A, B, C, and D.

In this admittedly contrived setup, each manager has produced exactly the same set of returns; only the order in which the returns were produced is different. It follows

Time	A	B	C	D
1	0.0%	−3.8%	−15.3%	−15.3%
2	−3.8%	−15.3%	−7.2%	−7.2%
3	−15.3%	3.8%	0.0%	−3.8%
4	−7.2%	−7.2%	−3.8%	15.3%
5	3.8%	0.0%	3.8%	0.0%
6	7.2%	7.2%	7.2%	7.2%
7	15.3%	15.3%	15.3%	3.8%

FIGURE 2-6 Funds returns.

Time	A + B	C + D
1	−1.9%	−15.3%
2	−9.5%	−7.2%
3	−5.8%	−1.9%
4	−7.2%	5.8%
5	1.9%	1.9%
6	7.2%	7.2%
7	15.3%	9.5%

FIGURE 2-7 Combined fund returns.

that the mean, standard deviation, skew, and kurtosis of the returns are exactly the same for each manager. In this example it is also the case that the covariance between managers A and B is the same as the covariance between managers C and D.

If we combine A and B in an equally weighted portfolio and combine C and D in a separate equally weighted portfolio, we get the returns shown in Figure 2-7.

The two portfolios have the same mean and standard deviation, but the skews of the portfolios are different. Whereas the worst return for A + B is −9.5%, the worst return for C + D is −15.3%. As a risk manager, knowing that the worst outcome for portfolio C + D is more than 1.6 times as bad as the worst outcome for A + B could be very important.

So how did two portfolios whose constituents seemed so similar end up being so different? One way to understand what is happening is to graph the two sets of returns for each portfolio against each other, as shown in Figures 2-8 and 2-9.

The two charts share a certain symmetry, but are clearly different. In the first portfolio, A + B, the two managers' best positive returns occur during the same time period, but their worst negative returns occur in different periods. This causes the distribution of points to be skewed toward the top-right of the chart. The situation is reversed for managers C and D: their worst negative returns occur in the same period, but their best positive returns occur in different periods. In the second chart, the points are skewed toward the bottom-left of the chart.

The reason the charts look different, and the reason the returns of the two portfolios are different, is because the coskewness between the managers in each of the portfolios is different. For two random variables, there are actually two nontrivial coskewness statistics. For example, for managers A and B, we have:

$$S_{AAB} = E[(A - \mu_A)^2(B - \mu_B)]/\sigma_A^2\sigma_B$$
$$S_{ABB} = E[(A - \mu_A)(B - \mu_B)^2]/\sigma_A\sigma_B^2 \tag{2.53}$$

The complete set of sample coskewness statistics for the sets of managers is shown in Figure 2-10.

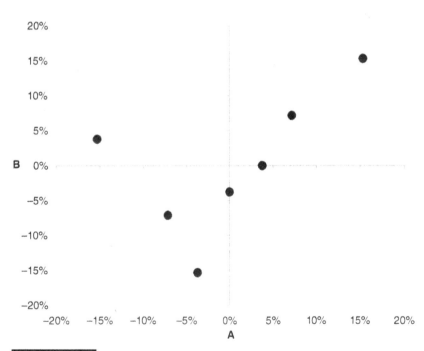

FIGURE 2-8 Funds A and B.

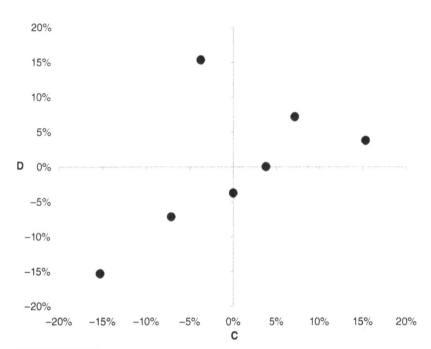

FIGURE 2-9 Funds C and D.

	A + B	C + D
S_{XXY}	0.99	−0.58
S_{XYY}	0.58	−0.99

FIGURE 2-10 Sample coskewness.

Both coskewness values for A and B are positive, whereas they are both negative for C and D. Just as with skewness, negative values of coskewness tend to be associated with greater risk.

In general, for n random variables, the number of nontrivial cross central moments of order m is:

$$k = \frac{(m+n-1)!}{m!(n-1)!} - n \qquad \textbf{(2.54)}$$

In this case, nontrivial means that we have excluded the cross moments that involve only one variable (i.e., our standard skewness and kurtosis). To include the nontrivial moments, we would simply add n to the preceding result.

For coskewness, Equation (2.54) simplifies to:

$$k_3 = \frac{(n+2)(n+1)n}{6} - n \qquad \textbf{(2.55)}$$

Despite their obvious relevance to risk management, many standard risk models do not explicitly define coskewness

or cokurtosis. One reason that many models avoid these higher-order cross moments is practical. As the number of variables increases, the number of nontrivial cross moments increases rapidly. With 10 variables there are 30 coskewness parameters and 65 cokurtosis parameters. With 100 variables, these numbers increase to 171,600 and over 4 million, respectively. Figure 2-11 compares the number of nontrivial cross moments for a variety of sample sizes. In most cases there is simply not enough data to calculate all of these cross moments.

Risk models with time-varying volatility (e.g., GARCH) or time-varying correlation can display a wide range of behaviors with very few free parameters. Copulas can also be used to describe complex interactions between variables that go beyond covariances, and have become popular in risk management in recent years. All of these approaches capture the essence of coskewness and cokurtosis, but in a more tractable framework. As a risk manager, it is important to differentiate between these models—which address the higher-order cross moments indirectly—and models that simply omit these risk factors altogether.

BEST LINEAR UNBIASED ESTIMATOR (BLUE)

In this chapter we have been careful to differentiate between the true parameters of a distribution and estimates of those parameters based on a sample of

n	Covariance	Coskewness	Cokurtosis
2	1	2	3
5	10	30	65
10	45	210	705
20	190	1,520	8,835
30	435	4,930	40,890
100	4,950	171,600	4,421,175

FIGURE 2-11 Number of nontrivial cross moments.

population data. In statistics we refer to these parameter estimates, or to the method of obtaining the estimate, as an estimator. For example, at the start of the chapter, we introduced an estimator for the sample mean:

$$\hat{\mu} = \frac{1}{n}\sum_{i=1}^{n} x_i \qquad \textbf{(2.56)}$$

This formula for computing the mean is so popular that we're likely to take it for granted. Why this equation, though? One justification that we gave earlier is that this particular estimator provides an unbiased estimate of the true mean. That is:

$$E[\hat{\mu}] = \mu \qquad \textbf{(2.57)}$$

Clearly, a good estimator should be unbiased. That said, for a given data set, we could imagine any number of unbiased estimators of the mean. For example, assuming there are three data points in our sample, x_1, x_2, and x_3, the following equation:

$$\hat{\mu} = 0.75x_1 + 0.25x_2 + 0.00x_3 \qquad \textbf{(2.58)}$$

is also an unbiased estimator of the mean. Intuitively, this new estimator seems strange; we have put three times as much weight on x_1 as on x_2, and we have put no weight on x_3. There is no reason, as we have described the problem, to believe that any one data point is better than any other, so distributing the weight equally might seem more logical. Still, the estimator in Equation (2.58) is unbiased, and our criterion for judging this estimator to be strange seems rather subjective. What we need is an objective measure for comparing different unbiased estimators.

As we will see in coming chapters, just as we can measure the variance of random variables, we can measure the variance of parameter estimators as well. For example, if we measure the sample mean of a random variable several times, we can get a different answer each time. Imagine rolling a die 10 times and taking the average of all the rolls. Then repeat this process again and again. The sample mean is potentially different for each sample of 10 rolls. It turns out that this variability of the sample mean, or any other distribution parameter, is a function not only of the underlying variable, but of the form of the estimator as well.

When choosing among all the unbiased estimators, statisticians typically try to come up with the estimator with the minimum variance. In other words, we want to choose a formula that produces estimates for the parameter that are consistently close to the true value of the parameter. If we limit ourselves to estimators that can be written as a linear combination of the data, we can often prove that a particular candidate has the minimum variance among all the potential unbiased estimators. We call an estimator with these properties the best linear unbiased estimator, or BLUE. All of the estimators that we produced in this chapter for the mean, variance, covariance, skewness, and kurtosis are either BLUE or the ratio of BLUE estimators.

Distributions

3

◼ Learning Objectives

Candidates, after completing this reading, should be able to:

- ◼ Distinguish the key properties among the following distributions: uniform distribution, Bernoulli distribution, Binomial distribution, Poisson distribution, normal distribution, lognormal distribution, Chi-squared distribution, Student's t, and F-distributions, and identify common occurrences of each distribution.

- ◼ Describe the central limit theorem and the implications it has when combining independent and identically distributed (i.i.d) random variables.
- ◼ Describe i.i.d random variables and the implications of the i.i.d. assumption when combining random variables.
- ◼ Describe a mixture distribution and explain the creation and characteristics of mixture distributions.

Excerpt is Chapter 4 of Mathematics and Statistics for Financial Risk Management, *Second Edition, by Michael B. Miller.*

In Chapter 1, we were introduced to random variables. In nature and in finance, random variables tend to follow certain patterns, or distributions. In this chapter we will learn about some of the most widely used probability distributions in risk management.

PARAMETRIC DISTRIBUTIONS

Distributions can be divided into two broad categories: parametric distributions and nonparametric distributions. A parametric distribution can be described by a mathematical function. In the following sections we explore a number of parametric distributions, including the uniform distribution and the normal distribution. A nonparametric distribution cannot be summarized by a mathematical formula. In its simplest form, a nonparametric distribution is just a collection of data. An example of a nonparametric distribution would be a collection of historical returns for a security.

Parametric distributions are often easier to work with, but they force us to make assumptions, which may not be supported by real-world data. Nonparametric distributions can fit the observed data perfectly. The drawback of nonparametric distributions is that they are potentially too specific, which can make it difficult to draw any general conclusions.

UNIFORM DISTRIBUTION

For a continuous random variable, X, recall that the probability of an outcome occurring between b_1 and b_2 can be found by integrating as follows:

$$P[b_1 \leq X \leq b_2] = \int_{b_1}^{b_2} f(x)dx$$

where $f(x)$ is the probability density function (PDF) of X.

The uniform distribution is one of the most fundamental distributions m statistics. The probability density function is given by the following formula:

$$u(b_1,b_2) = \begin{cases} c \ \forall \ b_1 \leq x \leq b_2 \\ 0 \ \forall \ b_1 > x > b_2 \end{cases} \text{s.t. } b_2 > b_1 \qquad \textbf{(3.1)}$$

In other words, the probability density is constant and equal to c between b_1 and b_2, and zero everywhere else. Figure 3-1 shows the plot of a uniform distribution's probability density function.

Because the probability of any outcome occurring must be one, we can find the value of c as follows:

$$\int_{-\infty}^{+\infty} u(b_1,b_2)dx = 1$$

$$\int_{-\infty}^{+\infty} u(b_1,b_2)dx = \int_{-\infty}^{b_1} 0dx + \int_{b_1}^{b_2} cdx + \int_{b_2}^{+\infty} 0dx = \int_{b_1}^{b_2} cdx$$

$$\int_{b_1}^{b_2} cdx = [cx]_{b_1}^{b_2} = c(b_2 - b_1) = 1$$

$$c = \frac{1}{b_2 - b_1} \qquad \textbf{(3.2)}$$

On reflection, this result should be obvious from the graph of the density function. That the probability of any outcome occurring must be one is equivalent to saying that the area under the probability density function must be equal to one. In Figure 3-1, we only need to know that the area of a rectangle is equal to the product of its width and its height to determine that c is equal to $1/(b_2 - b_1)$.

With the probability density function in hand, we can proceed to calculate the mean and the variance. For the mean:

$$\mu = \int_{b_1}^{b_2} cxdx = \frac{1}{2}(b_2 + b_1) \qquad \textbf{(3.3)}$$

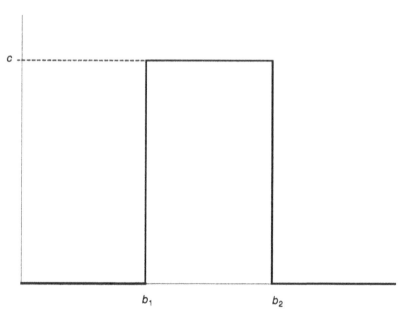

FIGURE 3-1 Probability density function of a uniform distribution.

In other words, the mean is just the average of the start and end values of the distribution.

Similarly, for the variance, we have:

$$\sigma^2 = \int_{b_1}^{b_2} c(x - \mu)^2 dx = \frac{1}{12}(b_2 - b_1)^2 \qquad \textbf{(3.4)}$$

This result is not as intuitive.

For the special case where $b_1 = 0$ and $b_2 = 1$, we refer to the distribution as a standard uniform distribution. Standard uniform distributions are extremely common. The default random number generator in most computer programs (technically a pseudo random number generator) is typically a standard uniform random variable. Because these random number generators are so ubiquitous, uniform distributions often serve as the building blocks for computer models in finance.

To calculate the cumulative distribution function (CDF) of the uniform distribution, we simply integrate the PDF. Again, assuming a lower bound of b_1 and an upper bound of b_2, we have:

$$P[X \le a] = \int_{b_1}^{a} c\,dz = c[z]_{b_1}^{a} = \frac{a - b_1}{b_2 - b_1} \qquad \textbf{(3.5)}$$

As required, when a equals b_1, we are at the minimum, and the CDF is zero. Similarly, when a equals b_2, we are at the maximum, and the CDF equals one.

As we will see later, we can use combinations of uniform distributions to approximate other more complex distributions. As we will see in the next section, uniform distributions can also serve as the basis of other simple distributions, including the Bernoulli distribution.

BERNOULLI DISTRIBUTION

Bernoulli's principle explains how the flow of fluids or gases leads to changes in pressure. It can be used to explain a number of phenomena, including how the wings of airplanes provide lift. Without it, modern aviation would be impossible. Bernoulli's principle is named after Daniel Bernoulli, an eighteenth-century Dutch-Swiss mathematician and scientist. Daniel came from a family of accomplished mathematicians. Daniel and his cousin Nicolas Bernoulli first described and presented a proof for the St. Petersburg paradox. But it is not Daniel or Nicolas, but rather their uncle, Jacob Bernoulli,

for whom the Bernoulli distribution is named. In addition to the Bernoulli distribution, Jacob is credited with first describing the concept of continuously compounded returns, and, along the way, discovering Euler's number, e.

The Bernoulli distribution is incredibly simple. A Bernoulli random variable is equal to either zero or one. If we define p as the probability that X equals one, we have:

$$P[X = 1] = p \text{ and } P[X = 0] = 1 - p \qquad \textbf{(3.6)}$$

We can easily calculate the mean and variance of a Bernoulli variable:

$$\mu = p \cdot 1 + (1 - p) \cdot 0 = p$$
$$\sigma^2 = p \cdot (1 - p)^2 + (1 - p) \cdot (0 - p)^2 = p(1 - p) \qquad \textbf{(3.7)}$$

Binary outcomes are quite common in finance: a bond can default or not default; the return of a stock can be positive or negative; a central bank can decide to raise rates or not to raise rates.

In a computer simulation, one way to model a Bernoulli variable is to start with a standard uniform variable. Conveniently, both the standard uniform variable and our Bernoulli probability, p, range between zero and one. If the draw from the standard uniform variable is less than p, we set our Bernoulli variable equal to one; likewise, if the draw is greater than or equal to p, we set the Bernoulli variable to zero (see Figure 3-2).

BINOMIAL DISTRIBUTION

A binomial distribution can be thought of as a collection of Bernoulli random variables. If we have two independent bonds and the probability of default for both is 10%, then there are three possible outcomes: no bond defaults, one bond defaults, or both bonds default. Labeling the number of defaults K:

$$P[K = 0] = (1 - 10\%)^2 = 81\%$$
$$P[K = 1] = 2 \cdot 10\% \cdot (1 - 10\%) = 18\%$$
$$P[K = 2] = 10\%^2 = 1\%$$

Notice that for $K = 1$ we have multiplied the probability of a bond defaulting, 10%, and the probability of a bond not defaulting, $1 - 10\%$, by 2. This is because there are two ways in which exactly one bond can default: The first bond defaults and the second does not, or the second bond defaults and the first does not.

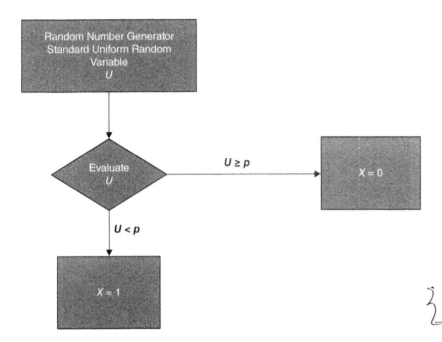

FIGURE 3-2 How to generate a Bernoulli distribution from a uniform distribution.

If we now have three bonds, still independent and with a 10% chance of defaulting, then:

$$P[K = 0] = (1 - 10\%)^3 = 72.9\%$$

$$P[K = 1] = 3 \cdot 10\% \cdot (1 - 10\%)^2 = 24.3\%$$

$$P[K = 2] = 3 \cdot 10\%^2 \cdot (1 - 10\%) = 2.7\%$$

$$P[K = 3] = 10\%^3 = 0.1\%$$

Notice that there are three ways in which we can get exactly one default and three ways in which we can get exactly two defaults.

We can extend this logic to any number of bonds. If we have n bonds, the number of ways in which k of those bonds can default is given by the number of combinations:

$$\binom{n}{k} = \frac{n!}{k!(n-k)!} \qquad (3.8)$$

Similarly, if the probability of one bond defaulting is p, then the probability of any *particular* k bonds defaulting is simply $p^k(1-p)^{n-k}$. Putting these two together, we can calculate the probability of any k bonds defaulting as:

$$P[K = k] = \binom{n}{k} p^k (1-p)^{n-k} \qquad (3.9)$$

This is the probability density function for the binomial distribution. You should check that this equation produces the same result as our examples with two and three bonds. While the general proof is somewhat complicated, it is not difficult to prove that the probabilities sum to one for $n = 2$ or $n = 3$, no matter what value p takes. It is a common mistake when calculating these probabilities to leave out the combinatorial term.

For the formulation in Equation (3.9), the mean of random variable K is equal to np. So for a bond portfolio with 40 bonds, each with a 20% chance of defaulting, we would expect eight bonds ($8 = 20 \times 0.40$) to default on average. The variance of a binomial distribution is $np(1 - p)$.

Example 3.1

Question:

Assume we have four bonds, each with a 10% probability of defaulting over the next year. The event of default for any given bond is independent of the other bonds defaulting. What is the probability that zero, one, two, three, or all of the bonds default? What is the mean number of defaults? The standard deviation?

Answer:

We can calculate the probability of each possible outcome as follows:

# of Defaults	$\binom{n}{k}$	$p^k(1 - p)^{n-k}$	Probability
0	1	65.61%	65.61%
1	4	7.29%	29.16%
2	6	0.81%	4.86%
3	4	0.09%	0.36%
4	1	0.01%	0.01%
			100.00%

We can calculate the mean number of defaults two ways. The first is to use our formula for the mean:

$$\mu = np = 4 \cdot 10\% = 0.40$$

On average there are 0.40 defaults. The other way we could arrive at this result is to use the probabilities from the table. We get:

$$\mu = \sum_{i=0}^{4} p_i x_i = 65.61\% \cdot 0 + 29.16\% \cdot 1 + 4.86\% \cdot 2 + 0.36\% \cdot 3$$
$$+ 0.01\% \cdot 4 = 0.40$$

This is consistent with our earlier result.

To calculate the standard deviation, we also have two choices. Using our formula for variance, we have:

$$\sigma^2 = np(1 - p) = 4 \cdot 10\%(1 - 10\%) = 0.36$$
$$\sigma = 0.60$$

As with the mean, we could also use the probabilities from the table:

$$\sigma^2 = \sum_{i=0}^{4} p_i (x_i - \mu)^2$$
$$\sigma^2 = 65.61\% \cdot 0.16 + 29.16\% \cdot 0.36 + 4.86\% \cdot 2.56 + 0.36\% \cdot 6.76$$
$$+ 0.01\% \cdot 12.96 = 0.36$$
$$\sigma = 0.60$$

Again, this is consistent with our earlier result.

Figure 3-3 shows binomial distributions with $p = 0.50$, for $n = 4, 16$, and 64. The highest point of each distribution

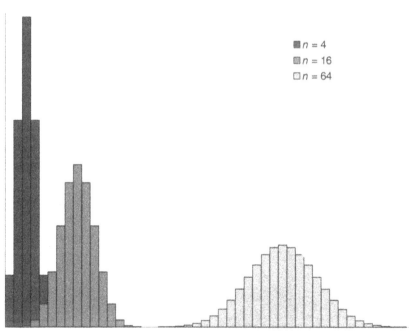

■ $n = 4$
■ $n = 16$
☐ $n = 64$

FIGURE 3-3 Binomial probability density functions.

occurs in the middle. In other words, when $p = 0.50$, the most likely outcome for a binomial random variable, the mode, is $n/2$ when n is even, or the whole numbers either side of $n/2$ when n is odd.

POISSON DISTRIBUTION

Another useful discrete distribution is the Poisson distribution, named for the French mathematician Simeon Denis Poisson.

For a Poisson random variable X,

$$P[X = n] = \frac{\lambda^n}{n!} e^{-\lambda} \qquad (3.10)$$

for some constant λ, it turns out that both the mean and variance of X are equal to λ. Figure 3-4 shows the probability density functions for three Poisson distributions.

The Poisson distribution is often used to model the occurrence of events over time—for example, the number of bond defaults in a portfolio or the number of crashes in equity markets. In this case, n is the number of events that occur in an interval, and λ is the expected number of events in the interval. Poisson distributions are often used to model jumps in jump-diffusion models.

If the rate at which events occur over time is constant, and the probability of any one event occurring is independent of all other events, then we say that the events follow a Poisson process, where:

$$P[X = n] = \frac{(\lambda t)^n}{n!} e^{-\lambda t} \qquad (3.11)$$

where t is the amount of time elapsed. In other words, the expected number of events before time t is equal to λt.

Example 3.2

Question:

Assume that defaults in a large bond portfolio follow a Poisson process. The expected number of defaults each month is four. What is the probability that there are exactly three defaults over the course of one month? Over two months?

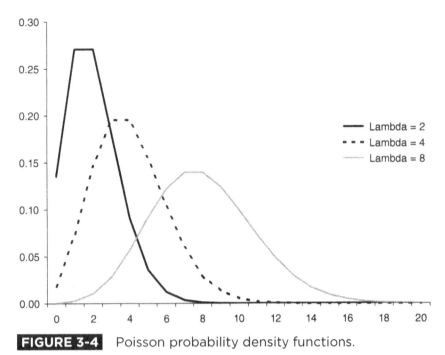

FIGURE 3-4 Poisson probability density functions.

Answer:

For the first question, we solve the following:

$$P[X = 3] = \frac{(\lambda t)^n}{n!}e^{-\lambda t} = \frac{(4 \cdot 1)^3}{3!}e^{-4 \cdot 1} = 19.5\%$$

Over two months, the answer is:

$$P[X = 3] = \frac{(\lambda t)^n}{n!}e^{-\lambda t} = \frac{(4 \cdot 2)^3}{3!}e^{-4 \cdot 2} = 2.9\%$$

NORMAL DISTRIBUTION

The normal distribution is probably the most widely used distribution in statistics, and is extremely popular in finance. The normal distribution occurs in a large number of settings, and is extremely easy to work with.

In popular literature, the normal distribution is often referred to as the bell curve because of the shape of its probability density function (see Figure 3-5).

The probability density function of the normal distribution is symmetrical, with the mean and median coinciding with the highest point of the PDF. Because it is symmetrical, the skew of a normal distribution is always zero. The kurtosis of a normal distribution is always 3. By definition, the excess kurtosis of a normal distribution is zero.

In some fields it is more common to refer to the normal distribution as the Gaussian distribution, after the famous German mathematician Johann Gauss, who is credited with some of the earliest work with the distribution. It is not the case that one name is more precise than the other as is the case with mean and average. Both normal distribution and Gaussian distribution are acceptable terms.

For a random variable X, the probability density function for the normal distribution is:

$$f(x) = \frac{1}{\sigma\sqrt{2\pi}}e^{-\frac{1}{2}\left(\frac{x-\mu}{\sigma}\right)^2} \qquad \textbf{(3.12)}$$

The distribution is described by two parameters, μ and σ; μ is the mean of the distribution and σ is the standard deviation.

Rather than writing out the entire density function, when a variable is normally distributed it is the convention to write:

$$X \sim N(\mu, \sigma^2) \qquad \textbf{(3.13)}$$

This would be read "X is normally distributed with a mean of μ and variance *of* σ^2."

One reason that normal distributions are easy to work with is that any linear combination of independent normal variables is also normal. If we have two normally distributed variables, X and Y, and two constants, a and b, then Z is also normally distributed:

$$Z = aX + bY \text{ s.t. } Z \sim N(a\mu_X + b\mu_Y, a^2\sigma_X^2 + b^2\sigma_Y^2) \qquad \textbf{(3.14)}$$

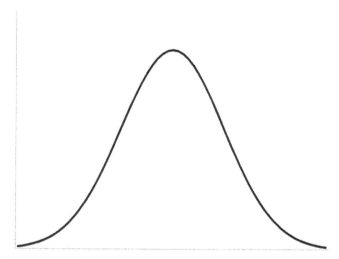

FIGURE 3-5 Normal distribution probability density function.

This is very convenient. For example, if the log returns of individual stocks are independent and normally distributed, then the average return of those stocks will also be normally distributed.

When a normal distribution has a mean of zero and a standard deviation of one, it is referred to as a standard normal distribution. $\mu = 0 \quad \sigma = 1$

$$\phi = \frac{1}{\sqrt{2\pi}}e^{-\frac{1}{2}x^2} \tag{3.15}$$

It is the convention to denote the standard normal PDF by ϕ, and the cumulative standard normal distribution by Φ.

Because a linear combination of independent normal distributions is also normal, standard normal distributions are the building blocks of many financial models. To get a normal variable with a standard deviation of σ and a mean of μ, we simply multiply the standard normal variable by σ and add μ.

$$X = \mu + \sigma\phi \Rightarrow X \sim N(\mu, \sigma^2) \tag{3.16}$$

To create two correlated normal variables, we can combine three independent standard normal variables, X_1, X_2, and X_3, as follows:

$$X_A = \sqrt{\rho}X_1 + \sqrt{1-\rho}X_2$$
$$X_B = \sqrt{\rho}X_1 + \sqrt{1-\rho}X_3 \tag{3.17}$$

In this formulation, X_A and X_B are also standard normal variables, but with a correlation of ρ.

Normal distributions are used throughout finance and risk management. Earlier, we suggested that log returns are extremely useful in financial modeling. One attribute that makes log returns particularly attractive is that they can be modeled using normal distributions. Normal distributions can generate numbers from negative infinity to positive infinity. For a particular normal distribution, the most extreme values might be extremely unlikely, but they can occur. This poses a problem for standard returns, which typically cannot be less than −100%. For log returns, though, there is no such constraint. Log returns also can range from negative to positive infinity.

Normally distributed log returns are widely used in financial simulations, and form the basis of a number of financial models, including the Black–Scholes option pricing model. As we will see in the coming chapters, while this normal assumption is often a convenient starting point, much of risk management is focused on addressing departures from this normality assumption.

There is no explicit solution for the cumulative standard normal distribution, or for its inverse. That said, most statistical packages will be able to calculate values for both functions. To calculate values for the CDF or inverse CDF for the normal distribution, there are a number of well-known numerical approximations.

Because the normal distribution is so widely used, most practitioners are expected to have at least a rough idea of how much of the distribution falls within one, two, or three standard deviations. In risk management it is also useful to know how many standard deviations are needed to encompass 95% or 99% of outcomes. Figure 3-6 lists some common values. Notice that for each row in the table, there is a "one-tailed" and "two-tailed" column. If we want to know how far we have to go to encompass 95% of the mass in the density function, the one-tailed value tells us that 95% of the values are less than 1.64 standard deviations above the mean. Because the normal distribution is symmetrical, it follows that 5% of the values are less than 1.64 standard deviations below the mean. The two-tailed value, in turn, tells us that 95% of the mass is within +/−1.96 standard deviations of the mean. It follows that 2.5% of the outcomes are less than −1.96 standard deviations from the mean, and 2.5% are greater than +1.96 standard deviations from the mean. Rather than one-tailed and two-tailed, some authors refer to "one-sided" and "two-sided" values.

	One-Tailed	Two-Tailed
1.0%	−2.33	−2.58
2.5%	−1.96	−2.24
5.0%	−1.64	−1.96
10.0%	−1.28	−1.64
90.0%	1.28	1.64
95.0%	1.64	1.96
97.5%	1.96	2.24
99.0%	2.33	2.58

FIGURE 3-6 Normal distribution confidence intervals.

LOGNORMAL DISTRIBUTION

It's natural to ask: if we assume that log returns are normally distributed, then how are standard returns distributed? To put it another way: rather than modeling log returns with a normal distribution, can we use another distribution and model standard returns directly?

The answer to these questions lies in the lognormal distribution, whose density function is given by:

$$f(x) = \frac{1}{x\sigma\sqrt{2\pi}} e^{-\frac{1}{2}\left(\frac{\ln x - \mu}{\sigma}\right)^2} \qquad \textbf{(3.18)}$$

If a variable has a lognormal distribution, then the log of that variable has a normal distribution. So, if log returns are assumed to be normally distributed, then one plus the standard return will be lognormally distributed.

Unlike the normal distribution, which ranges from negative infinity to positive infinity, the lognormal distribution is undefined, or zero, for negative values. Given an asset with a standard return, R, if we model $(1 + R)$ using the lognormal distribution, then R will have a minimum value of −100%. This feature, which we associate with limited liability, is common to most financial assets. Using the lognormal distribution provides an easy way to ensure that we avoid returns less than −100%. The probability density function for a lognormal distribution is shown in Figure 3-7.

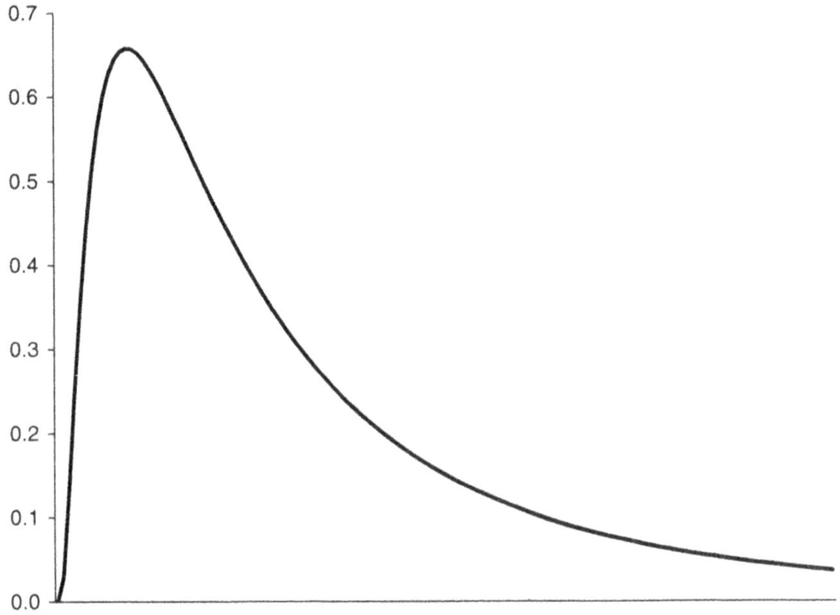

0.7
0.6
0.5
0.4
0.3
0.2
0.1
0.0

FIGURE 3-7 Lognormal probability density function.

Equation (3.18) looks almost exactly like the equation for the normal distribution, Equation (3.12), with x replaced by $\ln(x)$. Be careful, though, as there is also the x in the denominator of the leading fraction. At first it might not be clear what the x is doing there. By carefully rearranging Equation (3.18), we can get something that, while slightly longer, looks more like the normal distribution in form:

$$f(x) = e^{\frac{1}{2}\sigma^2 - \mu} \frac{1}{\sigma\sqrt{2\pi}} e^{-\frac{1}{2}\left(\frac{\ln x - (\mu - \sigma^2)}{\sigma}\right)^2} \qquad \textbf{(3.19)}$$

While not as pretty, this starts to hint at what we've actually done. Rather than being symmetrical around μ, as in the normal distribution, the lognormal distribution is asymmetrical and peaks at $\exp(\mu - \sigma^2)$.

Given μ and σ, the mean is given by:

$$E[X] = e^{\mu + \frac{1}{2}\sigma^2} \qquad \textbf{(3.20)}$$

This result looks very similar to the Taylor expansion of the natural logarithm around one. Remember, if R is a standard return and r the corresponding log return, then:

$$r \approx R - \frac{1}{2} R^2 \qquad \textbf{(3.21)}$$

Be careful: Because these equations are somewhat similar, it is very easy to get the signs in front of σ^2 and R^2 backward.

The variance of the lognormal distribution is given by:

$$E[(X - E[X])^2] = (e^{\sigma^2} - 1)e^{2\mu + \sigma^2} \qquad \textbf{(3.22)}$$

The equations for the mean and the variance hint at the difficulty of working with lognormal distributions directly. It is convenient to be able to describe the returns of a financial instrument as being lognormally distributed, rather than having to say the log returns of that instrument are normally distributed. When it comes to modeling, though, even though they are equivalent, it is often easier to work with log returns and normal distributions than with standard returns and lognormal distributions.

CENTRAL LIMIT THEOREM

Assume we have an index made up of a large number of equities, or a bond portfolio that contains a large number of similar bonds. In these situations and many more, it is often convenient to assume that the constituent elements—the equities or bonds—are made up of statistically identical random variables, and that these variables are uncorrelated with each other. As mentioned previously, in statistics we term these variables independent and identically distributed (i.i.d.). If the constituent elements are i.i.d., it turns out we can say a lot about the distribution of the population, even if the distribution of the individual elements is unknown.

We already know that if we add two i.i.d. normal distributions together we get a normal distribution, but what happens if we add two i.i.d. uniform variables together? Looking at the graph of the uniform distribution (Figure 3-1), you might think that we would get another uniform distribution, but this isn't the case. In fact, the probability density function resembles a triangle.

Assume we have two defaulted bonds, each with a face value of $100. The recovery rate for each bond is assumed to be uniform, between $0 and $100. At best we recover the full face value of the bond; at worst we get nothing. Further, assume the recovery rate for each bond is independent of the other. In other words, the bonds are i.i.d. uniform, between $0 and $100. What is the distribution for the portfolio of the two bonds? In the worst-case scenario, we recover $0 from both bonds, and the total recovery is $0. In the best-case scenario, we recover the full amount for both bonds, $200 for the portfolio. Because the bonds are independent, these extremes are actually very unlikely. The most likely scenario is right in the middle, where we recover $100. This could happen if we recover $40 from the first bond and $60 from the second, $90 from the first and $10 from the second, or any of an infinite number of combinations. Figure 3-8 shows the distribution of values for the portfolio of two i.i.d. bonds.

With three bonds, the distribution ranges from $0 to $300, with the mode at $150. With four bonds, the distribution ranges from $0 to $400, with the mode at $200.

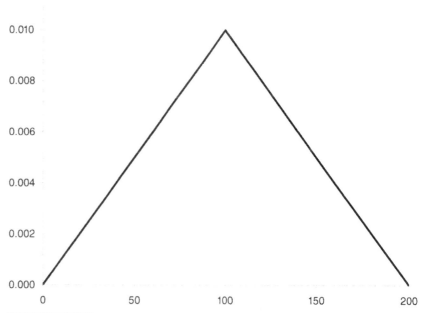

FIGURE 3-8 Sum of two i.i.d. uniform distributions.

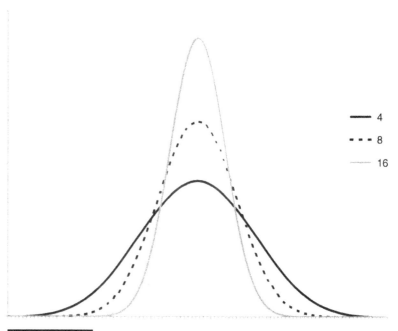

FIGURE 3-9 Sums of various i.i.d. uniform distributions.

As we continue to add more bonds, the shape of the distribution function continues to change. Figure 3-9 shows the density functions for the sums of 4, 8, and 16 i.i.d. uniform variables, scaled to have the same range.

Oddly enough, even though we started with uniform variables, the distribution is starting to look increasingly like a normal distribution. The resemblance is not just superficial; it turns out that as we add more and more variables, the distribution actually converges to a normal distribution. What's more, this is not just true if we start out with uniform distributions; it applies to any distributions with finite variance.[1] This result is known as the central limit theorem.

More formally, if we have n i.i.d. random variables, $X_1, X_2, \ldots, X_n$, each with mean μ and standard deviation σ, and we define S_n as the sum of those n variables, then:

$$\lim_{n \to \infty} S_n \sim N(n\mu, n\sigma^2) \qquad \textbf{(3.23)}$$

In other words, as n approaches infinity, the sum converges to a normal distribution. This result is one of the most important results in statistics and is the reason why the normal distribution is so ubiquitous. In risk, as in a number of other fields, we are often presented with data that either is i.i.d. by construction or is assumed to be i.i.d. Even when the underlying variables are not normal—which is rare in practice—the i.i.d. assumption, combined with the central limit theorem, allows us to approximate a large collection of data using a normal distribution. The central limit theorem is often used to justify the approximation of financial variables by a normal distribution.

APPLICATION: MONTE CARLO SIMULATIONS PART I: CREATING NORMAL RANDOM VARIABLES

While some problems in risk management have explicit analytic solutions, many problems have no exact mathematical solution. In these cases, we can often approximate a solution by creating a Monte Carlo simulation. A Monte Carlo simulation consists of a number of trials. For each trial we feed random inputs into a system of equations. By collecting the outputs from the system of equations for a large number of trials, we can estimate the statistical properties of the output variables.

Even in cases where explicit solutions might exist, a Monte Carlo solution might be preferable in practice if the explicit solution is difficult to derive or extremely complex.

---

[1] Even though we have not yet encountered any distributions with infinite variance, they can exist. The Cauchy distribution is an example of a parametric distribution with infinite variance. While rare in finance, it's good to know that these distributions can exist.

In some cases a simple Monte Carlo simulation can be easier to understand, thereby reducing operational risk.

As an example of a situation where we might use a Monte Carlo simulation, pretend we are asked to evaluate the mean and standard deviation of the profits from a fixed-strike arithmetic Asian option, where the value of the option, V, at expiry is:

$$V = \max\left[\frac{1}{T}\sum_{t=1}^{T} S_t - X, 0\right] \qquad \textbf{(3.24)}$$

Here X is the strike price, S_t is the closing price of the underlying asset at time t, and T is the number of periods in the life of the option. In other words, the value of the option at expiry is the greater of zero or the average price of the underlying asset less the strike price.

Assume there are 200 days until expiry. Further, we are told that the returns of the underlying asset are lognormal, with a mean of 10% and a standard deviation of 20%. The input to our Monte Carlo simulation would be lognormal variables with the appropriate mean and standard deviation. For each trial, we would generate 200 random daily returns, use the returns to calculate a series of random prices, calculate the average of the price series, and use the average to calculate the value of the option. We would repeat this process again and again, using a different realization of the random returns each time, and each time calculating a new value for the option.

The initial step in the Monte Carlo simulation, generating the random inputs, can itself be very complex. We will learn how to create correlated normally distributed random variables from a set of uncorrelated normally distributed random variables. How do we create the uncorrelated normally distributed random variables to start with? Many special-purpose statistical packages contain functions that will generate random draws from normal distributions. If the application we are using does not have this feature, but does have a standard random number generator, which generates a standard uniform distribution, there are two ways we can generate random normal variables. The first is to use an inverse normal transformation. As mentioned previously, there is no explicit formula for the inverse normal transformation, but there are a number of good approximations.

The second approach takes advantage of the central limit theorem. By adding together a large number of i.i.d. uniform distributions and then multiplying and adding the correct constants, a good approximation to any normal variable can be formed. A classic approach is to simply add 12 standard uniform variables together, and subtract 6:

$$X = \sum_{i=1}^{12} U_i - 6 \qquad (3.25)$$

Because the mean of a standard uniform variable is ½ and the variance is 1/12, this produces a good approximation to a standard normal variable, with mean zero and standard deviation of one. By utilizing a greater number of uniform variables, we could increase the accuracy of our approximation, but for most applications, this approximation is more than adequate.

CHI-SQUARED DISTRIBUTION

If we have k independent standard normal variables, $Z_1, Z_2, \ldots, Z_k$, then the sum of their squares, S, has a chi-squared distribution. We write:

$$S = \sum_{i=1}^{k} Z_i^2$$
$$S \sim \chi_k^2 \qquad (3.26)$$

The variable k is commonly referred to as the degrees of freedom. It follows that the sum of two independent chi-squared variables, with k_1 and k_2 degrees of freedom, will follow a chi-squared distribution, with $(k_1 + k_2)$ degrees of freedom.

Because the chi-squared variable is the sum of squared values, it can take on only nonnegative values and is asymmetrical. The mean of the distribution is k, and the variance is $2k$. As k increases, the chi-squared distribution becomes increasingly symmetrical. As k approaches infinity, the chi-squared distribution converges to the normal distribution. Figure 3-10 shows the probability density functions for some chi-squared distributions with different values for k.

For positive values of x, the probability density function for the chi-squared distribution is:

$$f(x) = \frac{1}{2^{k/2} \Gamma(k/2)} x^{\frac{k}{2}-1} e^{-\frac{x}{2}} \qquad (3.27)$$

where Γ is the gamma function:

$$\Gamma(n) = \int_0^\infty x^{n-1} e^{-x} dx \qquad (3.28)$$

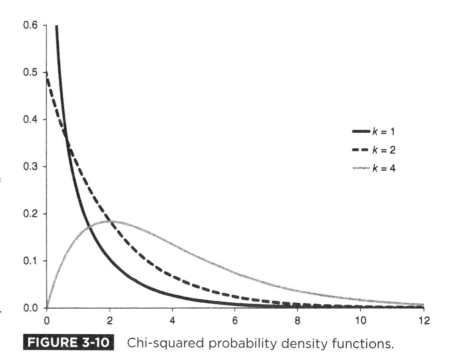

FIGURE 3-10 Chi-squared probability density functions.

The chi-squared distribution is widely used in risk management, and in statistics in general, for hypothesis testing.

STUDENT'S *t* DISTRIBUTION

Another extremely popular distribution in statistics and in risk management is Student's *t* distribution. The distribution was first described in English, in 1908, by William Sealy Gosset, an employee at the Guinness brewery in Dublin. In order to comply with his firm's policy on publishing in public journals, he submitted his work under the pseudonym Student. The distribution has been known as Student's *t* distribution ever since. In practice, it is often referred to simply as the *t* distribution.

If Z is a standard normal variable and U is a chi-square variable with k degrees of freedom, which is independent of Z, then the random variable X,

$$X = \frac{Z}{\sqrt{U/k}} \qquad (3.29)$$

follows a *t* distribution with k degrees of freedom.

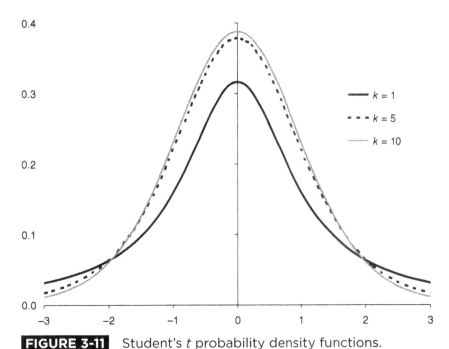

FIGURE 3-11 Student's t probability density functions.

Mathematically, the distribution is quite complicated. The probability density function can be written:

$$f(x) = \frac{\Gamma\left(\frac{k+1}{2}\right)}{\sqrt{k\pi}\,\Gamma\left(\frac{k}{2}\right)}\left(1 + \frac{x^2}{k}\right)^{-\frac{k+1}{2}} \quad \text{(3.30)}$$

where k is the degrees of freedom and Γ is the gamma function.

Very few risk managers will memorize this PDF equation, but it is important to understand the basic shape of the distribution and how it changes with k. Figure 3-11 shows the probability density function for three Student's t distributions. Notice how changing the value of k changes the shape of the distribution, specifically the tails.

The t distribution is symmetrical around its mean, which is equal to zero. For low values of k, the t distribution looks very similar to a standard normal distribution, except that it displays excess kurtosis. As k increases, this excess kurtosis decreases. In fact, as k approaches infinity, the t distribution converges to a standard normal distribution.

The variance of the t distribution for $k > 2$ is $k/(k-2)$. You can see that as k increases, the variance of the t distribution converges to one, the variance of the standard normal distribution.

The t distribution's popularity derives mainly from its use in hypothesis testing. The t distribution is also a popular

choice for modeling the returns of financial assets, since it displays excess kurtosis.

F-DISTRIBUTION

If U_1 and U_2 are two independent chi-squared distributions with k_1 and k_2 degrees of freedom, respectively, then X,

$$X = \frac{U_1/k_1}{U_2/k_2} \sim F(k_1, k_2) \quad \text{(3.31)}$$

follows an F-distribution with parameters k_1 and k_2.

The probability density function of the F-distribution, as with the chi-squared distribution, is rather complicated:

$$f(x) = \frac{\sqrt{\frac{(k_1 x)^{k_1} k_2^{k_2}}{(k_1 x + k_2)^{k_1+k_2}}}}{xB\left(\frac{k_1}{2}, \frac{k_2}{2}\right)} \quad \text{(3.32)}$$

where $B(x, y)$ is the beta function:

$$B(x, y) = \int_0^1 z^{x-1}(1-z)^{y-1}dz \quad \text{(3.33)}$$

As with the chi-squared and Student's t distributions, memorizing the probability density function is probably not something most risk managers would be expected to do; rather, it is important to understand the general shape and some properties of the distribution.

Figure 3-12 shows the probability density functions for several F-distributions. Because the chi-squared PDF is zero for negative values, the F-distributions density function is also zero for negative values. The mean and variance of the F-distribution are as follows:

$$\mu = \frac{k_2}{k_2 - 2} \text{ for } k_2 > 2$$

$$\sigma^2 = \frac{2k_2^2(k_1 + k_2 - 2)}{k_1(k_2 - 2)^2(k_2 - 4)} \text{ for } k_2 > 4 \quad \text{(3.34)}$$

As k_1 and k_2 increase, the mean and mode converge to one. As k_1 and k_2 approach infinity, the F-distribution converges to a normal distribution.

There is also a nice relationship between Student's t distribution and the F-distribution. From the description of the t distribution, Equation (3.29), it is easy to see

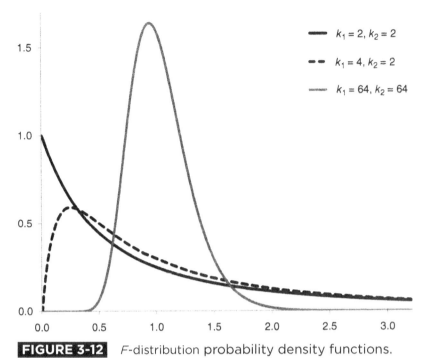

FIGURE 3-12 *F*-distribution probability density functions.

that the square of a variable with a *t* distribution has an *F*-distribution. More specifically, if X is a random variable with a *t* distribution with k degrees of freedom, then X^2 has an *F*-distribution with 1 and k degrees of freedom:

$$X^2 \sim F(1,k) \qquad (3.35)$$

TRIANGULAR DISTRIBUTION

It is often useful in risk management to have a distribution with a fixed minimum and maximum—for example, when modeling default rates and recovery rates, which by definition cannot be less than zero or greater than one. The uniform distribution is an example of a continuous distribution with a finite range. While the uniform distribution is extremely simple to work with (it is completely described by two parameters), it is rather limited in that the probability of an event is constant over its entire range.

The triangular distribution is a distribution whose PDF is a triangle. As with the uniform distribution, it has a finite range. Mathematically, the triangular distribution is only slightly more complex than a uniform distribution, but much more flexible. The triangular distribution has a unique mode, and can be symmetric, positively skewed, or negatively skewed.

The PDF for a triangular distribution with a minimum of a, a maximum of b, and a mode of c is described by the following two-part function:

$$f(x) = \begin{cases} \dfrac{2(x-a)}{(b-a)(c-a)} & a \le x \le c \\[2mm] \dfrac{2(b-x)}{(b-a)(b-c)} & c \le x \le b \end{cases} \qquad (3.36)$$

Figure 3-13 shows a triangular distribution where a, b, and c are 0.0, 1.0, and 0.8, respectively.

It is easily verified that the PDF is zero at both a and b, and that the value of $f(x)$ reaches a maximum, $2/(b-a)$, at c. Because the area of a triangle is simply one half the base multiplied by the height, it is also easy to confirm that the area under the PDF is equal to one.

The mean, μ, and variance, σ^2, of a triangular distribution are given by:

$$\mu = \frac{a+b+c}{3}$$
$$\sigma^2 = \frac{a^2+b^2+c^2-ab-ac-bc}{18} \qquad (3.37)$$

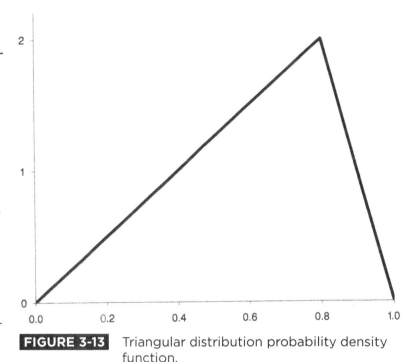

FIGURE 3-13 Triangular distribution probability density function.

BETA DISTRIBUTION

The beta distribution is another distribution with a finite range. It is more complicated than the triangular distribution mathematically, but it is also much more flexible.

As with the triangular distribution, the beta distribution can be used to model default rates and recovery rates. As we will see in Chapter 4, the beta distribution is also extremely useful in Bayesian analysis.

The beta distribution is defined on the interval from zero to one. The PDF is defined as follows, where a and b are two positive constants:

$$f(x) = \frac{1}{B(a,b)} x^{a-1}(1-x)^{b-1} \quad 0 \le x \le 1 \qquad \textbf{(3.38)}$$

where $B(a,b)$ is the beta function as described earlier for the F-distribution. The uniform distribution is a special case of the beta distribution, where both a and b are equal to one. Figure 3-14 shows four different parameterizations of the beta distribution.

The mean, μ, and variance, σ^2, of a beta distribution are given by:

$$\mu = \frac{a}{a+b}$$
$$\sigma^2 = \frac{ab}{(a+b)^2(a+b+1)} \qquad \textbf{(3.39)}$$

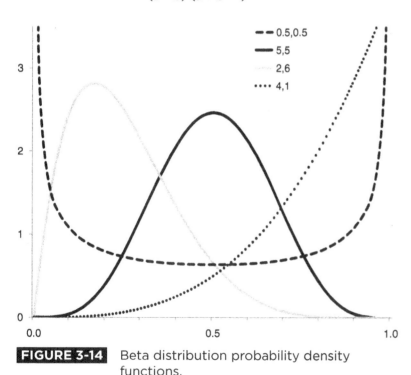

FIGURE 3-14 Beta distribution probability density functions.

MIXTURE DISTRIBUTIONS

Imagine a stock whose log returns follow a normal distribution with low volatility 90% of the time, and a normal distribution with high volatility 10% of the time. Most of the time the world is relatively dull, and the stock just bounces along. Occasionally, though—maybe there is an earnings announcement or some other news event—the stock's behavior is more extreme. We could write the combined density function as:

$$f(x) = w_L f_L(x) + w_H f_H(x) \qquad \textbf{(3.40)}$$

where $w_L = 0.90$ is the probability of the return coming from the low-volatility distribution, $f_L(x)$, and $w_H = 0.10$ is the probability of the return coming from the high-volatility distribution $f_H(x)$. We can think of this as a two-step process. First, we randomly choose the high or low distribution, with a 90% chance of picking the low distribution. Second, we generate a random return from the chosen normal distribution. The final distribution, $f(x)$, is a legitimate probability distribution in its own right, and although it is equally valid to describe a random draw directly from this distribution, it is often helpful to think in terms of this two-step process.

Note that the two-step process is not the same as the process described in a previous section for adding two random variables together. An example of adding two random variables together is a portfolio of two stocks. At each point in time, each stock generates a random return, and the portfolio return is the sum of *both* returns. In the case we are describing now, the return appears to come from *either* the low-volatility distribution *or* the high-volatility distribution.

The distribution that results from a weighted average distribution of density functions is known as a mixture distribution. More generally, we can create a distribution:

$$f(x) = \sum_{i=1}^{n} w_i f_i(x) \quad \text{s.t.} \sum_{i=1}^{n} w_i = 1 \qquad \textbf{(3.41)}$$

where the various $f_i(x)$'s are known as the component distributions, and the w_i's are known as the mixing proportions or weights. Notice that in order for the resulting mixture distribution to be a legitimate distribution, the sum of the component weights must equal one.

Mixture distributions are extremely flexible. In a sense they occupy a realm between parametric distributions and nonparametric distributions. In a typical mixture distribution, the component distributions are parametric, but the weights are based on empirical data, which is nonparametric. Just as there is a trade-off between parametric distributions and nonparametric distributions, there is a trade-off between using a low number and a high number of component distributions. By adding more and more component distributions, we can approximate any data set with increasing precision. At the same time, as we add more and more component distributions, the conclusions that we can draw tend to become less general in nature.

Just by adding two normal distributions together, we can develop a large number of interesting distributions. Similar to the previous example, if we combine two normal distributions with the same mean but different variances, we can get a symmetrical mixture distribution that displays excess kurtosis. By shifting the mean of one distribution, we can also create a distribution with positive or negative skew. Figure 3-15 shows an example of a skewed mixture distribution created from two normal distributions.

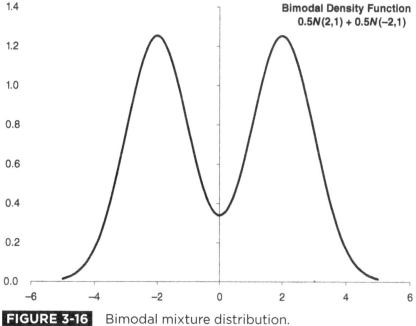

FIGURE 3-16   Bimodal mixture distribution.

Finally, if we move the means far enough apart, the resulting mixture distribution will be bimodal; that is, the PDF will have two distinct maxima, as shown in Figure 3-16.

Mixture distributions can be extremely useful in risk management. Securities whose return distributions are skewed or have excess kurtosis are often considered riskier than those with normal distributions, since extreme events can occur more frequently. Mixture distributions provide a ready method for modeling these attributes.

A bimodal distribution can be extremely risky. If one component of a security's returns has an extremely low mixing weight, we might be tempted to ignore that component. If the component has an extremely negative mean, though, ignoring it could lead us to severely underestimate the risk of the security. Equity market crashes are a perfect example of an extremely low-probability, highly negative mean event.

Example 3.3

Question:

Assume we have a mixture distribution with two independent components with equal variance. Prove that the variance of the mixture

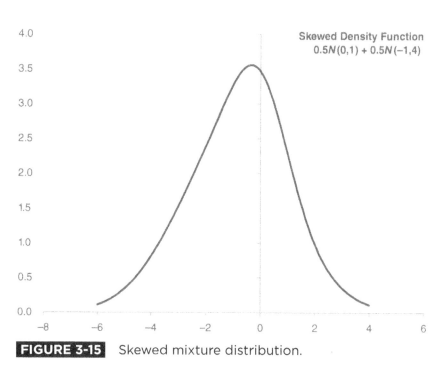

FIGURE 3-15   Skewed mixture distribution.

distribution must be greater than or equal to the variance of the two component distributions.

Answer:

Assume the two random variables, X_1 and X_2, have variance σ^2. The means are μ_1 and μ_2, with corresponding weights w and $(1 - w)$.

The mean of the mixture distribution, X, is just the weighted average of the two means:

$$\mu = E[X] = w_1 E[X_1] + w_2 E[X_2] = w\mu_1 + (1 - w)\mu_2$$

The variance is then:

$$E[(X - \mu)^2] = w_1 E[(X_1 - \mu)^2] + (1 - w)E[(X_2 - \mu)^2]$$

First, we solve for one term on the right-hand side:

$$
\begin{aligned}
E[(X_1 - \mu)^2] &= E[(X_1 - w\mu_1 - (1 - w)\mu_2)^2] \\
&= E[(X_1 - \mu_1 - (1 - w)(\mu_2 - \mu_1))^2] \\
&= E[(X_1 - \mu_1)^2 - 2(X_1 - \mu_1)(1 - w)(\mu_2 - \mu_1) \\
&\quad + (1 - w)^2(\mu_2 - \mu_1)^2] \\
&= \sigma^2 + (1 - w)^2(\mu_1 - \mu_2)^2
\end{aligned}
$$

Similarly for the second term:

$$E[(X_2 - \mu)^2] = \sigma^2 + w^2(\mu_1 - \mu_2)^2$$

Substituting back into our original equation for variance:

$$E[(X - \mu)^2] = \sigma^2 + w(1 - w)(\mu_1 - \mu_2)^2$$

Because w and $(1 - w)$ are always positive and $(\mu_1 - \mu_2)^2$ has a minimum of zero, $w(1 - w)(\mu_1 - \mu_2)^2$ must be greater than or equal to zero. Therefore, the variance of the mixture distribution must always be greater than or equal to σ^2.

Bayesian Analysis

Learning Objectives

Candidates, after completing this reading, should be able to:

- Describe Bayes' theorem and apply this theorem in the calculation of conditional probabilities.
- Compare the Bayesian approach to the frequentist approach.
- Apply Bayes' theorem to scenarios with more than two possible outcomes and calculate posterior probabilities.

Excerpt is Chapter 6 of Mathematics and Statistics for Financial Risk Management, *Second Edition, by Michael B. Miller*

Bayesian analysis is an extremely broad topic. In this chapter we introduce Bayes' theorem and other concepts related to Bayesian analysis. We will begin to see how Bayesian analysis can help us tackle some very difficult problems in risk management.

OVERVIEW

The foundation of Bayesian analysis is Bayes' theorem. Bayes' theorem is named after the eighteenth-century English mathematician Thomas Bayes, who first described the theorem. During his life, Bayes never actually publicized his eponymous theorem. Bayes' theorem might have been confined to the dustheap of history had not a friend submitted it to the Royal Society two years after his death.

Bayes' theorem itself is incredibly simple. For two random variables, A and B, Bayes' theorem states that:

$$P[A \mid B] = \frac{P[B \mid A] \cdot P[A]}{P[B]} \qquad (4.1)$$

In the next section we'll derive Bayes' theorem and explain how to interpret Equation (4.1). As we will see, the simplicity of Bayes' theorem is deceptive. Bayes' theorem can be applied to a wide range of problems, and its application can often be quite complex.

Bayesian analysis is used in a number of fields. It is most often associated with computer science and artificial intelligence, where it is used in everything from spam filters to machine translation and to the software that controls self-driving cars. The use of Bayesian analysis in finance and risk management has grown in recent years, and will likely continue to grow.

What follows makes heavy use of joint and conditional probabilities. If you have not already done so and you are not familiar with these topics, you can review them in Chapter 1.

BAYES' THEOREM

Assume we have two bonds, Bond A and Bond B, each with a 10% probability of defaulting over the next year. Further assume that the probability that both bonds default is 6%, and that the probability that neither bond defaults is 86%. It follows that the probability that only Bond A *or* Bond B defaults is 4%. We can summarize all

of this information in a probability matrix as shown in Figure 4-1.

		Bond A		
		No Default	**Default**	
Bond B	No Default	86%	4%	90%
	Default	4%	6%	10%
		90%	10%	100%

FIGURE 4-1 Probability matrix.

As required, the rows and columns of the matrix add up, and the sum of all the probabilities is equal to 100%.

In the probability matrix, notice that the probability of both bonds defaulting is 6%. This is higher than the 1% probability we would expect if the default events were independent (10% × 10% = 1%). The probability that neither bond defaults, 86%, is also higher than what we would expect if the defaults were independent (90% × 90% = 81%). Because bond issuers are often sensitive to broad economic trends, bond defaults are often highly correlated.

We can also express features of the probability matrix in terms of conditional probabilities. What is the probability that Bond A defaults, given that Bond B has defaulted? Bond B defaults in 10% of the scenarios, but the probability that both Bond A and Bond B default is only 6%. In other words, Bond A defaults in 60% of the scenarios in which Bond B defaults. We write this as follows:

$$P[A \mid B] = \frac{P[A \cap B]}{P[B]} = \frac{6\%}{10\%} = 60\% \qquad (4.2)$$

Notice that the conditional probability is different from the unconditional probability. The unconditional probability of default is 10%.

$$P[A] = 10\% \neq 60\% = P[A \mid B] \qquad (4.3)$$

It turns out that Equation (4.2) is true in general. More often the equation is written as follows:

$$P[A \cap B] = P[A \mid B] \cdot P[B] \qquad (4.4)$$

In other words, the probability of both A and B occurring is just the probability that A occurs, given B, multiplied by the probability of B occurring. What's more, the ordering of A and B doesn't matter. We could just as easily write:

$$P[A \cap B] = P[B \mid A] \cdot P[A] \qquad \textbf{(4.5)}$$

Combining the right-hand side of both of these equations and rearranging terms leads us to Bayes' theorem:

$$P[A \mid B] = \frac{P[B \mid A] \cdot P[A]}{P[B]} \qquad \textbf{(4.6)}$$

The following sample problem shows how Bayes' theorem can be applied to a very interesting statistical question.

Example 4.1

Question:

Imagine there is a disease that afflicts just 1 in every 100 people in the population. A new test has been developed to detect the disease that is 99% accurate. That is, for people with the disease, the test correctly indicates that they have the disease in 99% of cases. Similarly, for those who do not have the disease, the test correctly indicates that they do not have the disease in 99% of cases.

If a person takes the test and the result of the test is positive, what is the probability that he or she actually has the disease?

Answer:

While not exactly financial risk, this is a classic example of how conditional probability can be far from intuitive. This type of problem is also far from being an academic curiosity. A number of studies have asked doctors similar questions; see, for example, Gigerenzer and Edwards (2003). The results are often discouraging. The physicians' answers vary widely and are often far from correct.

If the test is 99% accurate, it is tempting to guess that there is a 99% chance that the person who tests positive actually has the disease. 99% is in fact a very bad guess. The correct answer is that there is only a 50% chance that the person who tests positive actually has the disease.

To calculate the correct answer, we first need to calculate the unconditional probability of a positive test. Remember from Chapter 1 that this is simply the probability of a positive test being produced by somebody with the disease plus the probability of a positive test being produced by somebody without the disease. Using a "+" to represent a positive test result, this can be calculated as:

$$P[+] = P[+ \cap \text{have disease}] + P[+ \cap \overline{\text{have disease}}]$$

$$\begin{aligned} P[+] = {}& P[+ \mid \text{have disease}] \cdot P[\text{have disease}] \\ & + P[+ \mid \overline{\text{have disease}}] \cdot P[\overline{\text{have disease}}] \end{aligned}$$

$$P[+] = 99\% \cdot 1\% + 1\% \cdot 99\%$$

$$P[+] = 2\% \cdot 99\%$$

Here we use the line above "have disease" to represent logical negation. In other words, $P[\overline{\text{have disease}}]$ is the probability of not having the disease.

We can then calculate the probability of having the disease given a positive test using Bayes' theorem:

$$P[\text{have disease} \mid +] = \frac{P[+ \mid \text{have disease}] \cdot P[\text{have disease}]}{P[+]}$$

$$P[\text{have disease} \mid +] = \frac{99\% \cdot 1\%}{2\% \cdot 99\%} = 50\%$$

The reason the answer is 50% and not 99% is because the disease is so rare. Most people don't have the disease, so even a small number of false positives overwhelms the number of actual positives. It is easy to see this in a matrix. Assume 10,000 trials:

		Actual		
		+	−	
Test	+	99	99	198
	−	1	9,801	9,802
		100	9,900	10,000

If you check the numbers, you'll see that they work out exactly as described: 1% of the population with the disease, and 99% accuracy in each column. In the end, though, the number of positive test results is identical for the two populations, 99 in each. This is why the probability of actually having the disease given a positive test is 50%.

In order for a test for a rare disease to be meaningful, it has to be extremely accurate. In the case just described, 99% accuracy was not nearly accurate enough.

Bayes' theorem is often described as a procedure for updating beliefs about the world when presented with new information. For example, pretend you had a coin that you believed was fair, with a 50% chance of landing heads or tails when flipped. If you flip the coin 10 times and it lands heads each time, you might start to suspect that the coin is not fair. Ten heads in a row could happen, but the odds of seeing 10 heads in a row is only 1:1,024 for a fair coin, $(\tfrac{1}{2})^{10} = \tfrac{1}{1,024}$. How do you update your beliefs after seeing 10 heads? If you believed there was a 90% probability that the coin was fair before you started flipping, then after seeing 10 heads your belief that the coin is fair should probably be somewhere between 0% and 90%. You believe it is less likely that the coin is fair after seeing 10 heads (so less than 90%), but there is still some probability that the coin is fair (so greater than 0%). As the following example will make clear, Bayes' theorem provides a framework for deciding exactly what our new beliefs should be.

Example 4.2

Question:

You are an analyst at Astra Fund of Funds. Based on an examination of historical data, you determine that all fund managers fall into one of two groups. Stars are the best managers. The probability that a star will beat the market in any given year is 75%. Ordinary, nonstar managers, by contrast, are just as likely to beat the market as they are to underperform it. For both types of managers, the probability of beating the market is independent from one year to the next.

Stars are rare. Of a given pool of managers, only 16% turn out to be stars. A new manager was added to your portfolio three years ago. Since then, the new manager has beaten the market every year. What was the probability that the manager was a star when the manager was first added to the portfolio? What is the probability that this manager is a star now? After observing the manager beat the market over the past three years, what is the probability that the manager will beat the market next year?

Answer:

We start by summarizing the information from the problem and introducing some notation. The probability that a manager beats the market given that the manager is a star is 75%:

$$P[B \mid S] = 75\% = \frac{3}{4}$$

The probability that a nonstar manager will beat the market is 50%:

$$P[B \mid \bar{S}] = 50\% = \frac{1}{2}$$

At the time the new manager was added to the portfolio, the probability that the manager was a star was just the

probability of any manager being a star, 16%, the unconditional probability:

$$P[S] = 16\% = \frac{4}{25}$$

To answer the second part of the question, we need to find $P[S \mid 3B]$, the probability that the manager is a star, given that the manager has beaten the market three years in a row. We can find this probability using Bayes' theorem:

$$P[S \mid 3B] = \frac{P[3B \mid S]P[S]}{P[3B]}$$

We already know $P[S]$. Because outperformance is independent from one year to the next, the other part of the numerator, $P[3B \mid S]$, is just the probability that a star beats the market in any given year to the third power:

$$P[3B \mid S] = \left(\frac{3}{4}\right)^3 = \frac{27}{64}$$

The denominator is the unconditional probability of beating the market for three years. This is just the weighted average probability of three market-beating years over both types of managers:

$$P[3B] = P[3B \mid S]P[S] + P[3B \mid \bar{S}]P[\bar{S}]$$

$$P[3B] = \left(\frac{3}{4}\right)^3 \frac{4}{25} + \left(\frac{1}{2}\right)^3 \frac{21}{25} = \frac{(27)}{(64)}\frac{(4)}{(25)} + \frac{(1)}{(8)}\frac{(21)}{(25)} = \frac{69}{400}$$

Putting it all together, we get our final result:

$$P[S \mid 3B] = \frac{\left(\frac{27}{64}\right)\left(\frac{4}{25}\right)}{\frac{69}{400}} = \frac{9}{23} = 39\%$$

Our updated belief about the manager being a star, having seen the manager beat the market three times, is 39%, a significant increase from our prior belief of 16%. A star is much more likely to beat the market three years in a row—more than three times as likely—so it makes sense that we believe our manager is more likely to be a star now.

Even though it is much more likely that a star will beat the market three years in a row, we are still far from certain that this manager is a star. In fact, at 39% the odds are more likely that the manager is *not* a star. As was the case in the medical test example, the reason has to do with the overwhelming number of false positives. There are so many nonstar managers that some of them are bound to beat the market three years in a row. The real stars are simply outnumbered by these lucky nonstar managers.

Next, we answer the final part of the question. The probability that the manager beats the market next year is just the probability that a star would beat the market plus the probability that a nonstar would beat the market, weighted by our new beliefs. Our updated belief about the manager being a star is 39% = $9/23$, so the probability that the manager is not a star must be 61% = $14/23$:

$$P[B] = P[B \mid S] \cdot P[S] + P[B \mid \bar{S}] \cdot P[\bar{S}]$$

$$P[B] = \frac{3}{4} \cdot \frac{9}{23} + \frac{1}{2} \cdot \frac{14}{23}$$

$$P[B] = 60\%$$

The probability that the manager will beat the market next year falls somewhere between the probability for a nonstar, 50%, and for a star, 75%, but is closer to the probability for a nonstar. This is consistent with our updated belief that there is only a 39% probability that the manager is a star.

When using Bayes' theorem to update beliefs, we often refer to prior and posterior beliefs and probabilities. In the preceding sample problem, the prior probability was 16%. That is, *before* seeing the manager beat the market three times, our belief that the manager was a star was 16%. The posterior probability for the sample problem was 39%. That is, *after* seeing the manager beat the market three times, our belief that the manager was a star was 39%.

We often use the terms *evidence* and *likelihood* when referring to the conditional probability on the right-hand side of Bayes' theorem. In the sample problem, the probability of beating the market, assuming that the manager was a star, $P[3B \mid S] = 27/64$, was the likelihood. In other words, the likelihood of the manager beating the market three times, assuming that the manager was a star, was $27/64$.

$$\text{posterior} \longrightarrow P[S \mid 3B] = \frac{P[3B \mid S] P[S]}{P[3B]} \longleftarrow \text{prior} \qquad \textbf{(4.7)}$$

where the upper label is "likelihood" and "prior" points to $P[S]$.

BAYES VERSUS FREQUENTISTS

Pretend that as an analyst you are given daily profit data for a fund, and that the fund has had positive returns for 560 of the past 1,000 trading days. What is the probability that the fund will generate a positive return tomorrow? Without any further instructions, it is tempting to say that the probability is 56%, ($560/1,000 = 56\%$). In the previous

sample problem, though, we were presented with a portfolio manager who beat the market three years in a row. Shouldn't we have concluded that the probability that the portfolio manager would beat the market the following year was 100% ($3/3 = 100\%$), and not 60%? How can both answers be correct?

The last approach, taking three out of three positive results and concluding that the probability of a positive result next year is 100%, is known as the frequentist approach. The conclusion is based only on the observed frequency of positive results. Prior to this chapter we had been using the frequentist approach to calculate probabilities and other parameters.

The Bayesian approach, which we have been exploring in this chapter, also counts the number of positive results. The conclusion is different because the Bayesian approach starts with a prior belief about the probability.

Which approach is better? It's hard to say. Within the statistics community there are those who believe that the frequentist approach is always correct. On the other end of the spectrum, there are those who believe the Bayesian approach is always superior.

Proponents of Bayesian analysis often point to the absurdity of the frequentist approach when applied to small data sets. Observing three out of three positive results and concluding that the probability of a positive result next year is 100% suggests that we are absolutely certain and that there is absolutely no possibility of a negative result. Clearly this certainty is unjustified.

Proponents of the frequentist approach often point to the arbitrariness of Bayesian priors. In the portfolio manager example, we started our analysis with the assumption that 16% of managers were stars. In a previous example we assumed that there was a 90% probability that a coin was fair. How did we arrive at these priors? In most cases the prior is either subjective or based on frequentist analysis.

Perhaps unsurprisingly, most practitioners tend to take a more balanced view, realizing that there are situations that lend themselves to frequentist analysis and others that lend themselves to Bayesian analysis. Situations in which there is very little data, or in which the signal-to-noise ratio is extremely low, often lend themselves to Bayesian analysis. When we have lots of data, the conclusions of frequentist analysis and Bayesian analysis are often very similar, and the frequentist results are often easier to calculate.

In the example with the portfolio manager, we had only three data points. Using the Bayesian approach for this problem made sense. In the example where we had 1,000 data points, most practitioners would probably utilize frequentist analysis. In risk management, performance analysis and stress testing are examples of areas where we often have very little data, and the data we do have is very noisy. These areas are likely to lend themselves to Bayesian analysis.

MANY-STATE PROBLEMS

In the two previous sample problems, each variable could exist in only one of two states: a person either had the disease or did not have the disease; a manager was either a star or a nonstar. We can easily extend Bayesian analysis to any number of possible outcomes. For example, suppose rather than stars and nonstars, we believe there are three types of managers: underperformers, in-line performers, and outperformers. The underperformers beat the market only 25% of the time, the in-line performers beat the market 50% of the time, and the outperformers beat the market 75% of the time. Initially we believe that a given manager is most likely to be an inline performer, and is less likely to be an underperformer or an outperformer. More specifically, our prior belief is that a manager has a 60% probability of being an in-line performer, a 20% chance of being an underperformer, and a 20% chance of being an outperformer. We can summarize this as:

$$P[p = 0.25] = 20\%$$

$$P[p = 0.50] = 60\%$$

$$P[p = 0.75] = 20\% \qquad \textbf{(4.8)}$$

Now suppose the manager beats the market two years in a row. What should our updated beliefs be? We start by calculating the likelihoods, the probability of beating the market two years in a row, for each type of manager:

$$P[2B \mid p = 0.25] = \left(\frac{1}{4}\right)^2 = \frac{1}{16}$$

$$P[2B \mid p = 0.50] = \left(\frac{1}{2}\right)^2 = \frac{1}{4} = \frac{4}{16}$$

$$P[2B \mid p = 0.75] = \left(\frac{3}{4}\right)^2 = \frac{9}{16} \qquad \textbf{(4.9)}$$

The unconditional probability of observing the manager beat the market two years in a row, given our prior beliefs about p, is:

$$P[2B] = 20\%\frac{1}{16} + 60\%\frac{4}{16} + 20\%\frac{9}{16}$$

$$P[2B] = \frac{2}{10}\frac{1}{16} + \frac{6}{10}\frac{4}{16} + \frac{2}{10}\frac{9}{16} = \frac{44}{160} = 27.5\% \qquad \textbf{(4.10)}$$

Putting this all together and using Bayes' theorem, we can calculate our posterior belief that the manager is an underperformer:

$$P[p = 0.25 \mid 2B] = \frac{P[2B \mid p = 0.25]P[p = 0.25]}{P[2B]}$$

$$= \frac{\frac{1}{16}\frac{2}{10}}{\frac{44}{160}} = \frac{2}{44} = \frac{1}{22} = 4.55\% \qquad \textbf{(4.11)}$$

Similarly, we can show that the posterior probability that the manager is an in-line performer is 54.55%:

$$P[p = 0.50 \mid 2B] = \frac{P[2B \mid p = 0.50]P[p = 0.50]}{P[2B]}$$

$$= \frac{\frac{4}{16}\frac{6}{10}}{\frac{44}{160}} = \frac{24}{44} = \frac{12}{22} = 54.55\% \qquad \textbf{(4.12)}$$

and that the posterior probability that the manager is an outperformer is 40.91%:

$$P[p = 0.75 \mid 2B] = \frac{P[2B \mid p = 0.75]P[p = 0.75]}{P[2B]}$$

$$= \frac{\frac{9}{16}\frac{2}{10}}{\frac{44}{160}} = \frac{18}{44} = \frac{9}{22} = 40.91\% \qquad \textbf{(4.13)}$$

As we would expect, given that the manager beat the market two years in a row, the posterior probability that the manager is an outperformer has increased, from 20% to 40.91%, and the posterior probability that the manager is an underperformer has decreased, from 20% to 4.55%. Even though the probabilities have changed, the sum of the probabilities is still equal to 100% (the percentages seem to add to 100.01%, but that is only a rounding error):

$$\frac{1}{22} + \frac{12}{22} + \frac{9}{22} = \frac{22}{22} = 1 \qquad \textbf{(4.14)}$$

At this point it is worth noting a useful shortcut. Notice that for each type of manager, the posterior probability was calculated as:

$$P[p = x \mid 2B] = \frac{P[2B \mid p = x]P[p = x]}{P[2B]} \qquad \textbf{(4.15)}$$

In each case, the denominator on the right-hand side is the same, $P[2B]$, or $^{44}/_{60}$. We can then rewrite this equation in terms of a constant, c:

$$P[p = x \mid 2B] = c \cdot P[2B \mid p = x]P[p = x] \qquad \textbf{(4.16)}$$

We also know that the sum of all the posterior probabilities must equal one:

$$\sum_{i=1}^{3} c \cdot P[2B \mid p = x_i]P[p = x_i]$$
$$= c\sum_{i=1}^{3} P[2B \mid p = x_i]P[p = x_i] = 1 \qquad \textbf{(4.17)}$$

In our current example we have:

$$c\left(\frac{1}{16}\frac{2}{10} + \frac{4}{16}\frac{6}{10} + \frac{9}{16}\frac{2}{10}\right) = c\frac{2 + 24 + 18}{160} = c\frac{44}{160} = 1$$
$$c = \frac{160}{44} \qquad \textbf{(4.18)}$$

We then use this to calculate each of the posterior probabilities. For example, the posterior probability that the manager is an underperformer is:

$$P[p = 0.25 \mid 2B] = c \cdot P[2B \mid p = 0.25]P[p = 0.25]$$
$$= \frac{160}{44}\frac{1}{16}\frac{2}{10} = \frac{2}{44} = \frac{1}{22} \qquad \textbf{(4.19)}$$

In the current example this might not seem like much of a shortcut, but with continuous distributions, this approach can make seemingly intractable problems very easy to solve.

Example 4.3

Question:

Using the same prior distributions as in the preceding example, what would the posterior probabilities be for an underperformer, an in-line performer, or an outperformer if instead of beating the market two years in a row, the manager beat the market in 6 of the next 10 years?

Answer:

For each possible type of manager, the likelihood of beating the market 6 times out of 10 can be determined using a binomial distribution (see Chapter 3):

$$P[6B \mid p] = \binom{10}{6}p^6(1-p)^4$$

Using our shortcut, we first calculate the posterior probabilities in terms of an arbitrary constant, c. If the manager is an underperformer:

$$P[p = 0.25 \mid 6B] = c \cdot P[6B \mid p = 0.25] \cdot P[p = 0.25]$$
$$P[p = 0.25 \mid 6B] = c \cdot \binom{10}{6}\left(\frac{1}{4}\right)^6\left(\frac{3}{4}\right)^4 \cdot \frac{2}{10}$$
$$P[p = 0.25 \mid 6B] = c\binom{10}{6}\frac{2 \cdot 3^4}{10 \cdot 4^{10}}$$

Similiarly, if the manager is an in-line performer or outperformer, we have:

$$P[p = 0.50 \mid 6B] = c\binom{10}{6}\frac{6 \cdot 2^{10}}{10 \cdot 4^{10}}$$
$$P[p = 0.75 \mid 6B] = c\binom{10}{6}\frac{2 \cdot 3^6}{10 \cdot 4^{10}}$$

Because all of the posterior probabilities sum to one, we have:

$$P[p = 0.25 \mid 6B] + P[p = 0.50 \mid 6B] + P[p = 0.75 \mid 6B] = 1$$
$$c\binom{10}{6}\frac{2 \cdot 3}{10 \cdot 4^{10}}(3^3 + 2^{10} + 3^5) = 1$$
$$c\binom{10}{6}\frac{2 \cdot 3}{10 \cdot 4^{10}}1{,}294 = 1$$
$$c = \frac{1}{\binom{10}{6}}\frac{10 \cdot 4^{10}}{2 \cdot 3}\frac{1}{1{,}294}$$

This may look unwieldy, but, as we will see, many of the terms will cancel out before we arrive at the final answers. Substituting back into the equations for the posterior probabilities, we have:

$$P[p = 0.25 \mid 6B] = c\binom{10}{6}\frac{2 \cdot 3^4}{10 \cdot 4^{10}} = \frac{3^3}{1{,}294} = \frac{27}{1{,}294} = 2.09\%$$
$$P[p = 0.50 \mid 6B] = c\binom{10}{6}\frac{6 \cdot 2^{10}}{10 \cdot 4^{10}} = \frac{2^{10}}{1{,}294} = \frac{1{,}024}{1{,}294} = 79.13\%$$
$$P[p = 0.75 \mid 6B] = c\binom{10}{6}\frac{2 \cdot 3^6}{10 \cdot 4^{10}} = \frac{3^5}{1{,}294} = \frac{243}{1{,}294} = 18.78\%$$

In this case, the probability that the manager is an in-line performer has increased from 60% to 79.13%. The probability that the manager is an outperformer decreased slightly from 20% to 18.78%. It now seems very unlikely that the manager is an underperformer (2.09% probability compared to our prior belief of 20%).

While the calculations looked rather complicated, using our shortcut saved us from actually having to calculate many of the more complicated terms. For more complex problems, and especially for problems involving continuous distributions, this shortcut can be extremely useful.

This example involved three possible states. The basic approach for solving a problem with four, five, or any finite number of states is exactly the same, only the number of calculations increases. Because the calculations are highly repetitive, it is often much easier to solve these problems using a spreadsheet or computer program.

Hypothesis Testing and Confidence Intervals

5

Learning Objectives

Candidates, after completing this reading, should be able to:

- Calculate and interpret the sample mean and sample variance.
- Construct and interpret a confidence interval.
- Construct an appropriate null and alternative hypothesis, and calculate an appropriate test statistic.

- Differentiate between a one-tailed and a two-tailed test and identify when to use each test.
- Interpret the results of hypothesis tests with a specific level of confidence.
- Demonstrate the process of backtesting VaR by calculating the number of exceedances.

Excerpt is Chapter 7 of Mathematics and Statistics for Financial Risk Management, *Second Edition, by Michael B. Miller.*

In this chapter we explore two closely related topics, confidence intervals and hypothesis testing. At the end of the chapter, we explore applications, including value-at-risk (VaR).

SAMPLE MEAN REVISITED

Imagine taking the output from a standard random number generator on a computer, and multiply it by 100. The resulting data-generating process (DGP) is a uniform random variable, which ranges between 0 and 100, with a mean of 50. If we generate 20 draws from this DGP and calculate the sample mean of those 20 draws, it is unlikely that the sample mean will be exactly 50. The sample mean might round to 50, say 50.03906724, but exactly 50 is next to impossible. In fact, given that we have only 20 data points, the sample mean might not even be close to the true mean.

The sample mean is actually a random variable itself. If we continue to repeat the experiment—generating 20 data points and calculating the sample mean each time—the calculated sample mean will be different every time. As we proved in Chapter 2, even though we never get exactly 50, the expected value of each sample mean is in fact 50. It might sound strange to say it, but the mean of our sample mean is the true mean of the distribution. Using our standard notation:

$$E[\hat{\mu}] = \mu \qquad \text{(5.1)}$$

If instead of 20 data points, what if we generate 1,000 data points? With 1,000 data points, the expected value of our sample mean is still 50, just as it was with 20 data points. While we still don't expect our sample mean to be exactly 50, our sample mean will tend to be closer when we are using 1,000 data points. The reason is simple: A single outlier won't have nearly the impact in a pool of 1,000 data points that it will in a pool of 20. If we continue to generate sets of 1,000 data points, it stands to reason that the standard deviation of our sample mean will be lower with 1,000 data points than it would be if our sets contained only 20 data points.

It turns out that the variance of our sample mean doesn't just decrease with the sample size; it decreases in a predictable way, in proportion to the sample size. If our sample size is n and the true variance of our DGP is σ^2, then the variance of the sample mean is:

$$\sigma_{\hat{\mu}}^2 = \frac{\sigma^2}{n} \qquad \text{(5.2)}$$

It follows that the standard deviation of the sample mean decreases with the square root of n. This square root is important. In order to reduce the standard deviation of the mean by a factor of 2, we need 4 times as many data points. To reduce it by a factor of 10, we need 100 times as much data. This is yet another example of the famous square root rule for independent and identically distributed (i.i.d.) variables.

In our current example, because the DGP follows a uniform distribution, we can easily calculate the variance of each data point using Equation (3.4). The variance of each data point is 833.33, $(100 - 0)^2/12 = 833.33$. This is equivalent to a standard deviation of 28.87. For 20 data points, the standard deviation of the mean will then be $28.87/\sqrt{20} = 6.45$, and for 1,000 data points, the standard deviation will be $28.87/\sqrt{1,000} = 0.91$.

We have the mean and the standard deviation of our sample mean, but what about the shape of the distribution? You might think that the shape of the distribution would depend on the shape of the underlying distribution of the DGP. If we recast our formula for the sample mean slightly, though:

$$\hat{\mu} = \frac{1}{n}\sum_{i=1}^{n} x_i = \sum_{i=1}^{n} \frac{1}{n} x_i \qquad \text{(5.3)}$$

and regard each of the $(1/n)x_i$'s as a random variable in its own right, we see that our sample mean is equivalent to the sum of n i.i.d. random variables, each with a mean of μ/n and a standard deviation of σ/n. Using the central limit theorem, we claim that the distribution of the sample mean converges to a normal distribution. For large values of n, the distribution of the sample mean will be extremely close to a normal distribution. Practitioners will often assume that the sample mean *is* normally distributed.

Example 5.1

Question:

You are given 10 years of monthly returns for a portfolio manager. The mean monthly return is 2.3%, and the standard deviation of the return series is 3.6%. What is the standard deviation of the mean?

The portfolio manager is being compared against a benchmark with a mean monthly return of 1.5%. What is the probability that the portfolio manager's mean return exceeds the benchmark? Assume the sample mean is normally distributed.

Answer:

There is a total of 120 data points in the sample (10 years × 12 months per year). The standard deviation of the mean is then 0.33%:

$$\sigma_{\hat{\mu}} = \frac{\sigma}{\sqrt{n}} = \frac{3.6\%}{\sqrt{120}} = 0.33\%$$

The distance between the portfolio manager's mean return and the benchmark is −2.43 standard deviations: (1.50% − 2.30%)/0.33% = −2.43. For a normal distribution, 99.25% of the distribution lies above −2.43 standard deviations, and only 0.75% lies below. The difference between the portfolio manager and the benchmark is highly significant.

SAMPLE VARIANCE REVISITED

Just as with the sample mean, we can treat the sample variance as a random variable. For a given DGP if we repeatedly calculate the sample variance, the expected value of the sample variance will equal the true variance, and the variance of the sample variance will equal:

$$E[(\hat{\sigma}^2 - \sigma^2)^2] = \sigma^4 \left(\frac{2}{n-1} + \frac{\kappa_{ex}}{n} \right) \tag{5.4}$$

where n is the sample size, and κ_{ex} is the excess kurtosis.

If the DGP has a normal distribution, then we can also say something about the shape of the distribution of the sample variance. If we have n sample points and $\hat{\sigma}^2$ is the sample variance, then our estimator will follow a chi-squared distribution with $(n - 1)$ degrees of freedom:

$$(n-1)\frac{\hat{\sigma}^2}{\sigma^2} \sim \chi^2_{n-1} \tag{5.5}$$

where σ^2 is the population variance. Note that this is true only when the DGP has a normal distribution. Unfortunately, unlike the case of the sample mean, we cannot apply the central limit theorem here. Even when the sample size is large, if the underlying distribution is nonnormal, the statistic in Equation (5.5) can vary significantly from a chi-squared distribution.

CONFIDENCE INTERVALS

In our discussion of the sample mean, we assumed that the standard deviation of the underlying distribution was known. In practice, the true standard deviation is likely to be unknown. At the same time we are measuring the sample mean, we will typically be measuring the sample variance as well.

It turns out that if we first standardize our estimate of the sample mean using the sample standard deviation, the new random variable follows a Student's t distribution with $(n-1)$ degrees of freedom:

$$t = \frac{\hat{\mu} - \mu}{\hat{\sigma}/\sqrt{n}} \tag{5.6}$$

Here the numerator is simply the difference between the sample mean and the population mean, while the denominator is the sample standard deviation divided by the square root of the sample size. To see why this new variable follows a t distribution, we simply need to divide both the numerator and the denominator by the population standard deviation. This creates a standard normal variable in the numerator, and the square root of a chi-square variable in the denominator with the appropriate constant. We know from the previous chapter on distributions that this combination of random variables follows a t distribution. This standardized version of the population mean is so frequently used that it is referred to as a t-statistic, or simply a t-stat.

Technically, this result requires that the underlying distribution be normally distributed. As was the case with the sample variance, the denominator may not follow a chi-squared distribution if the underlying distribution is nonnormal. Oddly enough, for large sample sizes the overall t-statistic still converges to a t distribution. However, if the sample size is small and the data distribution is nonnormal, the t-statistic, as defined here, may not be well approximated by a t distribution.

By looking up the appropriate values for the t distribution, we can establish the probability that our t-statistic is contained within a certain range:

$$P\left[x_L \leq \frac{\hat{\mu} - \mu}{\hat{\sigma}/\sqrt{n}} \leq x_U \right] = \gamma \tag{5.7}$$

where x_L and x_U are constants, which, respectively, define the lower and upper bounds of the range within the t distribution, and γ is the probability that our t-statistic will be found within that range. Typically γ is referred to as the confidence level. Rather than working directly with the confidence level, we often work with the quantity $1 - \gamma$, which is known as the significance level and is often denoted by α. The smaller the confidence level is, the higher the significance level.

In practice, the population mean, μ, is often unknown. By rearranging the previous equation we come to an equation with a more interesting form:

$$P\left[\hat{\mu} - \frac{x_L \hat{\sigma}}{\sqrt{n}} \leq \mu \leq \hat{\mu} + \frac{x_U \hat{\sigma}}{\sqrt{n}}\right] = \gamma \qquad \textbf{(5.8)}$$

Looked at this way, we are now giving the probability that the population mean will be contained within the defined range. When it is formulated this way, we call this range the confidence interval for the population mean. Confidence intervals are not limited to the population mean. Though it may not be as simple, in theory we can define a confidence level for any distribution parameter.

HYPOTHESIS TESTING

One problem with confidence intervals is that they require us to settle on an arbitrary confidence level. While 95% and 99% are common choices for the confidence level in risk management, there is nothing sacred about these numbers. It would be perfectly legitimate to construct a 74.92% confidence interval. At the same time, we are often concerned with the probability that a certain variable exceeds a threshold. For example, given the observed returns of a mutual fund, what is the probability that the standard deviation of those returns is less than 20%?

In a sense, we want to turn the confidence interval around. Rather than saying there is an x% probability that the population mean is contained within a given interval, we want to know what the probability is that the population mean is greater than y. When we pose the question this way, we are in the realm of hypothesis testing.

Traditionally the question is put in the form of a null hypothesis. If we are interested in knowing whether the expected return of a portfolio manager is greater than 10%, we would write:

$$H_0 : \mu_r > 10\% \qquad \textbf{(5.9)}$$

where H_0 is known as the null hypothesis. Even though the true population mean is unknown, for the hypothesis test we assume that the population mean *is* 10%. In effect, we are asking, *if* the true population mean *is* 10%, what is the probability that we would see a given sample mean? With our null hypothesis in hand, we gather our data, calculate the sample mean, and form the appropriate *t*-statistic. In this case, the appropriate *t-statistic* is:

$$t = \frac{\mu - 10\%}{\sigma/\sqrt{n}} \qquad \textbf{(5.10)}$$

We can then look up the corresponding probability from the *t* distribution.

In addition to the null hypothesis, we can offer an alternative hypothesis. In the previous example, where our null hypothesis is that the expected return is greater than 10%, the logical alternative would be that the expected return is less than or equal to 10%:

$$H_1 : \mu_r \leq 10\% \qquad \textbf{(5.11)}$$

In principle, we could test any number of hypotheses. In practice, as long as the alternative is trivial, we tend to limit ourselves to stating the null hypothesis.

Which Way to Test?

If we want to know if the expected return of a portfolio manager is greater than 10%, the obvious statement of the null hypothesis might seem to be $\mu_r > 10\%$. But we could just have easily have started with the alternative hypothesis, that $\mu_r \leq 10\%$. Finding that the first is true and finding that the second is false are logically equivalent.

Many practitioners construct the null hypothesis so that the desired result is false. If we are an investor trying to find good portfolio managers, then we would make the null hypothesis $\mu_r \leq 10\%$. That we want the expected return to be greater than 10% but we are testing for the opposite makes us seem objective. Unfortunately, in the case where there is a high probability that the manager's expected return is greater than 10% (a good result), we have to say, "We reject the null hypothesis that the manager's expected return is less than or equal to 10% at the x% level." This is very close to a double negative. Like a medical test where the good outcome is negative and the bad outcome is positive, we often find that the desired outcome for a null hypothesis is rejection.

To make matters more complicated, what happens if the portfolio manager doesn't seem to be that good? If we *rejected* the null hypothesis when there was a high probability that the portfolio manager's expected return was greater than 10%, should we *accept* the null hypothesis when there is a high probability that the expected return is less than 10%? In the realm of statistics, outright acceptance seems too certain. In practice, we can do two things. First, we can state that the probability of rejecting the null hypothesis is low (e.g., "The probability of rejecting the null hypothesis is only 4.2% "). More often, we say that we *fail to reject* the null hypothesis (e.g., "We fail to reject the null hypothesis at the 95.8% level").

Example 5.2

Question:

At the start of the year, you believed that the annualized volatility of XYZ Corporation's equity was 45%. At the end of the year, you have collected a year of daily returns, 256 business days' worth. You calculate the standard deviation, annualize it, and come up with a value of 48%. Can you reject the null hypothesis, $H_0: \sigma = 45\%$, at the 95% confidence level?

Answer:

The appropriate test statistic is:

$$(n-1)\frac{\hat{\sigma}^2}{\sigma^2} = (256-1)\frac{0.48^2}{0.45^2} = 290.13 \sim \chi^2_{255}$$

Notice that annualizing the standard deviation has no impact on the test statistic. The same factor would appear in the numerator and the denominator, leaving the ratio unchanged. For a chi-squared distribution with 255 degrees of freedom, 290.13 corresponds to a probability of 6.44%. We fail to reject the null hypothesis at the 95% confidence level.

One Tail or Two?

Novice statisticians often get confused about the choice between one-tailed and two-tailed critical values. In many scientific fields where positive and negative deviations are equally important, two-tailed confidence levels are more prevalent. In risk management, more often than not we are more concerned with the probability of extreme negative outcomes, and this concern naturally leads to one-tailed tests.

A two-tailed null hypothesis could take the form:

$$H_0 : \mu = 0$$
$$H_1 : \mu \neq 0 \tag{5.12}$$

In this case, H_1 implies that extreme positive or negative values would cause us to reject the null hypothesis. If we are concerned with both sides of the distribution (both tails), we should choose a two-tailed test.

A one-tailed test could be of the form:

$$H_0 : \mu > c$$
$$H_1 : \mu \leq c \tag{5.13}$$

In this case, we will reject H_0 only if the estimate of μ is significantly less than c. If we are only concerned with

deviations in one direction, we should use a one-tailed test. As long as the null hypothesis is clearly stated, the choice of a one-tailed or two-tailed confidence level should be obvious.

The 95% confidence level is a very popular choice for confidence levels, both in risk management and in the sciences. Many non-risk managers remember from their science classes that a 95% confidence level is equivalent to approximately 1.96 standard deviations. For a two-tailed test this is correct; for a normal distribution 95% of the mass is within +/−1.96 standard deviations. For a one-tailed test, though, 95% of the mass is within either +1.64 or −1.64 standard deviations. Using 1.96 instead of 1.64 is a common mistake for people new to risk management.

Figure 5-1 shows common critical values for *t-tests* of varying degrees of freedom and for a normal distribution. Notice that all distributions are symmetrical. For small sample sizes, extreme values are more likely, but as the sample size increases, the t distribution converges to the normal distribution. For 5% significance with 100 degrees of freedom, the difference between our rule of thumb based on the normal distribution, 1.64 standard deviations, is very close to the actual value of 1.66.

The Confidence Level Returns

As we stated at the beginning of this section, one of the great things about a hypothesis test is that we are not required to choose an arbitrary confidence level. In practice, though, 95% and 99% confidence levels are such gold standards that we often end up referring back to them. If

	t_{10}	t_{100}	$t_{1,000}$	N
1.0%	−2.76	−2.36	−2.33	−2.33
2.5%	−2.23	−1.98	−1.96	−1.96
5.0%	−1.81	−1.66	−1.65	−1.64
10.0%	−1.37	−1.29	−1.28	−1.28
90.0%	1.37	1.29	1.28	1.28
95.0%	1.81	1.66	1.65	1.64
97.5%	2.23	1.98	1.96	1.96
99.0%	2.76	2.36	2.33	2.33

FIGURE 5-1   Common critical values for Student's t distribution.

we can reject a null hypothesis at the 96.3% confidence level, some practitioners will simply say that the hypothesis was rejected at the 95% confidence level. The implication is that, even though we may be more confident, 95% is enough. This convention can be convenient when testing a hypothesis repeatedly. As an example, we might want to test the validity of a risk model against new market data every day and be alerted only when the hypothesis cannot be rejected at the 95% confidence level. In the end, our inability to decide on a universal confidence level should serve as a reminder that, in statistics, there is no such thing as a sure bet; there is no such thing as absolute certainty.

CHEBYSHEV'S INEQUALITY

In the preceding sections, we were working with sample statistics where the shape of the distribution was known. Amazingly, even if we do not know the entire distribution of a random variable, we can form a confidence interval, as long as we know the variance of the variable. For a random variable, X, with a standard deviation of σ, the probability that X is within n standard deviations of μ is less than or equal to $1/n^2$:

$$P[|X - \mu| \geq n\sigma] \leq \frac{1}{n^2} \qquad \textbf{(5.14)}$$

This is a result of what is known as Chebyshev's inequality.

For a given level of variance, Chebyshev's inequality places an upper limit on the probability of a variable being more than a certain distance from its mean. For a given distribution, the actual probability may be considerably less. Take, for example, a standard normal variable. Chebyshev's inequality tells us that the probability of being greater than two standard deviations from the mean is less than or equal to 25%. The exact probability for a standard normal variable is closer to 5%, which is indeed less than 25%.

Chebyshev's inequality makes clear how assuming normality can be very anti-conservative. If a variable is normally distributed, the probability of a three standard deviation event is very small, 0.27%. If we assume normality, we will assume that three standard deviation events are very rare. For other distributions, though, Chebyshev's inequality tells us that the probability could be as high as ⅑, or approximately 11 %. Eleven percent is hardly a rare occurrence. Assuming normality when a random variable is in fact not normal can lead to a severe underestimation of risk. Risk managers take note!

APPLICATION: VaR

Value-at-risk (VaR) is one of the most widely used risk measures in finance. VaR was popularized by J.P. Morgan in the 1990s. The executives at J.P. Morgan wanted their risk managers to generate one statistic at the end of each day, which summarized the risk of the firm's entire portfolio. What they came up with was VaR.

If the 95% VaR of a portfolio is $400, then we expect the portfolio will lose $400 or less in 95% of the scenarios, and lose more than $400 in 5% of the scenarios. We can define VaR for any confidence level, but 95% has become an extremely popular choice in finance. The time horizon also needs to be specified for VaR. On trading desks, with liquid portfolios, it is common to measure the one-day 95% VaR. In other settings, in which less liquid assets may be involved, time frames of up to one year are not uncommon. VaR is decidedly a one-tailed confidence interval.

If an actual loss equals or exceeds the predicted VaR threshold, that event is known as an exceedance. Another way to explain VaR is to say that for a one-day 95% VaR, the probability of an exceedance event on any given day is 5%.

Figure 5-2 provides a graphical representation of VaR at the 95% confidence level. The figure shows the probability density function for the returns of a portfolio. Because VaR is being measured at the 95% confidence level, 5% of the distribution is to the left of the VaR level, and 95% is to the right.

In order to formally define VaR, we begin by defining a random variable L, which represents the loss to our portfolio. L is simply the negative of the return to our portfolio. If the return of our portfolio is −$600, then the loss, L, is +$600. For a given confidence level, γ, then, we can define value-at-risk as:

$$P[L \geq \text{VaR}_\gamma] = 1 - \gamma \qquad \textbf{(5.15)}$$

If a risk manager says that the one-day 95% VaR of a portfolio is $400, this means that there is a 5% probability that the portfolio will *lose* $400 or more on any given day (that L will be more than $400).

We can also define VaR directly in terms of returns. If we multiply both sides of the inequality in Equation (5.15) by −1, and replace −L with R, we come up with Equation (5.16):

$$P[R \leq -\text{VaR}_\gamma] = 1 - \gamma \qquad \textbf{(5.16)}$$

Equations (5.15) and (5.16) are equivalent. A loss of $400 or more and a return of −$400 or less are exactly the same.

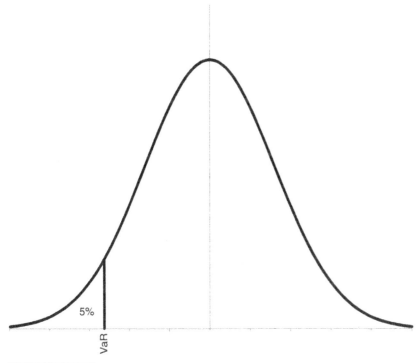

FIGURE 5-2 Example of 95% value-at-risk.

5%

VaR

$$p = \frac{1}{10} + \frac{1}{100}\pi \quad -10 \le \pi \le 0$$

$$p = \frac{1}{10} - \frac{1}{100}\pi \quad 0 < \pi \le 10$$

What is the one-day 95% VaR for Triangle Asset Management?

Answer:

To find the 95% VaR, we need to find *a*, such that:

$$\int_{-10}^{a} p\,d\pi = 0.05$$

By inspection, half the distribution is below zero, so we need only bother with the first half of the function:

$$\int_{-10}^{a}\left(\frac{1}{10} + \frac{1}{100}\pi\right)d\pi = \left[\frac{1}{10}\pi + \frac{1}{200}\pi^2\right]_{-10}^{a}$$

$$\int_{-10}^{a}\left(\frac{1}{10} + \frac{1}{100}\pi\right)d\pi = \frac{1}{10}a + \frac{1}{200}a^2 + 0.50 = 0.05$$

$$a^2 + 20a + 90 = 0$$

Using the quadratic formula, we can solve for *a*:

$$a = \frac{-20 \pm \sqrt{400 - 4 \cdot 90}}{2} = -10 \pm \sqrt{10}$$

Because the distribution is not defined for $\pi < -10$, we can ignore the negative, giving us the final answer:

$$a = -10 + \sqrt{10} = -6.84$$

While Equations (5.15) and (5.16) are equivalent, you should know that some risk managers go one step further and drop the negative sign from Equation (5.16). What we have described as a VaR of $400 they would describe as a VaR of −$400. The convention we have described is more popular. It has the advantage that for reasonable confidence levels for most portfolios, VaR will almost always be a positive number. The alternative convention is attractive because the VaR and returns will have the same sign. Under the alternative convention, if your VaR is −$400, then a return of −$400 is just at the VaR threshold. In practice, rather than just saying that your VaR is $400, it is often best to resolve any ambiguity by stating that your VaR is a *loss* of $400 or that your VaR is a *return* of −$400.

Example 5.3

Question:

The probability density function (PDF) for daily profits at Triangle Asset Management can be described by the following function (see Figure 5-3):

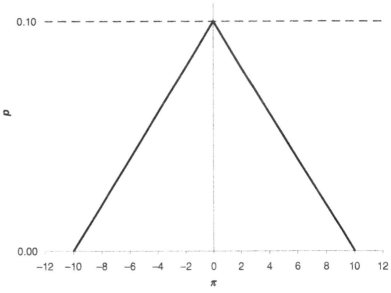

FIGURE 5-3 Triangular probability density function.

The one-day 95% VaR for Triangle Asset Management is a loss of 6.84.

Backtesting

An obvious concern when using VaR is choosing the appropriate confidence interval. As mentioned, 95% has become a very popular choice in risk management. In some settings there may be a natural choice for the confidence level, but most of the time the exact choice is arbitrary.

A common mistake for newcomers is to choose a confidence level that is too high. Naturally, a higher confidence level sounds more conservative. A risk manager who measures one-day VaR at the 95% confidence level will, on average, experience an exceedance event every 20 days. A risk manager who measures VaR at the 99.9% confidence level expects to see an exceedance only once every 1,000 days. Is an event that happens once every 20 days really something that we need to worry about? It is tempting to believe that the risk manager using the 99.9% confidence level is concerned with more serious, riskier outcomes, and is therefore doing a better job.

The problem is that, as we go further and further out into the tail of the distribution, we become less and less certain of the shape of the distribution. In most cases, the assumed distribution of returns for our portfolio will be based on historical data. If we have 1,000 data points, then there are 50 data points to back up our 95% confidence level, but only one to back up our 99.9% confidence level. As with any distribution parameter, the variance of our estimate of the parameter decreases with the sample size. One data point is hardly a good sample size on which to base a parameter estimate.

A related problem has to do with backtesting. Good risk managers should regularly backtest their models. Backtesting entails checking the predicted outcome of a model against actual data. Any model parameter can be backtested.

In the case of VaR, backtesting is easy. As we saw in a problem at the end of Chapter 3, when assessing a VaR model, each period can be viewed as a Bernoulli trial. In the case of one-day 95% VaR, there is a 5% chance of an exceedance event each day, and a 95% chance that there is no exceedance. Because exceedance events are independent, over the course of n days the distribution of exceedances follows a binomial distribution:

$$P[K = k] = \binom{n}{k} p^k (1 - p)^{n-k} \qquad (5.17)$$

Here, n is the number of periods that we are using in our back test, k is the number of exceedances, and $(1 - p)$ is our confidence level.

Example 5.4

Question:

As a risk manager, you are tasked with calculating a daily 95% VaR statistic for a large fixed income portfolio. Over the past 100 days, there have been four exceedances. How many exceedances should you have expected? What was the probability of exactly four exceedances during this time? The probability of four or less? Four or more?

Answer:

Over 100 days we would expect to see five exceedances: $(1 - 95\%) \times 100 = 5$. The probability of exactly four exceedances is 17.81 %:

$$P[K = 4] = \binom{100}{4} 0.05^4 (1 - 0.05)^{100-4} = 0.1781$$

Remember, by convention, for a 95% VaR the probability of an exceedance is 5%, not 95%.

The probability of four or fewer exceedances is 43.60%. Here we simply do the same calculation as in the first part of the problem, but for zero, one, two, three, and four exceedances. It's important not to forget zero:

$$P[K \leq 4] = \sum_{k=0}^{4} \binom{100}{k} 0.05^k (1 - 0.05)^{100-k}$$

$$P[K \leq 4] = 0.0059 + 0.0312 + 0.0812 + 0.1396 + 0.1781$$

$$P[K \leq 4] = 0.4360$$

For the final result, we could use the brute force approach and calculate the probability for $k = 4, 5, 6,$ . . . , 99, 100, a total of 97 calculations. Instead we realize that the sum of all probabilities from 0 to 100 must be 100%; therefore, if the probability of $K \leq 4$ is 43.60%, then the probability of $K > 4$ must be 100% − 43.60% = 56.40%. Be careful, though, as what we want is the probability for $K \geq 4$. To get this, we simply add the probability that $K = 4$, from the first part of our question, to get the final answer, 74.21%:

$$P[K \geq 4] = P[K > 4] + P[K = 4]$$

$$P[K \geq 4] = 0.5640 + 0.1781 = 0.7412$$

The probability of a VaR exceedance should be conditionally independent of all available information at the time the forecast is made. In other words, if we are calculating the 95% VaR for a portfolio, then the probability of an exceedance should always be 5%. The probability shouldn't be different because today is Tuesday, because it was sunny yesterday, or because your firm has been having a good month. Importantly, the probability should not vary because there was an exceedance the previous day, or because risk levels are elevated.

A common problem with VaR models in practice is that exceedances often end up being serially correlated. When exceedances are serially correlated, you are more likely to see another exceedance in the period immediately after an exceedance than expected. To test for serial correlation in exceedances, we can look at the periods immediately following any exceedance events. The number of exceedances in these periods should also follow a binomial distribution. For example, pretend we are calculating the one-day 95% VaR for a portfolio, and we observed 40 exceedances over the past 800 days. To test for serial correlation in the exceedances, we look at the 40 days immediately following the exceedance events, and count how many of those were also exceedances. In other words, we count the number of back-to-back exceedances. Because we are calculating VaR at the 95% confidence level, of the 40 day-after days, we would expect that 2 of them, 5% × 40 = 2, would also be exceedances. The actual number of these day-after exceedances should follow a binomial distribution with $n = 40$ and $p = 5\%$.

Another common problem with VaR models in practice is that exceedances tend to be correlated with the level of risk. It may seem counterintuitive, but we should be no more or less likely to see VaR exceedances in years when market volatility is high compared to when it is low. Positive correlation between exceedances and risk levels can happen when a model does not react quickly enough to changes in risk levels. Negative correlation can happen when model windows are too short. To test for correlation between exceedances and the level of risk, we can divide our exceedances into two or more buckets, based on the level of risk. As an example, pretend we have been calculating the one-day 95% VaR for a portfolio over the past 800 days. We divide the sample period in two, placing the 400 days with the highest forecasted VaR in one bucket and the 400 days with the lowest forecasted VaR in the other. After sorting the days, we would expect each 400-day bucket to contain 20 exceedances: 5% × 400 = 20.

The actual number of exceedances in each bucket should follow a binomial distribution with $n = 400$, and $p = 5\%$.

Subadditivity

There is a reason VaR has become so popular in risk management. The appeal of VaR is its simplicity. Because VaR can be calculated for any portfolio, it allows us to easily compare the risk of different portfolios. Because it boils risk down to a single number, VaR provides us with a convenient way to track the risk of a portfolio over time. Finally, the concept of VaR is intuitive, even to those not versed in statistics.

Because it is so popular, VaR has come under a lot of criticism. The criticism generally falls into one of three categories.

At a very high level, financial institutions have been criticized for being overly reliant on VaR. This is not so much a criticism of VaR as it is a criticism of financial institutions for trying to make risk too simple.

At the other end of the spectrum, many experts have criticized how VaR is measured in practice. This is not so much a criticism of VaR as it is a criticism of specific implementations of VaR. For example, in the early days of finance it was popular to make what is known as a delta-normal assumption. That is, when measuring VaR, you would assume that all asset returns were normally distributed, and that all options could be approximated by their delta exposures. Further, the relationship between assets was based entirely on a covariance matrix (no coskewness or cokurtosis). These assumptions made calculating VaR very easy, even for large portfolios, but the results were often disappointing. As computing power became cheaper and more widespread, this approach quickly fell out of favor. Today VaR models can be extremely complex, but many people outside of risk management still remember when delta-normal was the standard approach, and mistakenly believe that this is a fundamental shortcoming of VaR.

In between, there are more sophisticated criticisms. One such criticism is that VaR is not a subadditive risk measure. It is generally accepted that a logical risk measure should have certain properties; see, for example, Artzner, Delbaen, Eber, and Heath (1999). One such property is known as subadditivity. Subadditivity is basically a fancy way of saying that diversification is good, and a good risk measure should reflect that.

Assume that our risk measure is a function f that takes as its input a random variable representing an asset or portfolio of assets. Higher values of the risk measure are associated with greater risk. If we have two risky portfolios, X and Y, then f is said to be subadditive if:

$$f(X + Y) \leq f(X) + f(Y) \tag{5.18}$$

In other words, the risk of the combined portfolio, $X + Y$, is less than or equal to the sum of the risks of the separate portfolios. Variance and standard deviation are subadditive risk measures.

While there is a lot to recommend VaR, unfortunately it does not always satisfy the requirement of subadditivity. The following example demonstrates a violation of subadditivity.

Example 5.5

Question:

Imagine a portfolio with two bonds, each with a 4% probability of defaulting. Assume that default events are uncorrelated and that the recovery rate of both bonds is 0%. If a bond defaults, it is worth $0; if it does not, it is worth $100. What is the 95% VaR of each bond separately? What is the 95% VaR of the bond portfolio?

Answer:

For each bond separately, the 95% VaR is $0. For an individual bond, in (over) 95% of scenarios, there is no loss.

In the combined portfolio, however, there are three possibilities, with the following probabilities:

P[x]	x
0.16%	−$200
7.68%	−$100
92.16%	$0

As we can easily see, there are no defaults in only 92.16% of the scenarios, $(1 - 4\%)^2 = 92.16\%$. In the other 7.84% of scenarios, the loss is greater than or equal to $100. The 95% VaR of the portfolio is therefore $100.

For this portfolio, VaR is not subadditive. Because the VaR of the combined portfolio is greater than the sum of the VaRs of the separate portfolios, VaR seems to suggest that there is no diversification benefit, even though the bonds are uncorrelated. It seems to suggest that holding $200 of either bond would be less risky than holding a portfolio with $100 of each. Clearly this is not correct.

This example makes clear that when assets have payout functions that are discontinuous near the VaR critical level, we are likely to have problems with subadditivity. By the same token, if the payout functions of the assets in a portfolio are continuous, then VaR will be subadditive. In many settings this is not an onerous assumption. In between, we have large, diverse portfolios, which contain some assets with discontinuous payout functions. For these portfolios subadditivity will likely be only a minor issue.

Expected Shortfall

Another criticism of VaR is that it does not tell us anything about the tail of the distribution. Two portfolios could have the exact same 95% VaR but very different distributions beyond the 95% confidence level.

More than VaR, then, what we really want to know is how big the loss will be when we have an exceedance event. Using the concept of conditional probability, we can define the expected value of a loss, given an exceedance, as follows:

$$E[L \mid L \geq \text{VaR}_\gamma] = S \tag{5.19}$$

We refer to this conditional expected loss, S, as the expected shortfall.

If the profit function has a probability density function given by $f(x)$, and VaR is the VaR at the γ confidence level, we can find the expected shortfall as:

$$S = -\frac{1}{1 - \gamma} \int_{-\infty}^{\text{VaR}} x f(x) dx \tag{5.20}$$

As with VaR, we have defined expected shortfall in terms of losses. Just as VaR tends to be positive for reasonable confidence levels for most portfolios, expected shortfall, as we have defined it in Equation (5.20), will also tend to be positive. As with VaR, this convention is not universal, and risk managers should be careful to avoid ambiguity when quoting expected shortfall numbers.

Expected shortfall does answer an important question. What's more, expected shortfall turns out to be subadditive, thereby avoiding one of the major criticisms of

VaR. As our discussion on backtesting suggests, though, because it is concerned with the tail of the distribution, the reliability of our expected shortfall measure may be difficult to gauge.

Example 5.6

Question:

In a previous example, the probability density function of Triangle Asset Management's daily profits could be described by the following function:

$$p = \frac{1}{10} + \frac{1}{100}\pi \quad -10 \le \pi \le 0$$

$$p = \frac{1}{10} - \frac{1}{100}\pi \quad 0 < \pi \le 10$$

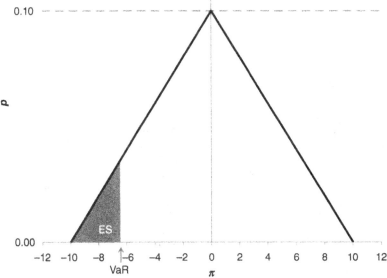

FIGURE 5-4 Triangular PDF, VaR, and expected shortfall.

The PDF is also shown in Figure 5-4. We calculated Triangle's one-day 95% VaR as a loss of $(10 - \sqrt{10}) = 6.84$. For the same confidence level and time horizon, what is the expected shortfall?

Answer:

Because the VaR occurs in the region where $\pi < 0$, we need to utilize only the first half of the function. Using Equation (5.20), we have:

$$S = \frac{1}{0.05}\int_{-10}^{VaR} \pi p\, d\pi = 20\int_{-10}^{VaR} \pi\left(\frac{1}{10} + \frac{1}{100}\pi\right)d\pi$$

$$S = \int_{-10}^{VaR}\left(2\pi + \frac{\pi^2}{5}\right)d\pi = \left[\pi^2 + \frac{1}{15}\pi^3\right]_{-10}^{VaR}$$

$$S = \left(\left(-10 + \sqrt{10}\right)^2 + \frac{1}{15}\left(-10 + \sqrt{10}\right)^3\right) - \left((-10)^2 + \frac{1}{15}(-10)^3\right)$$

$$S = -10 + \frac{2}{3}\sqrt{10} = -7.89$$

Thus, the expected shortfall is a loss of 7.89. Intuitively this should make sense. The expected shortfall must be greater than the VaR, 6.84, but less than the maximum loss of 10. Because extreme events are less likely (the height of the PDF decreases away from the center), it also makes sense that the expected shortfall is closer to the VaR than it is to the maximum loss.

Correlations and Copulas

6

Learning Objectives

Candidates, after completing this reading, should be able to:

- Define correlation and covariance and differentiate between correlation and dependence.
- Calculate covariance using the EWMA and GARCH (1,1) models.
- Apply the consistency condition to covariance.
- Describe the procedure of generating samples from a bivariate normal distribution.
- Describe properties of correlations between normally distributed variables when using a one-factor model.

- Define copula and describe the key properties of copula and copula correlation.
- Explain tail dependence.
- Describe Gaussian copula, Student's t-copula, multivariate copula, and one factor copula.

Excerpt is Chapter 11 of Risk Management and Financial Institutions, *Fourth Edition, by John C. Hull.*

Suppose that a company has an exposure to two different market variables. In the case of each variable, it gains $10 million if there is a one-standard-deviation increase and loses $10 million if there is a one-standard-deviation decrease. If changes in the two variables have a high positive correlation, the company's total exposure is very high; if they have a correlation of zero, the exposure is less but still quite large; if they have a high negative correlation, the exposure is quite low because a loss on one of the variables is likely to be offset by a gain on the other. This example shows that it is important for a risk manager to estimate correlations between the changes in market variables as well as their volatilities when assessing risk exposures.

This chapter explains how correlations can be monitored in a similar way to volatilities. It also covers what are known as copulas. These are tools that provide a way of defining a correlation structure between two or more variables, regardless of the shapes of their probability distributions. Copulas have a number of applications in risk management. The chapter shows how a copula can be used to create a model of default correlation for a portfolio of loans. This model is used in the Basel II capital requirements.

DEFINITION OF CORRELATION

The coefficient of correlation, ρ, between two variables V_1 and V_2 is defined as

$$\rho = \frac{E(V_1 V_2) - E(V_1)E(V_2)}{SD(V_1)SD(V_2)} \qquad \textbf{(6.1)}$$

where $E(.)$ denotes expected value and $SD(.)$ denotes standard deviation. If there is no correlation between the variables, $E(V_1 V_2) = E(V_1)E(V_2)$ and $\rho = 0$. If $V_1 = V_2$, both the numerator and the denominator in the expression for ρ equal the variance of V_1. As we would expect, $\rho = 1$ in this case.

The *covariance* between V_1 and V_2 is defined as

$$\text{cov}(V_1, V_2) = E(V_1 V_2) - E(V_1)E(V_2) \qquad \textbf{(6.2)}$$

so that the correlation can be written

$$\rho = \frac{\text{cov}(V_1, V_2)}{SD(V_1)SD(V_2)}$$

Although it is easier to develop intuition about the meaning of a correlation than a covariance, it is covariances that will prove to be the fundamental variables of our analysis.

An analogy here is that variance rates were the fundamental variables for the EWMA and GARCH models, even though it is easier to develop intuition about volatilities.

Correlation vs. Dependence

Two variables are defined as statistically independent if knowledge about one of them does not affect the probability distribution for the other. Formally, V_1 and V_2 are independent if:

$$f(V_2 | V_1 = x) = f(V_2)$$

for all x where $f(.)$ denotes the probability density function and | is the symbol denoting "conditional on."

If the coefficient of correlation between two variables is zero, does this mean that there is no dependence between the variables? The answer is no. We can illustrate this with a simple example. Suppose that there are three equally likely values for V_1: -1, 0, and $+1$. If $V_1 = -1$ or $V_1 = +1$, then $V_2 = +1$. If $V_1 = 0$, then $V_2 = 0$. In this case, there is clearly a dependence between V_1 and V_2. If we observe the value of V_1, we know the value of V_2. Also, a knowledge of the value of V_2 will cause us to change our probability distribution for V_1. However, the $E(V_1 V_2) = 0$ and $E(V_1) = 0$, it is easy to see that the coefficient of correlation between V_1 and V_2 is zero.

This example emphasizes the point that the coefficient of correlation measures one particular type of dependence between two variables. This is linear dependence. There are many other ways in which two variables can be related. We can characterize the nature of the dependence between V_1 and V_2 by plotting $E(V_2)$ against V_1. Three examples are shown in Figure 6-1. Figure 6-1(a) shows linear dependence where the expected value of V_2 depends linearly on V_1. Figure 6-1(b) shows a V-shaped relationship between the expected value of V_2 and the value of V_1. (This is similar to the simple example considered; a symmetrical V-shaped relationship, however strong, leads to zero coefficient of correlation.) Figure 6-1(c) shows a type of dependence that is often seen when V_1 and V_2 are percentage changes in financial variables. For the values of V_1 normally encountered, there is very little relation between V_1 and V_2. However, extreme values of V_1 tend to lead to extreme values of V_2. (This could be consistent with correlations increasing in stressed market conditions.)

Another aspect of the way in which V_2 depends on V_1 is found by examining the standard deviation of V_2

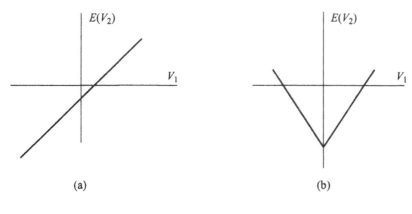

(a)   (b)

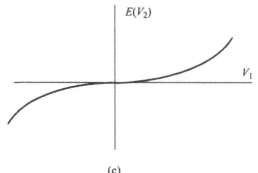

(c)

FIGURE 6-1 Examples of ways in which V_2 can be dependent on V_1.

conditional on V_1. As we will see later, this is constant when V_1 and V_2 have a bivariate normal distribution. But, in other situations, the standard deviation of V_2 is liable to depend on the value of V_1.

MONITORING CORRELATION

Exponentially weighted moving average and GARCH methods can be developed to monitor the variance rate of a variable. Similar approaches can be used to monitor the covariance rate between two variables. The variance rate per day of a variable is the variance of daily returns. Similarly, the *covariance rate* per day between two variables is defined as the covariance between the daily returns of the variables.

Suppose that X_i and Y_i are the values of two variables, X and Y, at the end of day i. The returns on the variables on day i are

$$x_i = \frac{X_i - X_{i-1}}{X_{i-1}} \quad y_i = \frac{Y_i - Y_{i-1}}{Y_{i-1}}$$

The covariance rate between X and Y on day n is from Equation (6.2):

$$\text{cov}_n = E(x_n y_n) - E(x_n)E(y_n)$$

Risk managers assume that expected daily returns are zero when the variance rate per day is calculated. They do the same when calculating the covariance rate per day. This means that the covariance rate per day between X and Y on day n is assumed to be

$$\text{cov}_n = E(x_n y_n)$$

Using equal weights for the last m observations on x_i and y_i gives the estimate

$$\text{cov}_n = \frac{1}{m}\sum_{i=1}^{m} x_{n-i} y_{n-i} \tag{6.3}$$

A similar weighting scheme for variances gives an estimate for the variance rate on day n for variable X as

$$\text{var}_{x,n} = \frac{1}{m}\sum_{i=1}^{m} x_{n-i}^2$$

and for variable Y as

$$\text{var}_{y,n} = \frac{1}{m}\sum_{i=1}^{m} y_{n-i}^2$$

The correlation estimate on day n is

$$\frac{\text{cov}_n}{\sqrt{\text{var}_{x,n}\text{var}_{y,n}}}$$

EWMA

Most risk managers would agree that observations from long ago should not have as much weight as recent observations. The exponentially weighted moving average (EWMA) model for variances leads to weights that decline exponentially as we move back through time. A similar weighting scheme can be used for covariances. The formula for updating a covariance estimate in the EWMA model is:

$$\text{cov}_n = \lambda\text{cov}_{n-1} + (1 - \lambda)x_{n-1}y_{n-1}$$

A similar analysis to that presented for the EWMA volatility model shows that the weight given to $x_{n-1}y_{n-1}$ declines as i increases (i.e., as we move back through time). The lower the value of λ, the greater the weight that is given to recent observations.

EXAMPLE 6.1

Suppose that $\lambda = 0.95$ and that the estimate of the correlation between two variables X and Y on day $n - 1$ is 0.6. Suppose further that the estimate of the volatilities for X and Y on day $n - 1$ are 1 % and 2%, respectively. From the relationship between correlation and covariance, the estimate of the covariance rate between X and Y on day $n - 1$ is

$$0.6 \times 0.01 \times 0.02 = 0.00012$$

Suppose that the percentage changes in X and Y on day $n - 1$ are 0.5% and 2.5%, respectively. The variance rates and covariance rate for day n would be updated as follows:

$$\sigma_{x,n}^2 = 0.95 \times 0.01^2 + 0.05 \times 0.005^2 = 0.00009625$$

$$\sigma_{y,n}^2 = 0.95 \times 0.02^2 + 0.05 \times 0.025^2 = 0.00041125$$

$$cov_n = 0.95 \times 0.00012 + 0.05 \times 0.005 \times 0.025$$
$$= 0.00012025$$

The new volatility of X is $\sqrt{0.00009625} = 0.981\%$, and the new volatility of Y is $\sqrt{0.00041125} = 2.028\%$. The new correlation between X and Y is

$$\frac{0.00012025}{0.00981 \times 0.02028} = 0.6044$$

GARCH

GARCH models can also be used for updating covariance rate estimates and forecasting the future level of covariance rates. For example, the GARCH(1,1) model for updating a covariance rate between X and Y is

$$cov_n = \omega + \alpha x_{n-1} y_{n-1} + \beta cov_{n-1}$$

This formula gives some weight to a long-run average covariance, some to the most recent covariance estimate, and some to the most recent observation on covariance (which is $x_{n-1} y_{n-1}$). The long-term average covariance rate is $\omega/(1 - \alpha - \beta)$. Formulas can be developed for forecasting future covariance rates and calculating the average covariance rate during a future time period.

Consistency Condition for Covariances

Once variance and covariance rates have been calculated for a set of market variables, a variance-covariance matrix can be constructed. When $i \neq j$, the (i, j) element of this

matrix shows the covariance rate between variable i and variable j. When $i = j$, it shows the variance rate of variable i.

Not all variance-covariance matrices are internally consistent. The condition for an $N \times N$ variance-covariance matrix, Ω, to be internally consistent is

$$\mathbf{w}^T \Omega \mathbf{w} \geq 0 \qquad \textbf{(6.4)}$$

for all $N \times 1$ vectors $\mathbf{w}$ where $\mathbf{w}^T$ is the transpose of $\mathbf{w}$. A matrix that satisfies this property is known as *positive-semidefinite.*

To understand why the condition in Equation (6.4) must hold, suppose that $\mathbf{w}$ is the (column) vector $(w_1, w_2, \ldots, w_N)$. The expression $\mathbf{w}^T \Omega \mathbf{w}$ is the variance rate of a portfolio where an amount w_i is invested in market variable i. As such, it cannot be negative.

To ensure that a positive-semidefinite matrix is produced, variances and covariances should be calculated consistently. For example, if variance rates are calculated by giving equal weight to the last m data items, the same should be done for covariance rates. If variance rates are updated using an EWMA model with $\lambda = 0.94$, the same should be done for covariance rates. Using a GARCH model to update a variance-covariance matrix in a consistent way is trickier and requires a multivariate GARCH model.[1]

An example of a variance-covariance matrix that is not internally consistent is

$$\begin{pmatrix} 1 & 0 & 0.9 \\ 0 & 1 & 0.9 \\ 0.9 & 0.9 & 1 \end{pmatrix}$$

The variance of each variable is 1.0 and so the covariances are also coefficients of correlation in this case. The first variable is highly correlated with the third variable, and the second variable is also highly correlated with the third variable. However, there is no correlation at all between the first and second variables. This seems strange. When we set $\mathbf{w}^T$ equal to $(1, 1, -1)$, we find that the condition in Equation (6.4) is not satisfied, proving that the matrix is not positive-semidefinite.[2]

---

[1] See R. Engle and J. Mezrich, "GARCH for Groups," *Risk* (August 1996): 36–40, for a discussion of alternative approaches.

[2] It can be shown that the condition for a 3×3 matrix of correlations to be internally consistent is

$$\rho_{12}^2 + \rho_{13}^2 + \rho_{23}^2 - 2\rho_{12}\rho_{13}\rho_{23} \leq 1$$

where ρ_{ij} is the coefficient of correlation between variables i and j.

If we make a small change to a positive-semidefinite matrix that is calculated from observations on three variables (e.g., for the purposes of doing a sensitivity analysis), it is likely that the matrix will remain positive-semidefinite. However, if we do the same thing for observations on 100 variables, we have to be much more careful. An arbitrary small change to a positive-semidefinite 100×100 matrix is quite likely to lead to it no longer being positive-semidefinite.

MULTIVARIATE NORMAL DISTRIBUTIONS

Multivariate normal distributions are well understood and relatively easy to deal with. As we will explain in the next section, they can be useful tools for specifying the correlation structure between variables, even when the distributions of the variables are not normal.

We start by considering a bivariate normal distribution where there are only two variables, V_1 and V_2. Suppose that we know V_1 has some value. Conditional on this, the value of V_2 is normal with mean

$$\mu_2 + \rho\sigma_2 \frac{V_1 - \mu_1}{\sigma_1}$$

and standard deviation

$$\sigma_2 \sqrt{1 - \rho^2}$$

Here μ_1 and μ_2 are the unconditional means of V_1 and V_2, σ_1 and σ_2 are their unconditional standard deviations, and ρ is the coefficient of correlation between V_1 and V_2. Note that the expected value of V_2 conditional on V_1 is linearly dependent on the value of V_1. This corresponds to Figure 6-1(a). Also, the standard deviation of V_2 conditional on the value of V_1 is the same for all values of V_1.

Generating Random Samples from Normal Distributions

Most programming languages have routines for sampling a random number between zero and one, and many have routines for sampling from a normal distribution.[3]

When samples ϵ_1 and ϵ_2 from a bivariate normal distribution (where both variables have mean zero and standard deviation one) are required, the usual procedure involves

---

[3] In Excel, the instruction =NORMSINV(RAND()) gives a random sample from a normal distribution.

first obtaining independent samples z_1 and z_2 from a univariate standardized normal distribution. The required samples ϵ_1 and ϵ_2 are then calculated as follows:

$$\epsilon_1 = z_1$$
$$\epsilon_2 = \rho z_1 + z_2\sqrt{1 - \rho^2}$$

where ρ is the coefficient of correlation in the bivariate normal distribution.

Consider next the situation where we require samples from a multivariate normal distribution (where all variables have mean zero and standard deviation one) and the coefficient of correlation between variable i and variable j is ρ_{ij}. We first sample n independent variables z_i $(1 \leq i \leq n)$ from univariate standardized normal distributions. The required samples are ϵ_i $(1 \leq i \leq n)$, where

$$\epsilon_i = \sum_{k=1}^{i} \alpha_{ik} z_k \qquad \textbf{(6.5)}$$

and the α_{ik} are parameters chosen to give the correct variances and the correct correlations for the ϵ_i. For $1 \leq j < i$, we must have

$$\sum_{k=1}^{i} \alpha_{ik}^2 = 1$$

and, for all $j < i$,

$$\sum_{k=1}^{j} \alpha_{ik}\alpha_{jk} = \rho_{ij}$$

The first sample, ϵ_1, is set equal to z_1. These equations can be solved so that ϵ_2 is calculated from z_1 and z_2, ϵ_3 is calculated from z_1, z_2, and z_3, and so on. The procedure is known as the *Cholesky decomposition*.

If we find ourselves trying to take the square root of a negative number when using the Cholesky decomposition, the variance-covariance matrix assumed for the variables is not internally consistent. As explained earlier, this is equivalent to saying that the matrix is not positive-semidefinite.

Factor Models

Sometimes the correlations between normally distributed variables are defined using a factor model. Suppose that $U_1, U_2, \ldots, U_N$ have standard normal distributions (i.e., normal distributions with mean zero and standard deviation one). In a one-factor model, each U_i has a component dependent on a common factor, F, and a component that is uncorrelated with the other variables. Formally,

$$U_i = a_i F + \sqrt{1 - a_i^2}\, Z_i \qquad \textbf{(6.6)}$$

where F and the Z_i have standard normal distributions and a_i is a constant between −1 and +1. The Z_i are uncorrelated with each other and uncorrelated with F. The coefficient of Z_i is chosen so that U_i has a mean of zero and a variance of one. In this model, all the correlation between U_i and U_j arises from their dependence on the common factor, F. The coefficient of correlation between U_i and U_j is $a_i a_j$.

A one-factor model imposes some structure on the correlations and has the advantage that the resulting covariance matrix is always positive-semidefinite. Without assuming a factor model, the number of correlations that have to be estimated for the N variables is $N(N − 1)/2$. With the one-factor model, we need only estimate N parameters: $a_1, a_2, \ldots, a_N$. An example of a one-factor model from the world of investments is the capital asset pricing model where the return on a stock has a component dependent on the return from the market and an idiosyncratic (nonsystematic) component that is independent of the return on other stocks.

The one-factor model can be extended to a two-factor, three-factor, or M-factor model. In the M-factor model

$$U_i = a_{i1}F_1 + a_{i2}F_2 + \ldots + a_{iM}F_M + \sqrt{1 - a_{i1}^2 - a_{i2}^2 - \ldots - a_{iM}^2}\, Z_i$$
$$\textbf{(6.7)}$$

The factors, $F_1, F_2, \ldots F_M$ have uncorrelated standard normal distributions and the Z_i are uncorrelated both with each other and with the factors. In this case, the correlation between U_i and U_j is

$$\sum_{m=1}^{M} a_{im} a_{jm}$$

COPULAS

Consider two correlated variables, V_1 and V_2. The *marginal distribution* of V_1 (sometimes also referred to as the unconditional distribution) is its distribution assuming we know nothing about V_2; similarly, the marginal distribution of V_2 is its distribution assuming we know nothing about V_1. Suppose we have estimated the marginal distributions of V_1 and V_2. How can we make an assumption about the correlation structure between the two variables to define their joint distribution?

If the marginal distributions of V_1 and V_2 are normal, a convenient and easy-to-work-with assumption is that the joint distribution of the variables is bivariate normal.[4] (The correlation structure between the variables is then as described earlier.) Similar assumptions are possible for some other marginal distributions. But often there is no natural way of defining a correlation structure between two marginal distributions. This is where copulas come in.

As an example of the application of copulas, suppose that variables V_1 and V_2 have the triangular probability density functions shown in Figure 6-2. Both variables have values between 0 and 1. The density function for V_1 peaks at 0.2. The density function for V_2 peaks at 0.5. For both density functions, the maximum height is 2.0 (so that the area under the density function is 1.0). To use what is known as a *Gaussian copula*, we map V_1 and V_2 into new variables U_1 and U_2 that have standard normal distributions. (A standard normal distribution is a normal distribution with mean zero and standard deviation one.) The mapping is accomplished on a percentile-to-percentile basis. The one-percentile point of the V_1 distribution is mapped to the one-percentile point of the U_1 distribution; the 10-percentile point of the V_1 distribution is mapped to the 10-percentile point of the U_1 distribution; and so on. V_2 is mapped into U_2 in a similar way. Table 6-1 shows how values of V_1 are mapped into values of U_1. Table 6-2 similarly shows how values of V_2 are mapped into values of U_2. Consider the $V_1 = 0.1$ calculation in Table 6-1. The cumulative probability that V_1 is less than 0.1 is (by calculating areas of triangles) $0.5 \times 0.1 \times 1 = 0.05$ or 5%. The value 0.1 for V_1 therefore gets mapped to the five-percentile point of the standard normal distribution. This is −1.64.[5]

---

[4] Although the bivariate normal assumption is a convenient one, it is not the only one that can be made. There are many other ways in which two normally distributed variables can be dependent on each other. For example, we could have $V_2 = V_1$ for $−k \leq V_1 \leq k$ and $V_2 = −V_1$ otherwise.

[5] It can be calculated using Excel: NORMSINV(0.05) = −1.64.

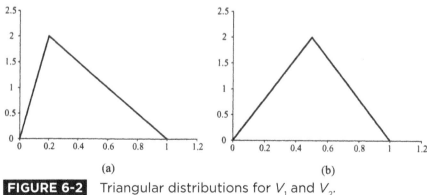

(a)   (b)

FIGURE 6-2 Triangular distributions for V_1 and V_2.

TABLE 6-1 Mapping of V_1 Which Has the Triangular Distribution in Figure 6-2(a) to U_1 Which Has a Standard Normal Distribution

V_1 Value	Percentile of Distribution	U_1 Value
0.1	5.00	−1.64
0.2	20.00	−0.84
0.3	38.75	−0.29
0.4	55.00	0.13
0.5	68.75	0.49
0.6	80.00	0.84
0.7	88.75	1.21
0.8	95.00	1.64
0.9	98.75	2.24

TABLE 6-2 Mapping of V_2 Which Has the Triangular Distribution in Figure 6-2(b) to U_2 Which Has a Standard Normal Distribution

V_2 Value	Percentile of Distribution	U_2 Value
0.1	2.00	−2.05
0.2	8.00	−1.41
0.3	18.00	−0.92
0.4	32.00	−0.47
0.5	50.00	0.00
0.6	68.00	0.47
0.7	82.00	0.92
0.8	92.00	1.41
0.9	98.00	2.05

The variables, U_1 and U_2, have normal distributions. We assume that they are jointly bivariate normal. This in turn implies a joint distribution and a correlation structure between V_1 and V_2. The essence of copula is therefore that, instead of defining a correlation structure between V_1 and V_2 directly, we do so indirectly. We map V_1 and V_2 into other variables which have well-behaved distributions and for which it is easy to define a correlation structure.

Suppose that we assume the correlation between U_1 and U_2 is 0.5. The joint cumulative probability distribution between V_1 and V_2 is shown in Table 6-3. To illustrate the calculations, consider the first one where we are calculating the probability that $V_1 < 0.1$ and $V_2 < 0.1$. From

TABLE 6-3 Cumulative Joint Probability Distribution for V_1 and V_2 in the Gaussian Copula Model (Correlation parameter = 0.5. Table shows the joint probability that V_1 and V_2 are less than the specified values.)

V_1	V_2								
	0.1	0.2	0.3	0.4	0.5	0.6	0.7	0.8	0.9
0.1	0.006	0.017	0.028	0.037	0.044	0.048	0.049	0.050	0.050
0.2	0.013	0.043	0.081	0.120	0.156	0.181	0.193	0.198	0.200
0.3	0.017	0.061	0.124	0.197	0.273	0.331	0.364	0.381	0.387
0.4	0.019	0.071	0.149	0.248	0.358	0.449	0.505	0.535	0.548
0.5	0.019	0.076	0.164	0.281	0.417	0.537	0.616	0.663	0.683
0.6	0.020	0.078	0.173	0.301	0.456	0.600	0.701	0.763	0.793
0.7	0.020	0.079	0.177	0.312	0.481	0.642	0.760	0.837	0.877
0.8	0.020	0.080	0.179	0.318	0.494	0.667	0.798	0.887	0.936
0.9	0.020	0.080	0.180	0.320	0.499	0.678	0.816	0.913	0.970

Tables 6-1 and 6-2, this is the same as the probability that $U_1 < -1.64$ and $U_2 < -2.05$. From the cumulative bivariate normal distribution, this is 0.006 when $\rho = 0.5$.[6] (Note that the probability would be only $0.02 \times 0.05 = 0.001$ if $\rho = 0$.)

The correlation between U_1 and U_2 is referred to as the *copula correlation*. This is not, in general, the same as the coefficient of correlation between V_1 and V_2. Because U_1 and U_2 are bivariate normal, the conditional mean of U_2 is linearly dependent on U_1 and the conditional standard deviation of U_2 is constant (as discussed earlier). However, a similar result does not in general apply to V_1 and V_2.

Expressing the Approach Algebraically

The way in which a Gaussian copula defines a joint distribution is illustrated in Figure 6-3. For a more formal description of the model, suppose that G_1 and G_2 are the cumulative marginal (i.e., unconditional) probability distribution of V_1 and V_2. We map $V_1 = v_1$ to $U_1 = u_1$ and $V_2 = v_2$ to $U_2 = u_2$ so that

---

[6] An Excel function for calculating the cumulative bivariate normal distribution is on the author's website: www-2.rotman .utoronto.ca/~hull/riskman.

$$G_1(v_1) = N(u_1)$$

and

$$G_2(v_2) = N(u_2)$$

where N is the cumulative normal distribution function. This means that

$$u_1 = N^{-1}[G_1(v_1)] \qquad u_2 = N^{-1}[G_2(v_2)]$$
$$v_1 = G_1^{-1}[N(u_1)] \qquad v_2 = G_2^{-1}[N(u_2)]$$

The variables U_1 and U_2 are then assumed to be bivariate normal. The key property of a copula model is that it preserves the marginal distributions of V_1 and V_2 (however unusual these may be) while defining a correlation structure between them.

Other Copulas

The Gaussian copula is just one copula that can be used to define a correlation structure between V_1 and V_2. There are many other copulas leading to many other correlation structures. One that is sometimes used is the *Student's t-copula*. This works in the same way as the Gaussian copula except that the variables U_1 and U_2 are assumed to have a bivariate Student's t-distribution instead of a bivariate normal distribution. To sample from a bivariate Student's t-distribution with f degrees of freedom and correlation ρ, the steps are as follows:

1. Sample from the inverse chi-square distribution to get a value χ. (In Excel, the CHIINV function can be used. The first argument is RAND() and the second is f.)

2. Sample from a bivariate normal distribution with correlation ρ as described earlier.

3. Multiply the normally distributed samples by $\sqrt{f/\chi}$.

Tail Dependence

Figure 6-4 shows plots of 5,000 random samples from a bivariate normal distribution while Figure 6-5 does the same for the bivariate Student's t. The correlation parameter is 0.5 and the number of degrees of freedom for the Student's t is 4. Define a tail value of a distribution as a value in the left or right 1% tail of the distribution. There is a tail value for the normal distribution when the variable is greater than 2.33 or less than −2.33. Similarly, there is a tail

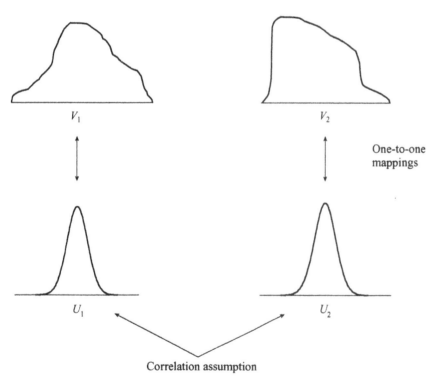

V_1 V_2

One-to-one mappings

U_1 U_2

Correlation assumption

FIGURE 6-3 The way in which a copula model defines a joint distribution.

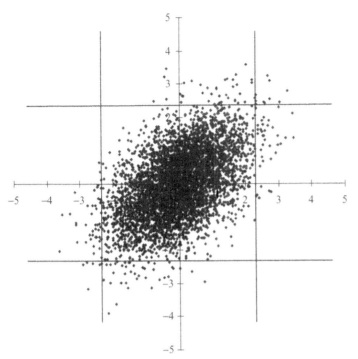

FIGURE 6-4 5,000 random samples from a bivariate normal distribution.

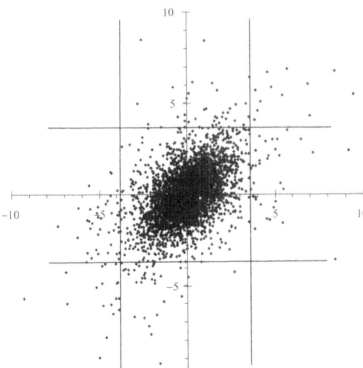

FIGURE 6-5 5,000 random samples from a bivariate Student's *t*-distribution with four degrees of freedom.

value in the Student's *t*-distribution when the value of the variable is greater than 3.75 or less than −3.75. Vertical and horizontal lines in the figures indicate when tail values occur. The figures illustrate that it is more common for the two variables to have tail values at the same time in the bivariate Student's *t*-distribution than in the bivariate normal distribution. To put this another way, the *tail dependence* is higher in a bivariate Student's *t*-distribution than in a bivariate normal distribution. We made the point earlier that correlations between market variables tend to increase in extreme market conditions, so that Figure 6-1(c) is sometimes a better description of the correlation structure between two variables than Figure 6-1(a). This has led some researchers to argue that the Student's *t*-copula provides a better description of the joint behavior of two market variables than the Gaussian copula.

Multivariate Copulas

Copulas can be used to define a correlation structure between more than two variables. The simplest example of this is the multivariate Gaussian copula. Suppose that there are N variables, $V_1, V_2, \ldots, V_N$ and that we know the marginal distribution of each variable. For each i ($1 \leq i \leq N$), we transform V_i into U_i where U_i has a standard normal distribution. (As described earlier, the transformation is accomplished on a percentile-to-percentile basis.) We then assume that the U_i have a multivariate normal distribution.

A Factor Copula Model

In multivariate copula models, analysts often assume a factor model for the correlation structure between the U_i. When there is only one factor, Equation (6.6) gives

$$U_i = a_i F + \sqrt{1 - a_i^2}\, Z_i \qquad \textbf{(6.8)}$$

where F and the Z_i have standard normal distributions. The Z_i are uncorrelated with each other and with F. Other factor copula models are obtained by choosing F and the Z_i to have other zero-mean unit-variance distributions. For example, if Z_i is normal and F has a Student's *t*-distribution, we obtain a multivariate Student's *t*-distribution for U_i. These distributional choices affect the nature of the dependence between the *U*-variables and therefore that between the *V*-variables.

APPLICATION TO LOAN PORTFOLIOS: VASICEK'S MODEL

We now present an application of the one-factor Gaussian copula model that will prove useful in understanding the Basel II capital requirements. Suppose a bank has a large portfolio of loans where the probability of default per year for each loan is 1%. If the loans default independently of each other, we would expect the default rate to be almost exactly 1% every year. In practice, loans do not default independently of each other. They are all influenced by macroeconomic conditions. As a result, in some years the default rate is high whereas in others it is low. This is illustrated by Table 6-4, which shows the default rate for all rated companies between 1970 and 2013. The default rate varies from a low of 0.088% in 1979 to a high of 6.002% in 2009. Other high-default-rate years were 1970, 1989, 1990, 1991, 1999, 2000, 2001, 2002, and 2008.

TABLE 6-4 Annual Percentage Default Rate for All Rated Companies, 1970–2013

Year	Default Rate	Year	Default Rate	Year	Default Rate
1970	2.621	1985	0.960	2000	2.852
1971	0.285	1986	1.875	2001	4.345
1972	0.451	1987	1.588	2002	3.319
1973	0.453	1988	1.372	2003	2.018
1974	0.274	1989	2.386	2004	0.939
1975	0.359	1990	3.750	2005	0.760
1976	0.175	1991	3.091	2006	0.721
1977	0.352	1992	1.500	2007	0.401
1978	0.352	1993	0.890	2008	2.252
1979	0.088	1994	0.663	2009	6.002
1980	0.342	1995	1.031	2010	1.408
1981	0.162	1996	0.588	2011	0.890
1982	1.032	1997	0.765	2012	1.381
1983	0.964	1998	1.317	2013	1.381
1984	0.934	1999	2.409		

Source: Moody's.

To model the defaults of the loans in a portfolio, we define T_i as the time when company i defaults. (There is an implicit assumption that all companies will default eventually—but the default may happen a long time, perhaps even hundreds of years, in the future.) We make the simplifying assumption that all loans have the same cumulative probability distribution for the time to default and define PD as the probability of default by time T:

$$PD = \text{Prob}(T_i < T).$$

The Gaussian copula model can be used to define a correlation structure between the times to default of the loans. Following the procedure we have described, each time to default T_i is mapped to a variable U_i that has a standard normal distribution on a percentile-to-percentile basis.

We assume the factor model in Equation (6.8) for the correlation structure between the U_i and make the simplifying assumption that the a_i are all the same and equal to a so that:

$$U_i = aF + \sqrt{1 - a^2}\, Z_i$$

As in Equation (6.8), the variables F and Z_i have independent standard normal distributions. The copula correlation between each pair of loans is in this case the same. It is

$$\rho = a^2$$

so that the expression for U_i can be written

$$U_i = \sqrt{\rho} F + \sqrt{1 - \rho}\, Z_i \qquad \textbf{(6.9)}$$

Define the "worst case default rate," WCDR(T, X), as the default rate (i.e., percentage of loans defaulting) during time T that will not be exceeded with probability X%. (In many applications T will be one year.) As shown in what follows, the assumptions we have made lead to

$$\text{WCDR}(T, X) = N\left(\frac{N^{-1}(PD) - \sqrt{\rho} N^{-1}(X)}{\sqrt{1 - \rho}} \right) \qquad \textbf{(6.10)}$$

This is a strange-looking result, but a very important one. It was first developed by Vasicek in 1987.[7] The right-hand side of the equation can easily be calculated using the NORMSDIST and NORMSINV functions in Excel. Note that if $\rho = 0$, the loans default independently of each other and WCDR = PD. AS ρ increases, WCDR increases.

---

[7] See O. Vasicek, "Probability of Loss on a Loan Portfolio" (Working Paper, KMV, 1987). Vasicek's results were published in *Risk* in December 2002 under the title "Loan Portfolio Value."

Example 6.2

Suppose that a bank has a large number of loans to retail customers. The one-year probability of default for each loan is 2% and the copula correlation parameter, ρ, in Vasicek's model is estimated as 0.1. In this case,

$$WCDR(1, 0.999) = N\left(\frac{N^{-1}(0.02) + \sqrt{0.1}N^{-1}(0.999)}{\sqrt{1-0.1}}\right) = 0.128$$

showing that the 99.9% worst case one-year default rate is 12.8%.

Proof of Vasicek's Result

From the properties of the Gaussian copula model

$$PD = Prob(T_i < T) = Prob(U_i < U)$$

where

$$U = N^{-1}[PD] \qquad \textbf{(6.11)}$$

The probability of default by time T depends on the value of the factor, F, in Equation (6.9). The factor can be thought of as an index of macroeconomic conditions. If F is high, macroeconomic conditions are good. Each U_i will then tend to be high and the corresponding T_i will therefore also tend to be high, meaning that the probability of an early default is low and therefore $Prob(T_i < T)$ is low. If F is low, macroeconomic conditions are bad. Each U_i and the corresponding T_i will then tend to be low so that the probability of an early default is high. To explore this further, we consider the probability of default conditional on F.

From Equation (6.9),

$$Z_i = \frac{U_i - \sqrt{\rho}F}{\sqrt{1-\rho}}$$

The probability that $U_i < U$ conditional on the factor value, F, is

$$Prob(U_i < U \mid F) = Prob\left(Z_i < \frac{U - \sqrt{\rho}F}{\sqrt{1-\rho}}\right) = N\left(\frac{U - \sqrt{\rho}F}{\sqrt{1-\rho}}\right)$$

This is also $Prob(T_i < T \mid F)$ so that

$$Prob(T_i < T \mid F) = N\left(\frac{U - \sqrt{\rho}F}{\sqrt{1-\rho}}\right) \qquad \textbf{(6.12)}$$

From Equation (6.11) this becomes

$$Prob(T_i < T \mid F) = N\left(\frac{N^{-1}(PD) - \sqrt{\rho}F}{\sqrt{1-\rho}}\right) \qquad \textbf{(6.13)}$$

For a large portfolio of loans with the same PD, where the copula correlation for each pair of loans is ρ, this equation provides a good estimate of the percentage of loans defaulting by time T conditional on F. We will refer to this as the default rate.

As F decreases, the default rate increases. How bad can the default rate become? Because F has a normal distribution, the probability that F will be less than $N^{-1}(Y)$ is Y. There is therefore a probability of Y that the default rate will be greater than

$$N\left(\frac{N^{-1}(PD) - \sqrt{\rho}N^{-1}(Y)}{\sqrt{1-\rho}}\right)$$

The default rate that we are X% certain will not be exceeded in time T is obtained by substituting $Y = 1 - X$ into the preceding expression. Because $N^{-1}(X) = -N^{-1}(1 - X)$, we obtain Equation (6.10).

Estimating PD and ρ

The maximum likelihood methods can be used to estimate PD and ρ from historical data on default rates. We used Equation (6.10) to calculate a high percentile of the default rate distribution, but it is actually true for all percentiles. If DR is the default rate and $G(DR)$ is the cumulative probability distribution function for DR, Equation (6.10) shows that

$$DR = N\left(\frac{N^{-1}(PD) + \sqrt{\rho}N^{-1}(G(DR))}{\sqrt{1-\rho}}\right)$$

Rearranging this equation

$$G(DR) = N\left(\frac{\sqrt{1-\rho}N^{-1}(DR) - N^{-1}(PD)}{\sqrt{\rho}}\right) \qquad \textbf{(6.14)}$$

Differentiating this, the probability density function for the default rate is

$$G(DR) = \sqrt{\frac{1-\rho}{\rho}} \exp$$

$$\left\{\frac{1}{2}\left[(N^{-1}(DR))^2 - \left(\frac{\sqrt{1-\rho}N^{-1}(DR) - N^{-1}(PD)}{\sqrt{\rho}}\right)^2\right]\right\} \qquad \textbf{(6.15)}$$

The procedure for calculating maximum likelihood estimates for PD and ρ from historical data is as follows:

1. Choose trial values for PD and ρ.

2. Calculate the logarithm of the probability density in Equation (6.15) for each of the observations on DR.

3. Use Solver to search for the values of PD and ρ that maximize the sum of the values in 2.

One application of this is to the data in Table 6-4. The estimates for ρ and PD given by this data are 0.108 and 1.41%, respectively. (See worksheet on the author's website for calculations). The probability distribution for the default rate is shown in Figure 6-6. The 99.9% worst case default rate is

$$N\left(\frac{N^{-1}(0.0141) + \sqrt{0.108}N^{-1}(0.999)}{\sqrt{1 - 0.108}}\right) = 0.106$$

or 10.6% per annum.

Alternatives to the Gaussian Copula

The one-factor Gaussian copula model has its limitations. As Figure 6-4 illustrates, it leads to very little tail dependence. This means that an unusually early default for one company does not often happen at the same time as an unusually early default time for another company. It can be difficult to find a ρ to fit data. For example, there is no ρ that is consistent with a PD of 1% and the situation where one year in 10 the default rate is greater than 3%. Other one-factor copula models with more tail dependence can provide a better fit to data.

An approach to developing other one-factor copulas is to choose F or Z_i, or both, as distributions with heavier tails than the normal distribution in Equation (6.9). (They have to be scaled so that they have a mean of zero and standard deviation of one.) The distribution of U_i is then determined (possibly numerically) from the distributions of F and Z_i. Equation (6.10) becomes

$$\text{WCDR}(T, X) = \Phi\left(\frac{\Psi^{-1}(\text{PD}) + \sqrt{\rho}\Theta^{-1}(X)}{\sqrt{1 - \rho}}\right)$$

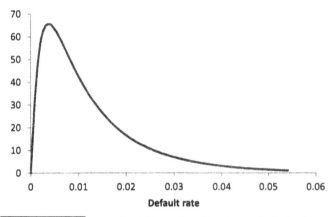

70
60
50
40
30
20
10
0

0   0.01   0.02   0.03   0.04   0.05   0.06

Default rate

FIGURE 6-6 Probability distribution of default rate when parameters are estimated using the data in Table 6-4.

where Φ, Θ, and Ψ are the cumulative probability distributions of Z_i, F, and U_i and Equation (6.14) becomes[8]

$$G(\text{DR}) = \Theta\left(\frac{\sqrt{1 - \rho}\Phi^{-1}(\text{DR}) - \Psi^{-1}(\text{PD})}{\sqrt{\rho}}\right)$$

SUMMARY

Risk managers use correlations or covariances to describe the relationship between two variables. The daily covariance rate is the correlation between the daily returns on the variables multiplied by the product of their daily volatilities. The methods for monitoring a covariance rate are similar to those for monitoring a variance rate. Risk managers often try to keep track of a variance–covariance matrix for all the variables to which they are exposed.

The marginal distribution of a variable is the unconditional distribution of the variable. Very often an analyst is in a situation where he or she has estimated the marginal distributions of a set of variables and wants to make an assumption about their correlation structure. If the marginal distributions of the variables happen to be normal, it is natural to assume that the variables have a multivariate normal distribution. In other situations, copulas are used. The marginal distributions are transformed on a percentile-to-percentile basis to normal distributions (or to some other distribution for which there is a multivariate counterpart). The correlation structure between the variables of interest is then defined indirectly from an assumed correlation structure between the transformed variables.

When there are many variables, analysts often use a factor model. This is a way of reducing the number of correlation estimates that have to be made. The correlation between any two variables is assumed to derive solely from their correlations with the factors. The default correlation between different companies can be modeled using a factor-based Gaussian copula model of their times to default.

---

[8] This approach is applied to evaluating the risk of tranches created from mortgages in J. Hull and A. White, "The Risk of Tranches Created from Mortgages," *Financial Analysts Journal* 66, no. 5 (September/October 2010): 54–67. It provides a better fit to historical data in many situations. Its main disadvantage is that the distributions used are not as easy to deal with as the normal distribution and numerical analysis may be necessary to determine Ψ and $G(\text{DR})$.

An important application of copulas for risk managers is to the calculation of the distribution of default rates for loan portfolios. Analysts often assume that a one-factor copula model relates the probability distributions of the times to default for different loans. The percentiles of the distribution of the number of defaults on a large portfolio can then be calculated from the percentiles of the probability distribution of the factor. This is the approach used in determining credit risk capital requirements for banks under Basel II.

Further Reading

Cherubini, U., E. Luciano, and W. Vecchiato. *Copula Methods in Finance.* Hoboken, NJ: John Wiley & Sons, 2004.

Demarta, S., and A. J. McNeil. "The *t*-Copula and Related Copulas." Working Paper, Department of Mathematics, ETH Zentrum, Zurich, Switzerland.

Engle, R. F., and J. Mezrich. "GARCH for Groups," *Risk* (August 1996): 36–40.

Vasicek, O. "Probability of Loss on a Loan Portfolio." Working Paper, KMV, 1987. (Published in *Risk* in December 2002 under the title "Loan Portfolio Value.")

Linear Regression with One Regressor

7

Learning Objectives

Candidates, after completing this reading, should be able to:

- Explain how regression analysis in econometrics measures the relationship between dependent and independent variables.
- Interpret a population regression function, regression coefficients, parameters, slope, intercept, and the error term.
- Interpret a sample regression function, regression coefficients, parameters, slope, intercept, and the error term.
- Describe the key properties of a linear regression.
- Define an ordinary least squares (OLS) regression and calculate the intercept and slope of the regression.

- Describe the method and three key assumptions of OLS for estimation of parameters.
- Summarize the benefits of using OLS estimators.
- Describe the properties of OLS estimators and their sampling distributions, and explain the properties of consistent estimators in general.
- Interpret the explained sum of squares, the total sum of squares, the residual sum of squares, the standard error of the regression, and the regression R^2.
- Interpret the results of an OLS regression.

Excerpt is Chapter 4 of Introduction to Econometrics, *Brief Edition, by James H. Stock and Mark W. Watson.*

A state implements tough new penalties on drunk drivers: What is the effect on highway fatalities? A school district cuts the size of its elementary school classes: What is the effect on its students' standardized test scores? You successfully complete one more year of college classes: What is the effect on your future earnings?

All three of these questions are about the unknown effect of changing one variable, X (X being penalties for drunk driving, class size, or years of schooling), on another variable, Y (Y being highway deaths, student test scores, or earnings).

This chapter introduces the linear regression model relating one variable, X, to another, Y. This model postulates a linear relationship between X and Y; the slope of the line relating X and Y is the effect of a one-unit change in X on Y. Just as the mean of Y is an unknown characteristic of the population distribution of Y, the slope of the line relating X and Y is an unknown characteristic of the population joint distribution of X and Y. The econometric problem is to estimate this slope—that is, to estimate the effect on Y of a unit change in X—using a sample of data on these two variables.

This chapter describes methods for estimating this slope using a random sample of data on X and Y. For instance, using data on class sizes and test scores from different school districts, we show how to estimate the expected effect on test scores of reducing class sizes by, say, one student per class. The slope and the intercept of the line relating X and Y can be estimated by a method called ordinary least squares (OLS).

THE LINEAR REGRESSION MODEL

The superintendent of an elementary school district must decide whether to hire additional teachers and she wants your advice. If she hires the teachers, she will reduce the number of students per teacher (the student–teacher ratio) by two. She faces a trade-off. Parents want smaller classes so that their children can receive more individualized attention. But hiring more teachers means spending more money, which is not to the liking of those paying the bill! So she asks you: If she cuts class sizes, what will the effect be on student performance?

In many school districts, student performance is measured by standardized tests, and the job status or pay of some administrators can depend in part on how well their students do on these tests. We therefore sharpen the superintendent's question: If she reduces the average class size by two students, what will the effect be on standardized test scores in her district?

A precise answer to this question requires a quantitative statement about changes. If the superintendent *changes* the class size by a certain amount, what would she expect the *change* in standardized test scores to be? We can write this as a mathematical relationship using the Greek letter beta, $\beta_{ClassSize}$, where the subscript "ClassSize" distinguishes the effect of changing the class size from other effects. Thus,

$$\beta_{ClassSize} = \frac{\text{change in TestScore}}{\text{change in ClassSize}} = \frac{\Delta \text{TestScore}}{\Delta \text{ClassSize}} \quad \textbf{(7.1)}$$

where the Greek letter Δ (delta) stands for "change in." That is, $\beta_{ClassSize}$ is the change in the test score that results from changing the class size, divided by the change in the class size.

If you were lucky enough to know $\beta_{ClassSize}$, you would be able to tell the superintendent that decreasing class size by one student would change districtwide test scores by $\beta_{ClassSize}$. You could also answer the superintendent's actual question, which concerned changing class size by two students per class. To do so, rearrange Equation (7.1) so that

$$\Delta TestScore = \beta_{ClassSize} \times \Delta ClassSize \quad \textbf{(7.2)}$$

Suppose that $\beta_{ClassSize} = -0.6$. Then a reduction in class size of two students per class would yield a predicted change in test scores of $(-0.6) \times (-2) = 1.2$; that is, you would predict that test scores would *rise* by 1.2 points as a result of the *reduction* in class sizes by two students per class.

Equation (7.1) is the definition of the slope of a straight line relating test scores and class size. This straight line can be written

$$TestScore = \beta_0 + \beta_{ClassSize} \times ClassSize \quad \textbf{(7.3)}$$

where β_0 is the intercept of this straight line, and, as before, $\beta_{ClassSize}$ is the slope. According to Equation (7.3), if you knew β_0 and $\beta_{ClassSize}$, not only would you be able to determine the *change* in test scores at a district associated with a *change* in class size, but you also would be able to predict the average test score itself for a given class size.

When you propose Equation (7.3) to the superintendent, she tells you that something is wrong with this formulation.

She points out that class size is just one of many facets of elementary education, and that two districts with the same class sizes will have different test scores for many reasons. One district might have better teachers or it might use better textbooks. Two districts with comparable class sizes, teachers, and textbooks still might have very different student populations; perhaps one district has more immigrants (and thus fewer native English speakers) or wealthier families. Finally, she points out that, even if two districts are the same in all these ways, they might have different test scores for essentially random reasons having to do with the performance of the individual students on the day of the test. She is right, of course; for all these reasons, Equation (7.3) will not hold exactly for all districts. Instead, it should be viewed as a statement about a relationship that holds *on average* across the population of districts.

A version of this linear relationship that holds for *each* district must incorporate these other factors influencing test scores, including each district's unique characteristics (for example, quality of their teachers, background of their students, how lucky the students were on test day). One approach would be to list the most important factors and to introduce them explicitly into Equation (7.3) (an idea we return to in Chapter 9). For now, however, we simply lump all these "other factors" together and write the relationship for a given district as

$$TestScore = \beta_0 + \beta_{ClassSize} \times ClassSize + \text{other factors} \quad \textbf{(7.4)}$$

Thus, the test score for the district is written in terms of one component, $\beta_0 + \beta_{ClassSize} \times ClassSize$, that represents the average effect of class size on scores in the population of school districts and a second component that represents all other factors.

Although this discussion has focused on test scores and class size, the idea expressed in Equation (7.4) is much more general, so it is useful to introduce more general notation. Suppose you have a sample of n districts. Let Y_i be the average test score in the ith district, let X_i be the average class size in the ith district, and let u_i denote the other factors influencing the test score in the ith district. Then Equation (7.4) can be written more generally as

$$Y_i = \beta_0 + \beta_1 X_i + u_i \quad \textbf{(7.5)}$$

for each district, (that is, $i = 1, \ldots, n$), where β_0 is the intercept of this line and β_1 is the slope. [The general notation "β_1" is used for the slope in Equation (7.5) instead of

"$\beta_{ClassSize}$" because this equation is written in terms of a general variable X_i.]

Equation (7.5) is the **linear regression model with a single regressor**, in which Y is the **dependent variable** and X is the **independent variable** or the **regressor**.

The first part of Equation (7.5), $\beta_0 + \beta_1 X_i$, is the **population regression line** or the **population regression function**. This is the relationship that holds between Y and X on average over the population. Thus, if you knew the value of X, according to this population regression line you would predict that the value of the dependent variable, Y, is $\beta_0 + \beta_1 X$.

The **intercept** β_0 and the **slope** β_1 are the **coefficients** of the population regression line, also known as the **parameters** of the population regression line. The slope β_1 is the change in Y associated with a unit change in X. The intercept is the value of the population regression line when $X = 0$; it is the point at which the population regression line intersects the Y axis. In some econometric applications, the intercept has a meaningful economic interpretation. In other applications, the intercept has no real-world meaning; for example, when X is the class size, strictly speaking the intercept is the predicted value of test scores when there are no students in the class! When the real-world meaning of the intercept is nonsensical it is best to think of it mathematically as the coefficient that determines the level of the regression line.

The term u_i in Equation (7.5) is the **error term**. The error term incorporates all of the factors responsible for the difference between the ith district's average test score and the value predicted by the population regression line. This error term contains all the other factors besides X that determine the value of the dependent variable, Y, for a specific observation, i. In the class size example, these other factors include all the unique features of the ith district that affect the performance of its students on the test, including teacher quality, student economic background, luck, and even any mistakes in grading the test.

The linear regression model and its terminology are summarized in Box 7-1.

Figure 7-1 summarizes the linear regression model with a single regressor for seven hypothetical observations on test scores (Y) and class size (X). The population regression line is the straight line $\beta_0 + \beta_1 X$. The population regression line slopes down ($\beta_1 < 0$), which means

Terminology for the Linear Regression Model with a Single Regressor

The linear regression model is

$$Y_i = \beta_0 + \beta_1 X_i + u_i$$

where

the subscript i runs over observations, $i = 1, \ldots, n$;

Y_i is the *dependent variable*, the *regressand*, or simply the *left-hand variable*;

X_i is the *independent variable*, the *regressor*, or simply the *right-hand variable*;

$\beta_0 + \beta_1 X$ is the *population regression line* or *population regression function*;

β_0 is the *intercept* of the population regression line;

β_1 is the *slope* of the population regression line; and

u_i is the *error term*.

as mentioned earlier, it has no real-world meaning in this example.

Because of the other factors that determine test performance, the hypothetical observations in Figure 7-1 do not fall exactly on the population regression line. For example, the value of Y for district #1, Y_1, is above the population regression line. This means that test scores in district #1 were better than predicted by the population regression line, so the error term for that district, u_1, is positive. In contrast, Y_2 is below the population regression line, so test scores for that district were worse than predicted, and $u_2 < 0$.

Now return to your problem as advisor to the superintendent: What is the expected effect on test scores of reducing the student–teacher ratio by two students per teacher? The answer is easy: The expected change is $(-2) \times \beta_{ClassSize}$. But what is the value of $\beta_{ClassSize}$?

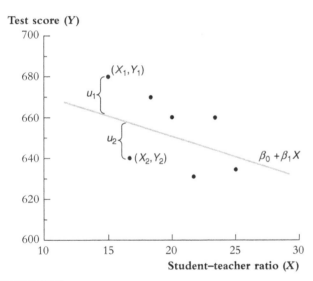

Test score (Y)

FIGURE 7-1 Scatter plot of test score vs. student–teacher ratio (hypothetical data).

The scatterplot shows hypothetical observations for seven school districts. The population regression line is $\beta_0 + \beta_1 X$. The vertical distance from the ith point to the population regression line is $Y_i - (\beta_0 + \beta_1 X_i)$, which is the population error term u_i for the ith observation.

ESTIMATING THE COEFFICIENTS OF THE LINEAR REGRESSION MODEL

In a practical situation, such as the application to class size and test scores, the intercept β_0 and slope β_1 of the population regression line are unknown. Therefore, we must use data to estimate the unknown slope and intercept of the population regression line.

This estimation problem is similar to others you have faced in statistics. For example, suppose you want to compare the mean earnings of men and women who recently graduated from college. Although the population mean earnings are unknown, we can estimate the population means using a random sample of male and female college graduates. Then the natural estimator of the unknown population mean earnings for women, for example, is the average earnings of the female college graduates in the sample.

The same idea extends to the linear regression model. We do not know the population value of $\beta_{ClassSize}$, the slope of the unknown population regression line relating X (class size) and Y (test scores). But just as it was possible to learn about the population mean using a sample of data drawn from that population, so is it possible to learn about the population slope $\beta_{ClassSize}$ using a sample of data.

that districts with lower student–teacher ratios (smaller classes) tend to have higher test scores. The intercept β_0 has a mathematical meaning as the value of the Y axis intersected by the population regression line, but,

TABLE 7-1 Summary of the Distribution of Student-Teacher Ratios and Fifth-Grade Test Scores for 420 K-8 Districts in California in 1998

| | Average | Standard Deviation | Percentile | | | | | | |
			10%	25%	40%	50% (median)	60%	75%	90%
Student-teacher ratio	19.6	1.9	17.3	18.6	19.3	19.7	20.1	20.9	21.9
Test score	665.2	19.1	630.4	640.0	649.1	654.5	659.4	666.7	679.1

The data we analyze here consist of test scores and class sizes in 1999 in 420 California school districts that serve kindergarten through eighth grade. The test score is the districtwide average of reading and math scores for fifth graders. Class size can be measured in various ways. The measure used here is one of the broadest, which is the number of students in the district divided by the number of teachers—that is, the district-wide student-teacher ratio. These data are described in more detail in Appendix A.

Table 7-1 summarizes the distributions of test scores and class sizes for this sample. The average student-teacher ratio is 19.6 students per teacher and the standard deviation is 1.9 students per teacher. The 10th percentile of the distribution of the student-teacher ratio is 17.3 (that is, only 10% of districts have student-teacher ratios below 17.3), while the district at the 90th percentile has a student-teacher ratio of 21.9.

A scatterplot of these 420 observations on test scores and the student-teacher ratio is shown in Figure 7-2. The sample correlation is −0.23, indicating a weak negative relationship between the two variables. Although larger classes in this sample tend to have lower test scores, there are other determinants of test scores that keep the observations from falling perfectly along a straight line.

Despite this low correlation, if one could somehow draw a straight line through these data, then the slope of this line would be an estimate of $\beta_{ClassSize}$ based on these data. One way to draw the line would be to take out a pencil and a ruler and to "eyeball" the best line you could. While this method is easy, it is very unscientific and different people will create different estimated lines.

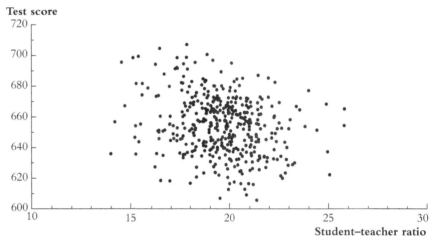

FIGURE 7-2 Scatterplot of test score vs. student-teacher ratio (California School District data).

Data from 420 California school districts. There is a weak negative relationship between the student-teacher ratio and test scores: The sample correlation is −0.23.

How, then, should you choose among the many possible lines? By far the most common way is to choose the line that produces the "least squares" fit to these data—that is, to use the ordinary least squares (OLS) estimator.

The Ordinary Least Squares Estimator

The OLS estimator chooses the regression coefficients so that the estimated regression line is as close as possible to the observed data, where closeness is measured by the sum of the squared mistakes made in predicting Y given X.

As discussed previously, the sample average, $\overline{Y}$, is the least squares estimator of the population mean, $E(Y)$; that is, $\overline{Y}$ minimizes the total squared estimation mistakes $\sum_{i=1}^{n}(Y_i - m)^2$ among all possible estimators m.

The OLS estimator extends this idea to the linear regression model. Let b_0 and b_1 be some estimators of β_0 and β_1. The regression line based on these estimators is $b_0 + b_1X$, so the value of Y_i predicted using this line is $b_0 + b_1X_i$. Thus, the mistake made in predicting the ith observation is $Y_i - (b_0 + b_1X_i) = Y_i - b_0 - b_1X_i$. The sum of these squared prediction mistakes over all n observations is

$$\sum_{i=1}^{n}(Y_i - b_0 - b_1X_i)^2 \qquad \textbf{(7.6)}$$

The sum of the squared mistakes for the linear regression model in Equation (7.6) is the extension of the sum of the squared mistakes for the problem of estimating the mean. In fact, if there is no regressor, then b_1 does not enter Equation (7.6) and the two problems are identical except for the different notation, b_0 in Equation (7.6). Just as there is a unique estimator, $\overline{Y}$, so is there a unique pair of estimators of β_0 and β_1 that minimize Equation (7.6).

The estimators of the intercept and slope that minimize the sum of squared mistakes in Equation (7.6) are called the **ordinary least squares (OLS) estimators** of β_0 and β_1.

OLS has its own special notation and terminology. The OLS estimator of β_0 is denoted $\hat{\beta}_0$, and the OLS estimator of β_1 is denoted $\hat{\beta}_1$. The **OLS regression line** is the straight line constructed using the OLS estimators: $\hat{\beta}_0 + \hat{\beta}_1X$. The **predicted value** of Y_i given X_i, based on the OLS regression line, is $\hat{Y}_i = \hat{\beta}_0 + \hat{\beta}_1X_i$. The **residual** for the ith observation is the difference between Y_i and its predicted value: $\hat{u}_i = Y_i - \hat{Y}_i$.

You could compute the OLS estimators $\hat{\beta}_0$ and $\hat{\beta}_1$ by trying different values of b_0 and b_1 repeatedly until you find those that minimize the total squared mistakes in Equation (7.6); they are the least squares estimates. This method would be quite tedious, however. Fortunately there are formulas, derived by minimizing Equation (7.6) using calculus, that streamline the calculation of the OLS estimators.

The OLS formulas and terminology are collected in Box 7-2. These formulas are implemented in virtually all statistical and spreadsheet programs. These formulas are derived in Appendix B.

BOX 7-2 The OLS Estimator, Predicted Values, and Residuals

The OLS estimators of the slope β_1 and the intercept β_0 are

$$\hat{\beta}_1 = \frac{\sum_{i=1}^{n}(X_i - \overline{X})(Y_i - \overline{Y})}{\sum_{i=1}^{n}(X_i - \overline{X})^2} = \frac{s_{XY}}{s_X^2} \qquad \textbf{(7.7)}$$

$$\hat{\beta}_0 = \overline{Y} - \hat{\beta}_1\overline{X}. \qquad \textbf{(7.8)}$$

The OLS predicted values $\hat{Y}_i$ and residuals $\hat{u}_i$ are

$$\hat{Y}_i = \hat{\beta}_0 + \hat{\beta}_1X_i, \; i = 1, \ldots, n \qquad \textbf{(7.9)}$$

$$\hat{u}_i = Y_i - \hat{Y}_i, \; i = 1, \ldots, n. \qquad \textbf{(7.10)}$$

The estimated intercept ($\hat{\beta}_0$), slope ($\hat{\beta}_1$), and residual ($\hat{u}_i$) are computed from a sample of n observations of X_i and Y_i, $i = 1, \ldots, n$. These are estimates of the unknown true population intercept (β_0), slope (β_1), and error term (u_i).

OLS Estimates of the Relationship Between Test Scores and the Student–Teacher Ratio

When OLS is used to estimate a line relating the student–teacher ratio to test scores using the 420 observations in Figure 7-2, the estimated slope is −2.28 and the estimated intercept is 698.9. Accordingly, the OLS regression line for these 420 observations is

$$\widehat{TestScore} = 698.9 - 2.28 \times STR, \qquad \textbf{(7.11)}$$

where *TestScore* is the average test score in the district and *STR* is the student–teacher ratio. The symbol " ˆ " over *TestScore* in Equation (7.11) indicates that this is the predicted value based on the OLS regression line. Figure 7-3 plots this OLS regression line superimposed over the scatterplot of the data previously shown in Figure 7-2.

The slope of −2.28 means that an increase in the student–teacher ratio by one student per class is, on average, associated with a decline in districtwide test scores by 2.28 points on the test. A decrease in the student–teacher ratio by 2 students per class is, on average, associated with an increase in test scores of 4.56 points [= −2 × (−2.28)].

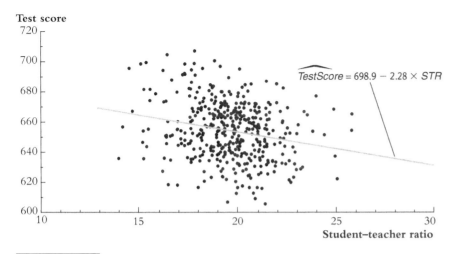

Test score

FIGURE 7-3 The estimated regression line for the California data.

The estimated regression line shows a negative relationship between test scores and the student–teacher ratio. If class sizes fall by 1 student, the estimated regression predicts that test scores will increase by 2.28 points.

The negative slope indicates that more students per teacher (larger classes) is associated with poorer performance on the test.

It is now possible to predict the districtwide test score given a value of the student–teacher ratio. For example, for a district with 20 students per teacher, the predicted test score is $698.9 - 2.28 \times 20 = 653.3$. Of course, this prediction will not be exactly right because of the other factors that determine a district's performance. But the regression line does give a prediction (the OLS prediction) of what test scores would be for that district, based on their student–teacher ratio, absent those other factors.

Is this estimate of the slope large or small? To answer this, we return to the superintendent's problem. Recall that she is contemplating hiring enough teachers to reduce the student–teacher ratio by 2. Suppose her district is at the median of the California districts. From Table 7-1, the median student–teacher ratio is 19.7 and the median test score is 654.5. A reduction of 2 students per class, from 19.7 to 17.7, would move her student–teacher ratio from the 50th percentile to very near the 10th percentile. This is a big change, and she would need to hire many new teachers. How would it affect test scores?

According to Equation (7.11), cutting the student–teacher ratio by 2 is predicted to increase test scores by approximately 4.6 points; if her district's test scores are at the median, 654.5, they are predicted to increase to 659.1. Is this improvement large or small? According to Table 7-1, this improvement would move her district from the median to just short of the 60th percentile. Thus, a decrease in class size that would place her district close to the 10% with the smallest classes would move her test scores from the 50th to the 60th percentile. According to these estimates, at least, cutting the student–teacher ratio by a large amount (2 students per teacher) would help and might be worth doing depending on her budgetary situation, but it would not be a panacea.

What if the superintendent were contemplating a far more radical change, such as reducing the student–teacher ratio from 20 students per teacher to 5? Unfortunately, the estimates in Equation (7.11) would not be very useful to her. This regression was estimated using the data in Figure 7-2, and as the figure shows, the smallest student–teacher ratio in these data is 14. These data contain no information on how districts with extremely small classes perform, so these data alone are not a reliable basis for predicting the effect of a radical move to such an extremely low student–teacher ratio.

Why Use the OLS Estimator?

There are both practical and theoretical reasons to use the OLS estimators $\hat{\beta}_0$ and $\hat{\beta}_1$. Because OLS is the dominant method used in practice, it has become the common language for regression analysis throughout economics, finance (see the box), and the social sciences more generally. Presenting results using OLS (or its variants discussed later in this book) means that you are "speaking the same language" as other economists and statisticians. The OLS formulas are built into virtually all spreadsheet and statistical software packages, making OLS easy to use.

The OLS estimators also have desirable theoretical properties. These are analogous to the desirable properties

The "Beta" of a Stock

A fundamental idea of modern finance is that an investor needs a financial incentive to take a risk. Said differently, the expected return[1] on a risky investment, R, must exceed the return on a safe, or risk-free, investment, R_f. Thus the expected excess return, $R - R_f$, on a risky investment, like owning stock in a company, should be positive.

At first it might seem like the risk of a stock should be measured by its variance. Much of that risk, however, can be reduced by holding other stocks in a "portfolio"—in other words, by diversifying your financial holdings. This means that the right way to measure the risk of a stock is not by its *variance* but rather by its *covariance* with the market.

The capital asset pricing model (CAPM) formalizes this idea. According to the CAPM, the expected excess return on an asset is proportional to the expected excess return on a portfolio of all available assets (the "market portfolio"). That is, the CAPM says that

$$R - R_f = \beta(R_m - R_f) \tag{7.12}$$

where R_m is the expected return on the market portfolio and β is the coefficient in the population regression

---

[1] The return on an investment is the change in its price plus any payout (dividend) from the investment as a percentage of its initial price. For example, a stock bought on January 1 for $100, which then paid a $2.50 dividend during the year and sold on December 31 for $105, would have a return of $R = [(\$105 - \$100) + \$2.50]/\$100 = 7.5\%$.

of $R - R_f$ on $R_m - R_f$. In practice, the risk-free return is often taken to be the rate of interest on short-term U.S. government debt. According to the CAPM, a stock with a $\beta < 1$ has less risk than the market portfolio and therefore has a lower expected excess return than the market portfolio. In contrast, a stock with a $\beta > 1$ is riskier than the market portfolio and thus commands a higher expected excess return.

The "beta" of a stock has become a workhorse of the investment industry, and you can obtain estimated β's for hundreds of stocks on investment firm Web sites. Those β's typically are estimated by OLS regression of the actual excess return on the stock against the actual excess return on a broad market index.

The table below gives estimated β's for six U.S. stocks. Low-risk consumer products firms like Kellogg have stocks with low β's; riskier technology stocks have high β's.

Company	Estimated β
Kellogg (breakfast cereal)	−0.03
Wal-Mart (discount retailer)	0.65
Waste Management (waste disposal)	0.70
Sprint Nextel (telecommunications)	0.78
Barnes and Noble (book retailer)	1.02
Microsoft (software)	1.27
Best Buy (electronic equipment retailer)	2.15
Amazon (online retailer)	2.65

Source: SmartMoney.com

---

of $\overline{Y}$ as an estimator of the population mean. Under the assumptions introduced in a later section, the OLS estimator is unbiased and consistent. The OLS estimator is also efficient among a certain class of unbiased estimators; however, this efficiency result holds under some additional special conditions, and further discussion of this result is deferred until Chapter 8.

MEASURES OF FIT

Having estimated a linear regression, you might wonder how well that regression line describes the data. Does the regressor account for much or for little of the variation in the dependent variable? Are the observations tightly clustered around the regression line, or are they spread out?

The R^2 and the standard error of the regression measure how well the OLS regression line fits the data. The R^2

ranges between 0 and 1 and measures the fraction of the variance of Y_i that is explained by X_i. The standard error of the regression measures how far Y_i typically is from its predicted value.

The R^2

The **regression R^2** is the fraction of the sample variance of Y_i explained by (or predicted by) X_i. The definitions of the predicted value and the residual (see Box 7-2) allow us to write the dependent variable Y_i as the sum of the predicted value, $\hat{Y}_i$, plus the residual $\hat{u}_i$:

$$Y_i = \hat{Y}_i + \hat{u}_i \tag{7.13}$$

In this notation, the R^2 is the ratio of the sample variance of $\hat{Y}_i$ to the sample variance of Y_i.

Mathematically, the R^2 can be written as the ratio of the explained sum of squares to the total sum of squares. The

explained sum of squares (ESS) is the sum of squared deviations of the predicted values of Y_i, $\hat{Y}_i$, from their average, and the **total sum of squares (TSS)** is the sum of squared deviations of Y_i from its average:

$$ESS = \sum_{i=1}^{n} (\hat{Y}_i - \overline{Y})^2 \qquad \textbf{(7.14)}$$

$$TSS = \sum_{i=1}^{n} (Y_i - \overline{Y})^2 \qquad \textbf{(7.15)}$$

Equation (7.14) uses the fact that the sample average OLS predicted value equals $\overline{Y}$.

The R^2 is the ratio of the explained sum of squares to the total sum of squares:

$$R^2 = \frac{ESS}{TSS} \qquad \textbf{(7.16)}$$

Alternatively, the R^2 can be written in terms of the fraction of the variance of Y_i not explained by X_i. The **sum of squared residuals**, or **SSR**, is the sum of the squared OLS residuals:

$$SSR = \sum_{i=1}^{n} \hat{u}_i^2 \qquad \textbf{(7.17)}$$

It can be shown that $TSS = ESS + SSR$. Thus the R^2 also can be expressed as 1 minus the ratio of the sum of squared residuals to the total sum of squares:

$$R^2 = 1 - \frac{SSR}{TSS} \qquad \textbf{(7.18)}$$

Finally, the R^2 of the regression of Y on the single regressor X is the square of the correlation coefficient between Y and X.

The R^2 ranges between 0 and 1. If $\hat{\beta}_1 = 0$, then X_i explains none of the variation of Y_i and the predicted value of Y_i based on the regression is just the sample average of Y_i. In this case, the explained sum of squares is zero and the sum of squared residuals equals the total sum of squares; thus the R^2 is zero. In contrast, if X_i explains all of the variation of Y_i, then $Y_i = \hat{Y}_i$ for all i and every residual is zero (that is, $\hat{u}_i = 0$), so that $ESS = TSS$ and $R^2 = 1$. In general, the R^2 does not take on the extreme values of 0 or 1 but falls somewhere in between. An R^2 near 1 indicates that the regressor is good at predicting Y_i, while an R^2 near 0 indicates that the regressor is not very good at predicting Y_i.

The Standard Error of the Regression

The **standard error of the regression (SER)** is an estimator of the standard deviation of the regression error u_i. The units of u_i and Y_i are the same, so the SER is a measure of the spread of the observations around the regression line, measured in the units of the dependent variable. For example, if the units of the dependent variable are dollars, then the SER measures the magnitude of a typical deviation from the regression line—that is, the magnitude of a typical regression error—in dollars.

Because the regression errors $u_1, \ldots, u_n$ are unobserved, the SER is computed using their sample counterparts, the OLS residuals $\hat{u}_1, \ldots, \hat{u}_n$. The formula for the SER is

$$SER = s_{\hat{u}}, \text{ where } s_{\hat{u}}^2 = \frac{1}{n-2} \sum_{i=1}^{n} \hat{u}_i^2 = \frac{SSR}{n-2} \qquad \textbf{(7.19)}$$

where the formula for $s_{\hat{u}}^2$ uses the fact that the sample average of the OLS residuals is zero.

The formula for the SER in Equation (7.19) is similar to the formula for the sample standard deviation of Y given earlier, except that $Y_i - \overline{Y}$ is replaced by $\hat{u}_i$, and the divisor is $n - 1$, whereas here it is $n - 2$. The reason for using the divisor $n - 2$ here (instead of n) is the same as the reason for using the divisor $n - 1$: It corrects for a slight downward bias introduced because two regression coefficients were estimated. This is called a "degrees of freedom" correction; because two coefficients were estimated (β_0 and β_1), two "degrees of freedom" of the data were lost, so the divisor in this factor is $n - 2$. (The mathematics behind this is discussed in Chapter 8.) When n is large, the difference between dividing by n, by $n - 1$, or by $n - 2$ is negligible.

Application to the Test Score Data

Equation (7.11) reports the regression line, estimated using the California test score data, relating the standardized test score (TestScore) to the student–teacher ratio (STR). The R^2 of this regression is 0.051, or 5.1%, and the SER is 18.6.

The R^2 of 0.051 means that the regressor STR explains 5.1% of the variance of the dependent variable TestScore. Figure 7-3 superimposes this regression line on the scatterplot of the TestScore and STR data. As the scatterplot shows, the student–teacher ratio explains some of the variation in test scores, but much variation remains unaccounted for.

The *SER* of 18.6 means that standard deviation of the regression residuals is 18.6, where the units are points on the standardized test. Because the standard deviation is a measure of spread, the *SER* of 18.6 means that there is a large spread of the scatterplot in Figure 7-3 around the regression line as measured in points on the test. This large spread means that predictions of test scores made using only the student–teacher ratio for that district will often be wrong by a large amount.

What should we make of this low R^2 and large *SER*? The fact that the R^2 of this regression is low (and the *SER* is large) does not, by itself, imply that this regression is either "good" or "bad." What the low R^2 *does* tell us is that other important factors influence test scores. These factors could include differences in the student body across districts, differences in school quality unrelated to the student–teacher ratio, or luck on the test. The low R^2 and high *SER* do not tell us what these factors are, but they do indicate that the student–teacher ratio alone explains only a small part of the variation in test scores in these data.

THE LEAST SQUARES ASSUMPTIONS

This section presents a set of three assumptions on the linear regression model and the sampling scheme under which OLS provides an appropriate estimator of the unknown regression coefficients, β_0 and β_1. Initially these assumptions might appear abstract. They do, however, have natural interpretations, and understanding these assumptions is essential for understanding when OLS will—and will not—give useful estimates of the regression coefficients.

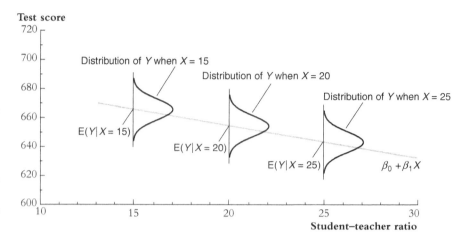

FIGURE 7-4 The conditional probability distributions and the population regression line.

The figure shows the conditional probability of test scores for districts with class sizes of 15, 20, and 25 students. The mean of the conditional distribution of test scores, given the student–teacher ratio, $E(Y|X)$, is the population regression line $\beta_0 + \beta_1 X$. At a given value of X, Y is distributed around the regression line and the error, $u = Y - (\beta_0 + \beta_1 X)$, has a conditional mean of zero for all values of X.

Assumption #1: The Conditional Distribution of u_i Given X_i Has a Mean of Zero

The first **least squares assumption** is that the conditional distribution of u_i given X_i has a mean of zero. This assumption is a formal mathematical statement about the "other factors" contained in u_i and asserts that these other factors are unrelated to X_i in the sense that, given a value of X_i, the mean of the distribution of these other factors is zero.

This is illustrated in Figure 7-4. The population regression is the relationship that holds on average between class size and test scores in the population, and the error term u_i represents the other factors that lead test scores at a given district to differ from the prediction based on the population regression line. As shown in Figure 7-4, at a given value of class size, say 20 students per class, sometimes these other factors lead to better performance than predicted ($u_i > 0$) and sometimes to worse performance ($u_i < 0$), but on average over the population the prediction is right. In other words, given $X_i = 20$, the mean of the distribution of u_i is zero. In Figure 7-4, this is shown as the distribution of u_i being centered on the population regression line at $X_i = 20$ and, more generally, at other values x of X_i as well. Said differently, the distribution of u_i, conditional on $X_i = x$, has a mean of zero; stated mathematically, $E(u_i|X_i = x) = 0$ or, in somewhat simpler notation, $E(u_i|X_i) = 0$.

As shown in Figure 7-4, the assumption that $E(u_i|X_i) = 0$ is equivalent to assuming that the population regression line is the conditional mean of Y_i given X_i.

The Conditional Mean of u in a Randomized Controlled Experiment

In a randomized controlled experiment, subjects are randomly assigned to the treatment group ($X = 1$) or to the control group ($X = 0$). The random assignment typically is done using a computer program that uses no information about the subject, ensuring that X is distributed independently of all personal characteristics of the subject. Random assignment makes X and u independent, which in turn implies that the conditional mean of u given X is zero.

In observational data, X is not randomly assigned in an experiment. Instead, the best that can be hoped for is that X is *as if* randomly assigned, in the precise sense that $E(u_i|X_i) = 0$. Whether this assumption holds in a given empirical application with observational data requires careful thought and judgment, and we return to this issue repeatedly.

Correlation and Conditional Mean

Recall that if the conditional mean of one random variable given another is zero, then the two random variables have zero covariance and thus are uncorrelated. Thus, the conditional mean assumption $E(u_i|X_i) = 0$ implies that X_i and u_i are uncorrelated, or $\text{corr}(X_i, u_i) = 0$. Because correlation is a measure of linear association, this implication does not go the other way; even if X_i and u_i are uncorrelated, the conditional mean of u_i given X_i might be nonzero. However, if X_i and u_i are correlated, then it must be the case that $E(u_i|X_i)$ is nonzero. It is therefore often convenient to discuss the conditional mean assumption in terms of possible correlation between X_i and u_i. If X_i and u_i are correlated, then the conditional mean assumption is violated.

Assumption #2: (X_i,Y_i), $i = 1, \ldots, n$ Are Independently and Identically Distributed

The second least squares assumption is that (X_i,Y_i), $i = 1, \ldots, n$ are independently and identically distributed (i.i.d.) across observations. This is a statement about how the sample is drawn. If the observations are drawn by simple random sampling from a single large population, then (X_i,Y_i), $i = 1, \ldots, n$ are i.i.d. For example, let X be the age of a worker and Y be his or her earnings, and imagine drawing a person at random from the population of workers. That randomly drawn person will have a certain age and earnings (that is, X and Y will take on some values). If a sample of n workers is drawn from this population, then (X_i,Y_i), $i = 1, \ldots, n$, necessarily have the same distribution. If they are drawn at random they are also distributed independently from one observation to the next; that is, they are i.i.d.

The i.i.d. assumption is a reasonable one for many data collection schemes. For example, survey data from a randomly chosen subset of the population typically can be treated as i.i.d.

Not all sampling schemes produce i.i.d. observations on (X_i,Y_i), however. One example is when the values of X are not drawn from a random sample of the population but rather are set by a researcher as part of an experiment. For example, suppose a horticulturalist wants to study the effects of different organic weeding methods (X) on tomato production (Y) and accordingly grows different plots of tomatoes using different organic weeding techniques. If she picks the techniques (the level of X) to be used on the ith plot and applies the same technique to the ith plot in all repetitions of the experiment, then the value of X_i does not change from one sample to the next. Thus X_i is nonrandom (although the outcome Y_i is random), so the sampling scheme is not i.i.d. The results presented in this chapter developed for i.i.d. regressors are also true if the regressors are nonrandom. The case of a nonrandom regressor is, however, quite special. For example, modern experimental protocols would have the horticulturalist assign the level of X to the different plots using a computerized random number generator, thereby circumventing any possible bias by the horticulturalist (she might use her favorite weeding method for the tomatoes in the sunniest plot). When this modern experimental protocol is used, the level of X is random and (X_i, Y_i) are i.i.d.

Another example of non-i.i.d. sampling is when observations refer to the same unit of observation over time. For example, we might have data on inventory levels (Y) at a firm and the interest rate at which the firm can borrow (X), where these data are collected over time from a specific firm; for example, they might be recorded four times a year (quarterly) for 30 years. This is an example of time series data, and a key feature of time series data is that observations falling close to each other in time are not independent but rather tend to be correlated with each other; if interest rates are low now, they are likely to be low next quarter. This pattern of correlation violates the "independence" part of the i.i.d. assumption. Time series data introduce a set of complications that are best handled after developing the basic tools of regression analysis.

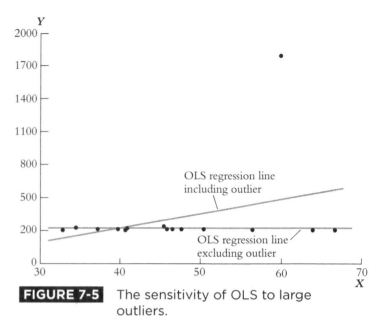

FIGURE 7-5 The sensitivity of OLS to large outliers.

This hypothetical data set has one outlier. The OLS regression line estimated with the outlier shows a strong positive relationship between X and Y, but the OLS regression line estimated without the outlier shows no relationship.

Assumption #3: Large Outliers Are Unlikely

The third least squares assumption is that large outliers—that is, observations with values of X_i and/or Y_i far outside the usual range of the data—are unlikely. Large outliers can make OLS regression results misleading. This potential sensitivity of OLS to extreme outliers is illustrated in Figure 7-5 using hypothetical data.

In this book, the assumption that large outliers are unlikely is made mathematically precise by assuming that X and Y have nonzero finite fourth moments: $0 < E(X_i^4) < \infty$ and $0 < E(Y_i^4) < \infty$. Another way to state this assumption is that X and Y have finite kurtosis.

The assumption of finite kurtosis is used in the mathematics that justify the large-sample approximations to the distributions of the OLS test statistics. We encountered this assumption when discussing the consistency of the sample variance. Specifically, the sample variance s_Y^2 is a consistent estimator of the population variance σ_Y^2 ($s_Y^2 \xrightarrow{p} \sigma_Y^2$). If $Y_1, \ldots, Y_n$ are i.i.d. and the fourth moment of Y_i is finite, then the law of large numbers applies to the average, $\frac{1}{n}\sum_{i=1}^{n}(Y_i - \mu_Y)^2$, a key step in the proof, showing that s_Y^2 is consistent.

One source of large outliers is data entry errors, such as a typographical error or incorrectly using different units for different observations: Imagine collecting data on the height of students in meters, but inadvertently recording one student's height in centimeters instead. One way to find outliers is to plot your data. If you decide that an outlier is due to a data entry error, then you can either correct the error or, if that is impossible, drop the observation from your data set.

Data entry errors aside, the assumption of finite kurtosis is a plausible one in many applications with economic data. Class size is capped by the physical capacity of a classroom; the best you can do on a standardized test is to get all the questions right and the worst you can do is to get all the questions wrong. Because class size and test scores have a finite range, they necessarily have finite kurtosis. More generally, commonly used distributions such as the normal distribution have four moments. Still, as a mathematical matter, some distributions have infinite fourth moments, and this assumption rules out those distributions. If this assumption holds then it is unlikely that statistical inferences using OLS will be dominated by a few observations.

The Least Squares Assumptions

$Y_i = \beta_0 + \beta_1 X_i + u_i, i = 1, \ldots, n$, where

1. The error term u_i has conditional mean zero given X_i: $E(u_i | X_i) = 0$;
2. $(X_i, Y_i), i = 1, \ldots, n$ are independent and identically distributed (i.i.d.) draws from their joint distribution; and
3. Large outliers are unlikely: X_i and Y_i have nonzero finite fourth moments.

Use of the Least Squares Assumptions

The three least squares assumptions for the linear regression model are summarized in Box 7-3. The least squares assumptions play twin roles, and we return to them repeatedly throughout this textbook.

Their first role is mathematical: If these assumptions hold, then, as is shown in the next section, in large samples the OLS estimators have sampling distributions that are normal. In turn, this large-sample normal distribution lets us develop methods for hypothesis testing and constructing confidence intervals using the OLS estimators.

Their second role is to organize the circumstances that pose difficulties for OLS regression. As we will see, the first least squares assumption is the most important to consider in practice. One reason why the first least squares assumption might not hold in practice is discussed in Chapter 9.

It is also important to consider whether the second assumption holds in an application. Although it plausibly holds in many cross-sectional data sets, the independence assumption is inappropriate for time series data. Therefore, the regression methods developed under assumption 2 require modification for some applications with time series data.

The third assumption serves as a reminder that OLS, just like the sample mean, can be sensitive to large outliers. If your data set contains large outliers, you should examine those outliers carefully to make sure those observations are correctly recorded and belong in the data set.

SAMPLING DISTRIBUTION OF THE OLS ESTIMATORS

Because the OLS estimators $\hat{\beta}_0$ and $\hat{\beta}_1$ are computed from a randomly drawn sample, the estimators themselves are random variables with a probability distribution—the sampling distribution—that describes the values they could take over different possible random samples. This section presents these sampling distributions. In small samples, these distributions are complicated, but in large samples, they are approximately normal because of the central limit theorem.

The Sampling Distribution of the OLS Estimators

Review of the Sampling Distribution of $\overline{Y}$

Recall the discussion about the sampling distribution of the sample average, $\overline{Y}$, an estimator of the unknown population mean of Y, μ_Y. Because $\overline{Y}$ is calculated using a randomly drawn sample, $\overline{Y}$ is a random variable that takes on different values from one sample to the next; the probability of these different values is summarized in its sampling distribution. Although the sampling distribution of $\overline{Y}$ can be complicated when the sample size is small, it is possible to make certain statements about it that hold for all n. In particular, the mean of the sampling distribution is μ_Y, that is, $E(\overline{Y}) = \mu_Y$, so $\overline{Y}$ is an unbiased estimator of μ_Y. If n is large, then more can be said about the sampling distribution. In particular, the central limit theorem states that this distribution is approximately normal.

The Sampling Distribution of $\hat{\beta}_0$ and $\hat{\beta}_1$

These ideas carry over to the OLS estimators $\hat{\beta}_0$ and $\hat{\beta}_1$ of the unknown intercept β_0 and slope β_1 of the population regression line. Because the OLS estimators are calculated using a random sample, $\hat{\beta}_0$ and $\hat{\beta}_1$ are random variables that take on different values from one sample to the next; the probability of these different values is summarized in their sampling distributions.

Although the sampling distribution of $\hat{\beta}_0$ and $\hat{\beta}_1$ can be complicated when the sample size is small, it is possible to make certain statements about it that hold for all n. In particular, the mean of the sampling distributions of $\hat{\beta}_0$ and

$\hat{\beta}_1$ are β_0 and β_1. In other words, under the least squares assumptions in Box 7-3,

$$E(\hat{\beta}_0) = \beta_0 \text{ and } E(\hat{\beta}_1) = \beta_1, \qquad \textbf{(7.20)}$$

that is, $\hat{\beta}_0$ and $\hat{\beta}_1$ are unbiased estimators of β_0 and β_1.

If the sample is sufficiently large, by the central limit theorem the sampling distribution of $\hat{\beta}_0$ and $\hat{\beta}_1$ is well approximated by the bivariate normal distribution. This implies that the marginal distributions of $\hat{\beta}_0$ and $\hat{\beta}_1$ are normal in large samples.

This argument invokes the central limit theorem. Technically, the central limit theorem concerns the distribution of averages (like $\overline{Y}$). If you examine the numerator in Equation (7.7) for $\hat{\beta}_1$, you will see that it, too, is a type of average—not a simple average, like $\overline{Y}$, but an average of the product, $(Y_i - \overline{Y})(X_i - \overline{X})$. The central limit theorem applies to this average so that, like the simpler average $\overline{Y}$, it is normally distributed in large samples.

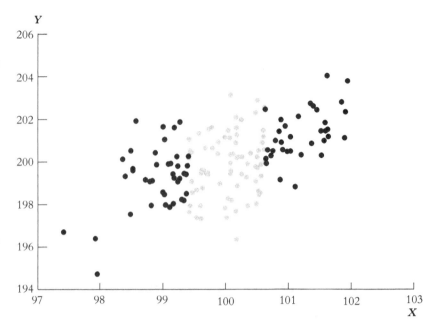

FIGURE 7-6 The variance of $\hat{\beta}_1$ and the variance of X.

The lighter dots represent a set of X_i's with a small variance. The black dots represent a set of X_i's with a large variance. The regression line can be estimated more accurately with the black dots than with the lighter dots.

The normal approximation to the distribution of the OLS estimators in large samples is summarized in Box 7-4. A relevant question in practice is how large n must be for these approximations to be reliable. We suggested that $n = 100$ is sufficiently large for the sampling distribution of $\overline{Y}$ to be well approximated by a normal distribution, and sometimes smaller n suffices. This criterion carries over to the more complicated averages appearing in regression analysis. In virtually all modern econometric applications $n > 100$, so we will treat the normal approximations to the distributions of the OLS estimators as reliable unless there are good reasons to think otherwise.

The results in Box 7-4 imply that the OLS estimators are consistent—that is, when the sample size is large, $\hat{\beta}_0$ and $\hat{\beta}_1$ will be close to the true population coefficients β_0 and β_1 with high probability. This is because the variances $\sigma^2_{\hat{\beta}_0}$ and $\sigma^2_{\hat{\beta}_1}$ of the estimators decrease to zero as n increases (n appears in the denominator of the formulas for the variances), so the distribution of the OLS estimators will be tightly concentrated around their means, β_0 and β_1, when n is large.

Another implication of the distributions in Box 7-4 is that, in general, the larger the variance of X_i, the smaller the variance $\sigma^2_{\hat{\beta}_1}$ of $\hat{\beta}_1$. Mathematically, this arises because the variance of $\hat{\beta}_1$ in Equation (7.21) is inversely proportional to the square of the variance of X_i: the larger is $\text{VaR}(X_i)$, the larger is the denominator in Equation (7.21) so the smaller is $\sigma^2_{\hat{\beta}_1}$. To get a better sense of why this is so, look

---

BOX 7-4 Large-Sample Distributions of $\hat{\beta}_0$ and $\hat{\beta}_1$

If the least squares assumptions in Box 7-3 hold, then in large samples $\hat{\beta}_0$ and $\hat{\beta}_1$ have a jointly normal sampling distribution. The large-sample normal distribution of $\hat{\beta}_1$ is $N(\beta_1, \sigma^2_{\hat{\beta}_1})$, where the variance of this distribution, $\sigma^2_{\hat{\beta}_1}$, is

$$\sigma^2_{\hat{\beta}_1} = \frac{1}{n} \frac{\text{var}[(X_i - \mu_X)u_i]}{[\text{var}(X_i)]^2}. \qquad \textbf{(7.21)}$$

The large-sample normal distribution of $\hat{\beta}_0$ is $N(\beta_0, \sigma^2_{\hat{\beta}_0})$, where

$$\sigma^2_{\hat{\beta}_0} = \frac{1}{n} \frac{\text{var}(H_i u_i)}{[E(H_i^2)]^2}, \text{ where } H_i = 1 - \left(\frac{\mu_X}{E(X_i^2)}\right) X_i. \qquad \textbf{(7.22)}$$

at Figure 7-6, which presents a scatterplot of 150 artificial data points on X and Y. The data points indicated by the colored dots are the 75 observations closest to $\overline{X}$. Suppose you were asked to draw a line as accurately as possible through *either* the colored or the black dots—which would you choose? It would be easier to draw a precise line through the black dots, which have a larger variance than the colored dots. Similarly, the larger the variance of X, the more precise is $\hat{\beta}_1$.

The normal approximation to the sampling distribution of $\hat{\beta}_0$ and $\hat{\beta}_1$ is a powerful tool. With this approximation in hand, we are able to develop methods for making inferences about the true population values of the regression coefficients using only a sample of data.

CONCLUSION

This chapter has focused on the use of ordinary least squares to estimate the intercept and slope of a population regression line using a sample of n observations on a dependent variable, Y, and a single regressor, X. There are many ways to draw a straight line through a scatterplot, but doing so using OLS has several virtues. If the least squares assumptions hold, then the OLS estimators of the slope and intercept are unbiased, are consistent, and have a sampling distribution with a variance that is inversely proportional to the sample size n. Moreover, if n is large, then the sampling distribution of the OLS estimator is normal.

These important properties of the sampling distribution of the OLS estimator hold under the three least squares assumptions.

The first assumption is that the error term in the linear regression model has a conditional mean of zero, given the regressor X. This assumption implies that the OLS estimator is unbiased.

The second assumption is that (X_i, Y_i) are i.i.d., as is the case if the data are collected by simple random sampling. This assumption yields the formula, presented in Box 7-4, for the variance of the sampling distribution of the OLS estimator.

The third assumption is that large outliers are unlikely. Stated more formally, X and Y have finite fourth moments (finite kurtosis). The reason for this assumption is that OLS can be unreliable if there are large outliers.

The results in this chapter describe the sampling distribution of the OLS estimator. By themselves, however, these results are not sufficient to test a hypothesis about the value of β_1 or to construct a confidence interval for β_1. Doing so requires an estimator of the standard deviation of the sampling distribution—that is, the standard error of the OLS estimator. This step—moving from the sampling distribution of $\hat{\beta}_1$ to its standard error, hypothesis tests, and confidence intervals—is taken in the next chapter.

SUMMARY

1. The population regression line, $\beta_0 + \beta_1 X$, is the mean of Y as a function of the value of X. The slope, β_1, is the expected change in Y associated with a 1-unit change in X. The intercept, β_0, determines the level (or height) of the regression line. Box 7-1 summarizes the terminology of the population linear regression model.

2. The population regression line can be estimated using sample observations (Y_i, X_i), $i = 1, \ldots, n$ by ordinary least squares (OLS). The OLS estimators of the regression intercept and slope are denoted by $\hat{\beta}_0$ and $\hat{\beta}_1$.

3. The R^2 and standard error of the regression (SER) are measures of how close the values of Y_i are to the estimated regression line. The R^2 is between 0 and 1, with a larger value indicating that the Y_i's are closer to the line. The standard error of the regression is an estimator of the standard deviation of the regression error.

4. There are three key assumptions for the linear regression model: (1) The regression errors, u_i, have a mean of zero conditional on the regressors X_i; (2) the sample observations are i.i.d. random draws from the population; and (3) large outliers are unlikely. If these assumptions hold, the OLS estimators $\hat{\beta}_0$ and $\hat{\beta}_1$ are (1) unbiased; (2) consistent; and (3) normally distributed when the sample is large.

Key Terms

linear regression model with a single regressor (85)
dependent variable (85)
independent variable (85)
regressor (85)
population regression line (85)
population regression function (85)

APPENDIX A

The California Test Score Data Set

The California Standardized Testing and Reporting data set contains data on test performance, school characteristics, and student demographic backgrounds. The data used here are from all 420 K–6 and K–8 districts in California with data available for 1998 and 1999. Test scores are the average of the reading and math scores on the Stanford 9 Achievement Test, a standardized test administered to fifth-grade students. School characteristics (averaged across the district) include enrollment, number of teachers (measured as "full-time equivalents"), number of computers per classroom, and expenditures per student. The student–teacher ratio used here is the number of students in the district, divided by the number of full-time equivalent teachers. Demographic variables for the students also are averaged across the district. The demographic variables include the percentage of students who are in the public assistance program CalWorks (formerly AFDC), the percentage of students who qualify for a reduced price lunch, and the percentage of students who are English learners (that is, students for whom English is a second language). All of these data were obtained from the California Department of Education (www.cde.ca.gov).

APPENDIX B

Derivation of the OLS Estimators

This appendix uses calculus to derive the formulas for the OLS estimators given in Box 7-2. To minimize the sum of squared prediction mistakes $\sum_{i=1}^{n} (Y_i - b_0 - b_1 X_i)^2$ [Equation (7.6)], first take the partial derivatives with respect to b_0 and b_1:

$$\frac{\partial}{\partial b_0} \sum_{i=1}^{n} (Y_i - b_0 - b_1 X_i)^2 = -2 \sum_{i=1}^{n} (Y_i - b_0 - b_1 X_i) \text{ and} \quad \textbf{(7.23)}$$

$$\frac{\partial}{\partial b_1} \sum_{i=1}^{n} (Y_i - b_0 - b_1 X_i)^2 = -2 \sum_{i=1}^{n} (Y_i - b_0 - b_1 X_i) X_i. \quad \textbf{(7.24)}$$

The OLS estimators, $\hat{\beta}_0$ and $\hat{\beta}_1$, are the values of b_0 and b_1 that minimize $\sum_{i=1}^{n} (Y_i - b_0 - b_1 X_i)^2$ or, equivalently, the values of b_0 and b_1 for which the derivatives in Equations (7.23) and (7.24) equal zero. Accordingly, setting these derivatives equal to zero, collecting terms, and dividing by n shows that the OLS estimators, $\hat{\beta}_0$ and $\hat{\beta}_1$, must satisfy the two equations,

$$\overline{Y} - \hat{\beta}_0 - \hat{\beta}_1 \overline{X} = 0 \text{ and} \quad \textbf{(7.25)}$$

$$\frac{1}{n} \sum_{i=1}^{n} X_i Y_i - \hat{\beta}_0 \overline{X} - \hat{\beta}_1 \frac{1}{n} \sum_{i=1}^{n} X_i^2 = 0 \quad \textbf{(7.26)}$$

Solving this pair of equations for $\hat{\beta}_0$ and $\hat{\beta}_1$ yields

$$\hat{\beta}_1 = \frac{\frac{1}{n} \sum_{i=1}^{n} X_i Y_i - \overline{X}\,\overline{Y}}{\frac{1}{n} \sum_{i=1}^{n} X_i^2 - (\overline{X})^2} = \frac{\sum_{i=1}^{n} (X_i - \overline{X})(Y_i - \overline{Y})}{\sum_{i=1}^{n} (X_i - \overline{X})^2} \quad \textbf{(7.27)}$$

$$\hat{\beta}_0 = \overline{Y} - \hat{\beta}_1 \overline{X} \quad \textbf{(7.28)}$$

Equations (7.27) and (7.28) are the formulas for $\hat{\beta}_0$ and $\hat{\beta}_1$ given in Box 7-2; the formula $\hat{\beta}_1 = s_{XY}/s_X^2$ is obtained by dividing the numerator and denominator in Equation (7.27) by $n - 1$.

Regression with a Single Regressor
Hypothesis Tests and Confidence Intervals

8

Learning Objectives

Candidates, after completing this reading, should be able to:

- Calculate and interpret confidence intervals for regression coefficients.
- Interpret the *p*-value.
- Interpret hypothesis tests about regression coefficients.
- Evaluate the implications of homoskedasticity and heteroskedasticity.

- Determine the conditions under which the OLS is the best linear conditionally unbiased estimator.
- Explain the Gauss-Markov Theorem and its limitations, and alternatives to the OLS.
- Apply and interpret the *t*-statistic when the sample size is small.

Excerpt is Chapter 5 of Introduction to Econometrics, *Brief Edition, by James H. Stock and Mark W. Watson.*

This chapter continues the treatment of linear regression with a single regressor. Chapter 7 explained how the OLS estimator $\hat{\beta}_1$ of the slope coefficient β_1 differs from one sample to the next—that is, how $\hat{\beta}_1$ has a sampling distribution. In this chapter, we show how knowledge of this sampling distribution can be used to make statements about β_1 that accurately summarize the sampling uncertainty. The starting point is the standard error of the OLS estimator, which measures the spread of the sampling distribution of $\hat{\beta}_1$. The first section provides an expression for this standard error (and for the standard error of the OLS estimator of the intercept), then shows how to use $\hat{\beta}_1$ and its standard error to test hypotheses. The next section explains how to construct confidence intervals for β_1. The third section takes up the special case of a binary regressor.

The first three sections assume that the three least squares assumptions of Chapter 7 hold. If, in addition, some stronger conditions hold, then some stronger results can be derived regarding the distribution of the OLS estimator. One of these stronger conditions is that the errors are homoskedastic, a concept introduced later. The Gauss-Markov theorem, which states that, under certain conditions, OLS is efficient (has the smallest variance) among a certain class of estimators is also discussed. The final section discusses the distribution of the OLS estimator when the population distribution of the regression errors is normal.

TESTING HYPOTHESES ABOUT ONE OF THE REGRESSION COEFFICIENTS

Your client, the superintendent, calls you with a problem. She has an angry taxpayer in her office who asserts that cutting class size will not help boost test scores, so that reducing them further is a waste of money. Class size, the taxpayer claims, has no effect on test scores.

The taxpayer's claim can be rephrased in the language of regression analysis. Because the effect on test scores of a unit change in class size is $\beta_{ClassSize}$, the taxpayer is asserting that the population regression line is flat—that is, the slope $\beta_{ClassSize}$ of the population regression line is zero. Is there, the superintendent asks, evidence in your sample of 420 observations on California school districts that this

slope is nonzero? Can you reject the taxpayer's hypothesis that $\beta_{ClassSize} = 0$, or should you accept it, at least tentatively pending further new evidence?

This section discusses tests of hypotheses about the slope β_1 or intercept β_0 of the population regression line. We start by discussing two-sided tests of the slope β_1 in detail, then turn to one-sided tests and to tests of hypotheses regarding the intercept β_0.

Two-Sided Hypotheses Concerning β_1

The general approach to testing hypotheses about these coefficients is the same as to testing hypotheses about the population mean, so we begin with a brief review.

Testing Hypotheses About the Population Mean

Recall that the null hypothesis that the mean of Y is a specific value $\mu_{Y,0}$ can be written as $H_0: E(Y) = \mu_{Y,0}$, and the two-sided alternative is $H_1: E(Y) \neq \mu_{Y,0}$.

The test of the null hypothesis H_0 against the two-sided alternative proceeds as in the three steps summarized. The first is to compute the standard error of $\overline{Y}$, $SE(\overline{Y})$, which is an estimator of the standard deviation of the sampling distribution of $\overline{Y}$. The second step is to compute the t-statistic, which has the general form given in Box 8-1; applied here, the t-statistic is $t = (\overline{Y} - \mu_{Y,0})/SE(\overline{Y})$.

The third step is to compute the p-value, which is the smallest significance level at which the null hypothesis could be rejected, based on the test statistic actually observed; equivalently, the p-value is the probability of obtaining a statistic, by random sampling variation, at least as different from the null hypothesis value as is the statistic actually observed, assuming that the null hypothesis is correct. Because the t-statistic has a standard normal distribution in large samples under the null hypothesis, the p-value for a two-sided hypothesis test is $2\Phi(-|t^{act}|)$, where t^{act} is the value of the t-statistic

---

BOX 8-1 General Form of the t-Statistic

In general, the t-statistic has the form

$$t = \frac{\text{estimator} - \text{hypothesized value}}{\text{standard error of the estimator}} \tag{8.1}$$

---

actually computed and Φ is the cumulative standard normal distribution. Alternatively, the third step can be replaced by simply comparing the t-statistic to the critical value appropriate for the test with the desired significance level. For example, a two-sided test with a 5% significance level would reject the null hypothesis if $|t^{act}| > 1.96$. In this case, the population mean is said to be statistically significantly different than the hypothesized value at the 5% significance level.

Testing Hypotheses About the Slope β_1

At a theoretical level, the critical feature justifying the foregoing testing procedure for the population mean is that, in large samples, the sampling distribution of $\overline{Y}$ is approximately normal. Because $\hat{\beta}_1$ also has a normal sampling distribution in large samples, hypotheses about the true value of the slope β_1 can be tested using the same general approach.

The null and alternative hypotheses need to be stated precisely before they can be tested. The angry taxpayer's hypothesis is that $\beta_{ClassSize} = 0$. More generally, under the null hypothesis the true population slope β_1 takes on some specific value, $\beta_{1,0}$. Under the two-sided alternative, β_1 does not equal $\beta_{1,0}$. That is, the **null hypothesis** and the **two-sided alternative hypothesis** are

$$H_0: \beta_1 = \beta_{1,0} \text{ vs. } H_1: \beta_1 \neq \beta_{1,0} \qquad (8.2)$$
$$\text{(two-sided alternative)}$$

To test the null hypothesis H_0, we follow the same three steps as for the population mean.

The first step is to compute the **standard error of $\hat{\beta}_1$, $SE(\hat{\beta}_1)$**. The standard error of $\hat{\beta}_1$ is an estimator of $\sigma_{\hat{\beta}_1}$, the standard deviation of the sampling distribution of $\hat{\beta}_1$. Specifically,

$$SE(\hat{\beta}_1) = \sqrt{\hat{\sigma}_{\hat{\beta}_1}^2} \qquad (8.3)$$

where

$$\hat{\sigma}_{\hat{\beta}_1}^2 = \frac{1}{n} \times \frac{\frac{1}{n-2} \sum_{i=1}^{n} (X_i - \overline{X})^2 \hat{u}_i^2}{\left[\frac{1}{n} \sum_{i=1}^{n} (X_i - \overline{X})^2 \right]^2} \qquad (8.4)$$

Although the formula for $\hat{\sigma}_{\hat{\beta}_1}^2$ is complicated, in applications the standard error is computed by regression software so that it is easy to use in practice.

The second step is to compute the **t-statistic**,

$$t = \frac{\hat{\beta}_1 - \beta_{1,0}}{SE(\hat{\beta}_1)} \qquad (8.5)$$

The third step is to compute the **p-value**, the probability of observing a value of $\hat{\beta}_1$ at least as different from $\beta_{1,0}$ as the estimate actually computed ($\hat{\beta}_1^{act}$), assuming that the null hypothesis is correct. Stated mathematically,

$$p\text{-value} = \Pr_{H_0}[|\hat{\beta}_1 - \beta_{1,0}| > |\hat{\beta}_1^{act} - \beta_{1,0}|] \qquad (8.6)$$
$$= \Pr_{H_0}\left[\left| \frac{\hat{\beta}_1 - \beta_{1,0}}{SE(\hat{\beta}_1)} \right| > \left| \frac{\hat{\beta}_1^{act} - \beta_{1,0}}{SE(\hat{\beta}_1)} \right| \right]$$
$$= \Pr_{H_0}(|t| > |t^{act}|)$$

where $\Pr_{H_0}$ denotes the probability computed under the null hypothesis, the second equality follows by dividing by $SE(\hat{\beta}_1)$, and t^{act} is the value of the t-statistic actually computed. Because $\hat{\beta}_1$ is approximately normally distributed in large samples, under the null hypothesis the t-statistic is approximately distributed as a standard normal random variable, so in large samples,

$$p\text{-value} = \Pr(|Z| > |t^{act}|) = 2\Phi(-|t^{act}|) \qquad (8.7)$$

A small value of the p-value, say less than 5%, provides evidence against the null hypothesis in the sense that the chance of obtaining a value of $\hat{\beta}_1$ by pure random variation from one sample to the next is less than 5% if, in fact, the null hypothesis is correct. If so, the null hypothesis is rejected at the 5% significance level.

Alternatively, the hypothesis can be tested at the 5% significance level simply by comparing the value of the t-statistic to ± 1.96, the critical value for a two-sided test, and rejecting the null hypothesis at the 5% level if $|t^{act}| > 1.96$.

These steps are summarized in Box 8-2.

Reporting Regression Equations and Application to Test Scores

The OLS regression of the test score against the student–teacher ratio, reported in Equation (7.11), yielded $\hat{\beta}_0 = 698.9$ and $\hat{\beta}_1 = -2.28$. The standard errors of these estimates are $SE(\hat{\beta}_0) = 10.4$ and $SE(\hat{\beta}_1) = 0.52$.

Because of the importance of the standard errors, by convention they are included when reporting the estimated OLS coefficients. One compact way to report the standard errors is to place them in parentheses below the respective coefficients of the OLS regression line:

$$\widehat{TestScore} = 698.9 - 2.28 \times STR, \; R^2 = 0.051, \; SER = 18.6.$$
$$(10.4) \; (0.52) \qquad\qquad\qquad\qquad \textbf{(8.8)}$$

Equation (8.8) also reports the regression R^2 and the standard error of the regression (SER) following the estimated regression line. Thus Equation (8.8) provides the estimated regression line, estimates of the sampling uncertainty of the slope and the intercept (the standard errors), and two measures of the fit of this regression line (the R^2 and the SER). This is a common format for reporting a single regression equation, and it will be used throughout the rest of this book.

Suppose you wish to test the null hypothesis that the slope β_1 is zero in the population counterpart of Equation (8.8) at the 5% significance level. To do so, construct the t-statistic and compare it to 1.96, the 5% (two-sided) critical value taken from the standard normal distribution. The t-statistic is constructed by substituting the hypothesized value of β_1 under the null hypothesis (zero), the estimated slope, and its standard error from Equation (8.8) into the general formula in Equation (8.5); the result is $t^{act} = (-2.28 - 0)/0.52 = -4.38$. This t-statistic exceeds (in absolute value) the 5% two-sided critical value of 1.96, so the null hypothesis is rejected in favor of the two-sided alternative at the 5% significance level.

Alternatively, we can compute the p-value associated with $t^{act} = -4.38$. This probability is the area in the tails of standard normal distribution, as shown in Figure 8-1. This probability is extremely small, approximately 0.00001, or 0.001%. That is, if the null hypothesis $\beta_{ClassSize} = 0$ is true, the probability of obtaining a value of $\hat{\beta}_1$ as far from the

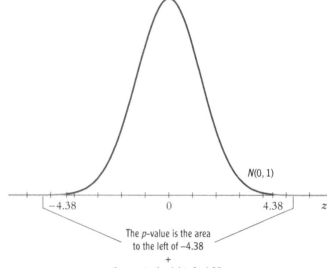

FIGURE 8-1 Calculating the p-value of a two-sided test when $t^{act} = -4.38$.

The p-value of a two-sided test is the probability that $|Z| > |t^{act}|$, where Z is a standard normal random variable and t^{act} is the value of the t-statistic calculated from the sample. When $t^{act} = -4.38$, the p-value is only 0.00001.

null as the value we actually obtained is extremely small, less than 0.001%. Because this event is so unlikely, it is reasonable to conclude that the null hypothesis is false.

One-Sided Hypotheses Concerning β_1

The discussion so far has focused on testing the hypothesis that $\beta_1 = \beta_{1,0}$ against the hypothesis that $\beta_1 \neq \beta_{1,0}$. This is a two-sided hypothesis test, because under the alternative β_1 could be either larger or smaller than $\beta_{1,0}$. Sometimes, however, it is appropriate to use a one-sided hypothesis test. For example, in the student–teacher ratio/test score problem, many people think that smaller classes provide a better learning environment. Under that hypothesis, β_1 is negative: Smaller classes lead to higher scores. It might make sense, therefore, to test the null hypothesis that $\beta_1 = 0$ (no effect) against the one-sided alternative that $\beta_1 < 0$.

For a one-sided test, the null hypothesis and the one-sided alternative hypothesis are

$$H_0: \beta_1 = \beta_{1,0} \; \text{vs.} \; H_1: \beta_1 < \beta_{1,0}, \quad \text{(one-sided alternative)} \qquad \textbf{(8.9)}$$

where $\beta_{1,0}$ is the value of β_1 under the null (0 in the student–teacher ratio example) and the alternative is that

β_1 is less than $\beta_{1,0}$. If the alternative is that β_1 is greater than $\beta_{1,0}$, the inequality in Equation (8.9) is reversed.

Because the null hypothesis is the same for a one- and a two-sided hypothesis test, the construction of the t-statistic is the same. The only difference between a one- and two-sided hypothesis test is how you interpret the t-statistic. For the one-sided alternative in Equation (8.9), the null hypothesis is rejected against the one-sided alternative for large negative, but not large positive, values of the t-statistic: Instead of rejecting if $|t^{act}| > 1.96$, the hypothesis is rejected at the 5% significance level if $t^{act} < -1.645$.

The p-value for a one-sided test is obtained from the cumulative standard normal distribution as

$$p\text{-value} = \Pr(Z < t^{act}) \qquad \textbf{(8.10)}$$
$$= \Phi(t^{act}) \ (p\text{-value, one-sided left-tail test})$$

If the alternative hypothesis is that β_1 is greater than $\beta_{1,0}$, the inequalities in Equations (8.9) and (8.10) are reversed, so the p-value is the right-tail probability, $\Pr(Z > t^{act})$.

When Should a One-Sided Test Be Used?

In practice, one-sided alternative hypotheses should be used only when there is a clear reason for doing so. This reason could come from economic theory, prior empirical evidence, or both. However, even if it initially seems that the relevant alternative is one-sided, upon reflection this might not necessarily be so. A newly formulated drug undergoing clinical trials actually could prove harmful because of previously unrecognized side effects. In the class size example, we are reminded of the graduation joke that a university's secret of success is to admit talented students and then make sure that the faculty stays out of their way and does as little damage as possible. In practice, such ambiguity often leads econometricians to use two-sided tests.

Application to Test Scores

The t-statistic testing the hypothesis that there is no effect of class size on test scores [so $\beta_{1,0} = 0$ in Equation (8.9)] is $t^{act} = -4.38$. This is less than -2.33 (the critical value for a one-sided test with a 1% significance level), so the null hypothesis is rejected against the one-sided alternative at the 1% level. In fact, the p-value is less than 0.0006%. Based on these data, you can reject the angry taxpayer's assertion that the negative estimate of the slope arose purely because of random sampling variation at the 1% significance level.

Testing Hypotheses about the Intercept β_0

This discussion has focused on testing hypotheses about the slope, β_1. Occasionally, however, the hypothesis concerns the intercept, β_0. The null hypothesis concerning the intercept and the two-sided alternative are

$$H_0\text{: } \beta_0 = \beta_{0,0} \text{ vs. } H_1\text{: } \beta_0 \neq \beta_{0,0} \qquad \textbf{(8.11)}$$
$$(\text{two-sided alternative})$$

The general approach to testing this null hypothesis consists of the three steps in Box 8-2, applied to β_0. If the alternative is one-sided, this approach is modified as was discussed in the previous subsection for hypotheses about the slope.

Hypothesis tests are useful if you have a specific null hypothesis in mind (as did our angry taxpayer). Being able to accept or to reject this null hypothesis based on the statistical evidence provides a powerful tool for coping with the uncertainty inherent in using a sample to learn about the population. Yet, there are many times that no single hypothesis about a regression coefficient is dominant, and instead one would like to know a range of values of the coefficient that are consistent with the data. This calls for constructing a confidence interval.

CONFIDENCE INTERVALS FOR A REGRESSION COEFFICIENT

Because any statistical estimate of the slope β_1 necessarily has sampling uncertainty, we cannot determine the true value of β_1 exactly from a sample of data. It is, however, possible to use the OLS estimator and its standard error to construct a confidence interval for the slope β_1 or for the intercept β_0.

Confidence Interval for β_1

Recall that a 95% **confidence interval for β_1** has two equivalent definitions. First, it is the set of values that cannot be rejected using a two-sided hypothesis test with a 5% significance level. Second, it is an interval that has a

95% probability of containing the true value of β_1; that is, in 95% of possible samples that might be drawn, the confidence interval will contain the true value of β_1. Because this interval contains the true value in 95% of all samples, it is said to have a **confidence level** of 95%.

The reason these two definitions are equivalent is as follows. A hypothesis test with a 5% significance level will, by definition, reject the true value of β_1 in only 5% of all possible samples; that is, in 95% of all possible samples the true value of β_1 will *not* be rejected. Because the 95% confidence interval (as defined in the first definition) is the set of all values of β_1 that are *not* rejected at the 5% significance level, it follows that the true value of β_1 will be contained in the confidence interval in 95% of all possible samples.

As in the case of a confidence interval for the population mean, in principle a 95% confidence interval can be computed by testing all possible values of β_1 (that is, testing the null hypothesis $\beta_1 = \beta_{1,0}$ for all values of $\beta_{1,0}$) at the 5% significance level using the t-statistic. The 95% confidence interval is then the collection of all the values of β_1 that are not rejected. But constructing the t-statistic for all values of β_1 would take forever.

An easier way to construct the confidence interval is to note that the t-statistic will reject the hypothesized value $\beta_{1,0}$ whenever $\beta_{1,0}$ is outside the range $\hat{\beta}_1 \pm 1.96SE(\hat{\beta}_1)$. That is, the 95% confidence interval for β_1 is the interval $[\hat{\beta}_1 - 1.96SE(\hat{\beta}_1), \hat{\beta}_1 + 1.96SE(\hat{\beta}_1)]$. This argument parallels the argument used to develop a confidence interval for the population mean.

The construction of a confidence interval for β_1 is summarized in Box 8-3.

BOX 8-3 Confidence Interval for β_1

A 95% two-sided confidence interval for β_1 is an interval that contains the true value of β_1 with a 95% probability; that is, it contains the true value of β_1 in 95% of all possible randomly drawn samples. Equivalently, it is the set of values of β_1 that cannot be rejected by a 5% two-sided hypothesis test. When the sample size is large, it is constructed as

$$95\% \text{ confidence interval for } \beta_1 = \quad (8.12)$$
$$[\hat{\beta}_1 - 1.96SE(\hat{\beta}_1), \hat{\beta}_1 + 1.96SE(\hat{\beta}_1)].$$

Confidence Interval for β_0

A 95% confidence interval for β_0 is constructed as in Box 8-3, with $\hat{\beta}_0$ and $SE(\hat{\beta}_0)$ replacing $\hat{\beta}_1$ and $SE(\hat{\beta}_1)$.

Application to Test Scores

The OLS regression of the test score against the student–teacher ratio, reported in Equation (8.8), yielded $\hat{\beta}_1 = -2.28$ and $SE(\hat{\beta}_1) = 0.52$. The 95% two-sided confidence interval for β_1 is $\{-2.28 \pm 1.96 \times 0.52\}$, or $-3.30 \le \beta_1 \le -1.26$. The value $\beta_1 = 0$ is not contained in this confidence interval, so (as we knew already) the hypothesis $\beta_1 = 0$ can be rejected at the 5% significance level.

Confidence Intervals for Predicted Effects of Changing X

The 95% confidence interval for β_1 can be used to construct a 95% confidence interval for the predicted effect of a general change in X.

Consider changing X by a given amount, Δx. The predicted change in Y associated with this change in X is $\beta_1 \Delta x$. The population slope β_1 is unknown, but because we can construct a confidence interval for β_1, we can construct a confidence interval for the predicted effect $\beta_1 \Delta x$. Because one end of a 95% confidence interval for β_1 is $\hat{\beta}_1 - 1.96SE(\hat{\beta}_1)$, the predicted effect of the change Δx using this estimate of β_1 is $[\hat{\beta}_1 - 1.96SE(\hat{\beta}_1)] \times \Delta x$. The other end of the confidence interval is $\hat{\beta}_1 + 1.96SE(\hat{\beta}_1)$, and the predicted effect of the change using that estimate is $[\hat{\beta}_1 + 1.96SE(\hat{\beta}_1)] \times \Delta x$. Thus a 95% confidence interval for the effect of changing x by the amount Δx can be expressed as

$$95\% \text{ confidence interval for } \beta_1 \Delta x = \quad (8.13)$$
$$[\hat{\beta}_1 \Delta x - 1.96SE(\hat{\beta}_1) \times \Delta x, \ \hat{\beta}_1 \Delta x + 1.96SE(\hat{\beta}_1) \times \Delta x]$$

For example, our hypothetical superintendent is contemplating reducing the student–teacher ratio by 2. Because the 95% confidence interval for β_1 is $[-3.30, -1.26]$, the effect of reducing the student–teacher ratio by 2 could be as great as $-3.30 \times (-2) = 6.60$, or as little as $-1.26 \times (-2) = 2.52$. Thus decreasing the student–teacher ratio by 2 is predicted to increase test scores by between 2.52 and 6.60 points, with a 95% confidence level.

REGRESSION WHEN X IS A BINARY VARIABLE

The discussion so far has focused on the case that the regressor is a continuous variable. Regression analysis can also be used when the regressor is binary—that is, when it takes on only two values, 0 or 1. For example, X might be a worker's gender (= 1 if female, = 0 if male), whether a school district is urban or rural (= 1 if urban, = 0 if rural), or whether the district's class size is small or large (= 1 if small, = 0 if large). A binary variable is also called an **indicator variable** or sometimes a **dummy variable**.

Interpretation of the Regression Coefficients

The mechanics of regression with a binary regressor are the same as if it is continuous. The interpretation of β_1, however, is different, and it turns out that regression with a binary variable is equivalent to performing a difference of means analysis, as described previously.

To see this, suppose you have a variable D_i that equals either 0 or 1, depending on whether the student–teacher ratio is less than 20:

$$D_i = \begin{cases} 1 \text{ if the student–teacher ratio in } i^{th} \text{ district } < 20 \\ 0 \text{ if the student–teacher ratio in } i^{th} \text{ district } \geq 20 \end{cases}$$

$$\text{(8.14)}$$

The population regression model with D_i as the regressor is

$$Y_i = \beta_0 + \beta_1 D_i + u_i, \quad i = 1, \ldots, n \qquad \text{(8.15)}$$

This is the same as the regression model with the continuous regressor X_i, except that now the regressor is the binary variable D_i. Because D_i is not continuous, it is not useful to think of β_1 as a slope; indeed, because D_i can take on only two values, there is no "line" so it makes no sense to talk about a slope. Thus we will not refer to β_1 as the slope in Equation (8.15); instead we will simply refer to β_1 as the **coefficient multiplying D_i** in this regression or, more compactly, the **coefficient on D_i**.

If β_1 in Equation (8.15) is not a slope, then what is it? The best way to interpret β_0 and β_1 in a regression with a binary regressor is to consider, one at a time, the two possible cases, $D_i = 0$ and $D_i = 1$. If the student–teacher ratio is high, then $D_i = 0$ and Equation (8.15) becomes

$$Y_i = \beta_0 + u_i \quad (D_i = 0) \qquad \text{(8.16)}$$

Because $E(u_i | D_i) = 0$, the conditional expectation of Y_i when $D_i = 0$ is $E(Y_i | D_i = 0) = \beta_0$; that is, β_0 is the population mean value of test scores when the student–teacher ratio is high. Similarly, when $D_i = 1$,

$$Y_i = \beta_0 + \beta_1 + u_i \quad (D_i = 1) \qquad \text{(8.17)}$$

Thus, when $D_i = 1$, $E(Y_i | D_i = 1) = \beta_0 + \beta_1$; that is, $\beta_0 + \beta_1$ is the population mean value of test scores when the student–teacher ratio is low.

Because $\beta_0 + \beta_1$ is the population mean of Y_i when $D_i = 1$ and β_0 is the population mean of Y_i when $D_i = 0$, the difference $(\beta_0 + \beta_1) - \beta_0 = \beta_1$ is the difference between these two means. In other words, β_1 is the difference between the conditional expectation of Y_i when $D_i = 1$ and when $D_i = 0$, or $\beta_1 = E(Y_i | D_i = 1) - E(Y_i | D_i = 0)$. In the test score example, β_1 is the difference between mean test score in districts with low student–teacher ratios and the mean test score in districts with high student–teacher ratios.

Because β_1 is the difference in the population means, it makes sense that the OLS estimator β_1 is the difference between the sample averages of Y_i in the two groups, and in fact this is the case.

Hypothesis Tests and Confidence Intervals

If the two population means are the same, then β_1 in Equation (8.15) is zero. Thus, the null hypothesis that the two population means are the same can be tested against the alternative hypothesis that they differ by testing the null hypothesis $\beta_1 = 0$ against the alternative $\beta_1 \neq 0$. This hypothesis can be tested using the procedure outlined in the first section of this chapter. Specifically, the null hypothesis can be rejected at the 5% level against the two-sided alternative when the OLS t-statistic $t = \hat{\beta}_1 / SE(\hat{\beta}_1)$ exceeds 1.96 in absolute value. Similarly, a 95% confidence interval for β_1, constructed as $\hat{\beta}_1 \pm 1.96 SE(\hat{\beta}_1)$ as described earlier, provides a 95% confidence interval for the difference between the two population means.

Application to Test Scores

As an example, a regression of the test score against the student–teacher ratio binary variable D defined in Equation (8.14) estimated by OLS using the 420 observations in Figure 7-2, yields

$$\widehat{TestScore} = 650.0 + 7.4D, \; R^2 = 0.037, \quad \textbf{(8.18)}$$
$$(1.3) \quad (1.8)$$
$$SER = 18.7$$

where the standard errors of the OLS estimates of the coefficients β_0 and β_1 are given in parentheses below the OLS estimates. Thus the average test score for the subsample with student–teacher ratios greater than or equal to 20 (that is, for which $D = 0$) is 650.0, and the average test score for the subsample with student–teacher ratios less than 20 (so $D = 1$) is $650.0 + 7.4 = 657.4$. The difference between the sample average test scores for the two groups is 7.4. This is the OLS estimate of β_1, the coefficient on the student–teacher ratio binary variable D.

Is the difference in the population mean test scores in the two groups statistically significantly different from zero at the 5% level? To find out, construct the t-statistic on β_1: $t = 7.4/1.8 = 4.04$. This exceeds 1.96 in absolute value, so the hypothesis that the population mean test scores in districts with high and low student–teacher ratios is the same can be rejected at the 5% significance level.

The OLS estimator and its standard error can be used to construct a 95% confidence interval for the true difference in means. This is $7.4 \pm 1.96 \times 1.8 = (3.9, 10.9)$. This confidence interval excludes $\beta_1 = 0$, so that (as we know from the previous paragraph) the hypothesis $\beta_1 = 0$ can be rejected at the 5% significance level.

HETEROSKEDASTICITY AND HOMOSKEDASTICITY

Our only assumption about the distribution of u_i conditional on X_i is that it has a mean of zero (the first least squares assumption). If, furthermore, the *variance* of this conditional distribution does not depend on X_i, then the errors are said to be homoskedastic. This section discusses homoskedasticity, its theoretical implications, the simplified formulas for the standard errors of the OLS estimators that arise if the errors are homoskedastic, and the risks you run if you use these simplified formulas in practice.

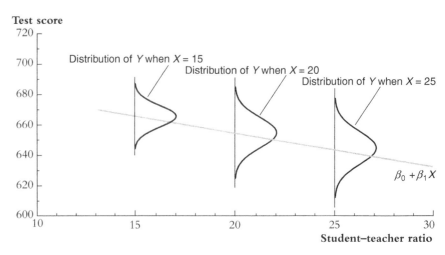

FIGURE 8-2   An example of heteroskedasticity.

Like Figure 7-4, this shows the conditional distribution of test scores for three different class sizes. Unlike Figure 7-4, these distributions become more spread out (have a larger variance) for larger class sizes. Because the variance of the distribution of u given X, $\text{VaR}(u \mid X)$, depends on X, u is heteroskedastic.

What Are Heteroskedasticity and Homoskedasticity?

Definitions of Heteroskedasticity and Homoskedasticity

The error term u_i is **homoskedastic** if the variance of the conditional distribution of u_i given X_i is constant for $i = 1, \ldots, n$ and in particular does not depend on X_i. Otherwise, the error term is **heteroskedastic**.

As an illustration, return to Figure 7-4. The distribution of the errors u_i is shown for various values of x. Because this distribution applies specifically for the indicated value of x, this is the conditional distribution of u_i given $X_i = x$. As drawn in that figure, all these conditional distributions have the same spread; more precisely, the variance of these distributions is the same for the various values of x. That is, in Figure 7-4, the conditional variance of u_i given $X_i = x$ does not depend on x, so the errors illustrated in Figure 7-4 are homoskedastic.

In contrast, Figure 8-2 illustrates a case in which the conditional distribution of u_i spreads out as x increases. For small values of x, this distribution is tight, but for larger values of x, it has a greater spread. Thus, in Figure 8-2 the variance of u_i given $X_i = x$ increases with x, so that the errors in Figure 8-2 are heteroskedastic.

Heteroskedasticity and Homoskedasticity

The error term u_i is homoskedastic if the variance of the conditional distribution of u_i given X_i, $\mathrm{VaR}(u_i | X_i = x)$, is constant for $i = 1, \ldots, n$, and in particular does not depend on x. Otherwise, the error term is heteroskedastic.

The definitions of heteroskedasticity and homoskedasticity are summarized in Box 8-4.

Example

These terms are a mouthful and the definitions might seem abstract. To help clarify them with an example, we digress from the student–teacher ratio/test score problem and instead return to the example of earnings of male versus female college graduates. Let $MALE_i$ be a binary variable that equals 1 for male college graduates and equals 0 for female graduates. The binary variable regression model relating someone's earnings to his or her gender is

$$Earnings_i = \beta_0 + \beta_1 MALE_i + u_i \qquad \textbf{(8.19)}$$

for $i = 1, \ldots, n$. Because the regressor is binary, β_1 is the difference in the population means of the two groups—in this case, the difference in mean earnings between men and women who graduated from college.

The definition of homoskedasticity states that the variance of u_i does not depend on the regressor. Here the regressor is $MALE_i$, so at issue is whether the variance of the error term depends on $MALE_i$. In other words, is the variance of the error term the same for men and for women? If so, the error is homoskedastic; if not, it is heteroskedastic.

Deciding whether the variance of u_i depends on $MALE_i$ requires thinking hard about what the error term actually is. In this regard, it is useful to write Equation (8.19) as two separate equations, one for men and one for women:

$$Earnings_i = \beta_0 + u_i \quad \text{(women) and} \qquad \textbf{(8.20)}$$

$$Earnings_i = \beta_0 + \beta_1 + u_i \quad \text{(men)} \qquad \textbf{(8.21)}$$

Thus, for women, u_i is the deviation of the ith woman's earnings from the population mean earnings for women (β_0), and for men, u_i is the deviation of the ith man's earnings from the population mean earnings for men ($\beta_0 + \beta_1$). It follows that the statement, "the variance of u_i does not depend on $MALE$," is equivalent to the statement, "the variance of earnings is the same for men as it is for women." In other words, in this example, the error term is homoskedastic if the variance of the population distribution of earnings is the same for men and women; if these variances differ, the error term is heteroskedastic.

Mathematical Implications of Homoskedasticity

The OLS Estimators Remain Unbiased and Asymptotically Normal

Because the least squares assumptions in Box 7-3 place no restrictions on the conditional variance, they apply to both the general case of heteroskedasticity and the special case of homoskedasticity. Therefore, the OLS estimators remain unbiased and consistent even if the errors are homoskedastic. In addition, the OLS estimators have sampling distributions that are normal in large samples even if the errors are homoskedastic. Whether the errors are homoskedastic or heteroskedastic, the OLS estimator is unbiased, consistent, and asymptotically normal.

Efficiency of the OLS Estimator When the Errors Are Homoskedastic

If the least squares assumptions in Box 7-3 hold and the errors are homoskedastic, then the OLS estimators $\hat{\beta}_0$ and $\hat{\beta}_1$ are efficient among all estimators that are linear in $Y_1, \ldots, Y_n$ and are unbiased, conditional on $X_1, \ldots, X_n$. This result, which is called the Gauss-Markov theorem, is discussed in the next section.

Homoskedasticity-Only Variance Formula

If the error term is homoskedastic, then the formulas for the variances of $\hat{\beta}_0$ and $\hat{\beta}_1$ in Box 7-4 simplify. Consequently, if the errors are homoskedastic, then there is a specialized formula that can be used for the standard errors of $\hat{\beta}_0$ and $\hat{\beta}_1$. The **homoskedasticity-only standard error** of $\hat{\beta}_1$ is $SE(\hat{\beta}_1) = \sqrt{\tilde{\sigma}^2_{\hat{\beta}_1}}$, where $\tilde{\sigma}^2_{\hat{\beta}_1}$ is the homoskedasticity-only estimator of the variance of $\hat{\beta}_1$:

$$\tilde{\sigma}^2_{\hat{\beta}_1} = \frac{s^2_{\hat{u}}}{\displaystyle\sum_{i=1}^{n}(X_i - \bar{X})^2} \quad \text{(homoskedasticity-only)} \qquad \textbf{(8.22)}$$

where $s_{\hat{u}}^2$ is given in Equation (7.19). In the special case that X is a binary variable, the estimator of the variance of $\hat{\beta}_1$ under homoskedasticity (that is, the square of the standard error of $\hat{\beta}_1$ under homoskedasticity) is the so-called pooled variance formula for the difference in means.

Because these alternative formulas are derived for the special case that the errors are homoskedastic and do not apply if the errors are heteroskedastic, they will be referred to as the "homoskedasticity-only" formulas for the variance and standard error of the OLS estimators. As the name suggests, if the errors are heteroskedastic, then the homoskedasticity-only standard errors are inappropriate. Specifically, if the errors are heteroskedastic, then the t-statistic computed using the homoskedasticity-only standard error does not have a standard normal distribution, even in large samples. In fact, the correct critical values to use for this homoskedasticity-only t-statistic depend on the precise nature of the heteroskedasticity, so those critical values cannot be tabulated. Similarly, if the errors are heteroskedastic but a confidence interval is constructed as ±1.96 homoskedasticity-only standard errors, in general the probability that this interval contains the true value of the coefficient is not 95%, even in large samples.

In contrast, because homoskedasticity is a special case of heteroskedasticity, the estimators $\hat{\sigma}_{\hat{\beta}_1}^2$ and $\hat{\sigma}_{\hat{\beta}_0}^2$ of the variances of $\hat{\beta}_1$ and $\hat{\beta}_0$ given in Equations (8.4) and (8.26) produce valid statistical inferences whether the errors are heteroskedastic or homoskedastic. Thus hypothesis tests and confidence intervals based on those standard errors are valid whether or not the errors are heteroskedastic. Because the standard errors we have used so far [i.e., those based on Equations (8.4) and (8.26)] lead to statistical inferences that are valid whether or not the errors are heteroskedastic, they are called **heteroskedasticity-robust standard errors**. Because such formulas were proposed by Eicker (1967), Huber (1967), and White (1980), they are also referred to as Eicker-Huber-White standard errors.

What Does This Mean in Practice?

Which Is More Realistic, Heteroskedasticity or Homoskedasticity?

The answer to this question depends on the application. However, the issues can be clarified by returning to the example of the gender gap in earnings among college graduates. Familiarity with how people are paid in the world around us gives some clues as to which assumption is more sensible. For many years—and, to a lesser extent, today—women were not found in the top-paying jobs: There have always been poorly paid men, but there have rarely been highly paid women. This suggests that the distribution of earnings among women is tighter than among men. In other words, the variance of the error term in Equation (8.20) for women is plausibly less than the variance of the error term in Equation (8.21) for men. Thus, the presence of a "glass ceiling" for women's jobs and pay suggests that the error term in the binary variable regression model in Equation (8.19) is heteroskedastic. Unless there are compelling reasons to the contrary—and we can think of none—it makes sense to treat the error term in this example as heteroskedastic.

As this example of modeling earnings illustrates, heteroskedasticity arises in many econometric applications. At a general level, economic theory rarely gives any reason to believe that the errors are homoskedastic. It therefore is prudent to assume that the errors might be heteroskedastic unless you have compelling reasons to believe otherwise.

Practical Implications

The main issue of practical relevance in this discussion is whether one should use heteroskedasticity-robust or homoskedasticity-only standard errors. In this regard, it is useful to imagine computing both, then choosing between them. If the homoskedasticity-only and heteroskedasticity-robust standard errors are the same, nothing is lost by using the heteroskedasticity-robust standard errors; if they differ, however, then you should use the more reliable ones that allow for heteroskedasticity. The simplest thing, then, is always to use the heteroskedasticity-robust standard errors.

For historical reasons, many software programs use the homoskedasticity-only standard errors as their default setting, so it is up to the user to specify the option of heteroskedasticity-robust standard errors. The details of how to implement heteroskedasticity-robust standard errors depend on the software package you use.

The Economic Value of a Year of Education: Homoskedasticity or Heteroskedasticity?

On average, workers with more education have higher earnings than workers with less education. But if the best-paying jobs mainly go to the college educated, it might also be that the *spread* of the distribution of earnings is greater for workers with more education. Does the distribution of earnings spread out as education increases?

This is an empirical question, so answering it requires analyzing data. Figure 8-3 is a scatterplot of the hourly earnings and the number of years of education for a sample of 2950 full-time workers in the United States in 2004, ages 29 and 30, with between 6 and 18 years of

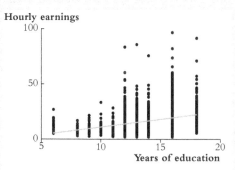

Hourly earnings

FIGURE 8-3 Scatterplot of hourly earnings and years of education for 29- to 30-year-olds in the United States in 2004.

Hourly earnings are plotted against years of education for 2950 full-time, 29- to 30-year-old workers. The spread around the regression line increases with the years of education, indicating that the regression errors are heteroskedastic.

education. The data come from the March 2005 Current Population Survey.

Figure 8-3 has two striking features. The first is that the mean of the distribution of earnings increases with the number of years of education. This increase is summarized by the OLS regression line,

$$\widehat{Earnings} = -3.13 + 1.47 \; Years \; Education, \quad \textbf{(8.23)}$$
$$(0.93) \; (0.07)$$

$$R^2 = 0.130, \; SER = 8.77.$$

This line is plotted in Figure 8-3. The coefficient of 1.47 in the OLS regression line means that, on average, hourly earnings increase by $1.47 for each additional year of education. The 95% confidence interval for this coefficient is $1.47 \pm 1.96 \times 0.07$, or 1.33 to 1.61.

The second striking feature of Figure 8-3 is that the spread of the distribution of earnings increases with the years of education. While some workers with many years of education have low-paying jobs, very few workers with low levels of education have high-paying jobs. This can be stated more precisely by looking at the spread of the residuals around the OLS regression line. For workers with ten years of education, the standard deviation of the residuals is $5.46; for workers with a high school diploma, this standard deviation is $7.43; and for workers with a college degree, this standard deviation increases to $10.78. Because these standard deviations differ for different levels of education, the variance of the residuals in the regression of Equation (8.23) depends on the value of the regressor (the years of education); in other words, the regression errors are heteroskedastic. In real-world terms, not all college graduates will be earning $50/hour by the time they are 29, but some will, and workers with only ten years of education have no shot at those jobs.

All of the empirical examples in this book employ heteroskedasticity-robust standard errors unless explicitly stated otherwise.[1]

THE THEORETICAL FOUNDATIONS OF ORDINARY LEAST SQUARES*

As discussed in Chapter 7, the OLS estimator is unbiased, is consistent, has a variance that is inversely proportional to *n*, and has a normal sampling distribution when the sample size is large. In addition, under certain conditions the OLS estimator is more efficient than some other

---

[1] In case this book is used in conjunction with other texts, it might be helpful to note that some textbooks add homoskedasticity to the list of least squares assumptions. As just discussed, however, this additional assumption is not needed for the validity of OLS regression analysis as long as heteroskedasticity-robust standard errors are used.

---

* This section is optional and is not used in later chapters.

candidate estimators. Specifically, if the least squares assumptions hold and if the errors are homoskedastic, then the OLS estimator has the smallest variance of all conditionally unbiased estimators that are linear functions of $Y_1, \ldots, Y_n$. This section explains and discusses this result, which is a consequence of the Gauss-Markov theorem. The section concludes with a discussion of alternative estimators that are more efficient than OLS when the conditions of the Gauss-Markov theorem do not hold.

Linear Conditionally Unbiased Estimators and the Gauss-Markov Theorem

If the three least squares assumptions (Box 7-3) hold and if the error is homoskedastic, then the OLS estimator has the smallest variance, conditional on $X_1, \ldots, X_n$, among all estimators in the class of linear conditionally unbiased estimators. In other words, the OLS estimator is the **B**est **L**inear conditionally **U**nbiased **E**stimator—that is, it is BLUE. This result extends to regression the result that the sample average $\overline{Y}$ is the most efficient estimator of the population mean among the class of all estimators that are unbiased and are linear functions (weighted averages) of $Y_1, \ldots, Y_n$.

Linear Conditionally Unbiased Estimators

The class of linear conditionally unbiased estimators consists of all estimators of β_1 that are linear functions of $Y_1, \ldots, Y_n$ and that are unbiased, conditional on $X_1, \ldots, X_n$. That is, if $\tilde{\beta}_1$ is a linear estimator, then it can be written as

$$\tilde{\beta}_1 = \sum_{i=1}^{n} a_i Y_i \quad (\tilde{\beta}_1 \text{ is linear}) \qquad \textbf{(8.24)}$$

where the weights $a_1, \ldots, a_n$ can depend on $X_1, \ldots, X_n$ but *not* on $Y_1, \ldots, Y_n$. The estimator $\tilde{\beta}_1$ is conditionally unbiased if the mean of its conditional sampling distribution, given $X_1, \ldots, X_n$, is β_1. That is, the estimator $\tilde{\beta}_1$ is conditionally unbiased if

$E(\tilde{\beta}_1 | X_1, \ldots, X_n) = \beta_1 \quad (\tilde{\beta}_1 \text{ is conditionally unbiased})$ **(8.25)**

The estimator $\tilde{\beta}_1$ is a linear conditionally unbiased estimator if it can be written in the form of Equation (8.24) (it is linear) and if Equation (8.25) holds (it is conditionally unbiased). It can be shown that the OLS estimator is linear and conditionally unbiased.

BOX 8-5 The Gauss-Markov Theorem for $\hat{\beta}_1$

If the three least squares assumptions in Box 7-3 hold *and* if errors are homoskedastic, then the OLS estimator $\hat{\beta}_1$ is the **B**est (most efficient) **L**inear conditionally **U**nbiased **E**stimator (is **BLUE**).

The Gauss-Markov Theorem

The **Gauss-Markov** theorem states that, under a set of conditions known as the Gauss-Markov conditions, the OLS estimator $\hat{\beta}_1$ has the smallest conditional variance, given $X_1, \ldots, X_n$, of all linear conditionally unbiased estimators of β_1; that is, the OLS estimator is BLUE. The Gauss-Markov conditions, which are stated in the chapter Appendix, are implied by the three least squares assumptions plus the assumption that the errors are homoskedastic. Consequently, if the three least squares assumptions hold and the errors are homoskedastic, then OLS is BLUE.

Limitations of the Gauss-Markov Theorem

The Gauss-Markov theorem provides a theoretical justification for using OLS. However, the theorem has two important limitations. First, its conditions might not hold in practice. In particular, if the error term is heteroskedastic—as it often is in economic applications—then the OLS estimator is no longer BLUE. As discussed previously, the presence of heteroskedasticity does not pose a threat to inference based on heteroskedasticity-robust standard errors, but it does mean that OLS is no longer the efficient linear conditionally unbiased estimator. An alternative to OLS when there is heteroskedasticity of a known form, called the weighted least squares estimator, is discussed below.

The second limitation of the Gauss-Markov theorem is that even if the conditions of the theorem hold, there are other candidate estimators that are not linear and conditionally unbiased; under some conditions, these other estimators are more efficient than OLS.

Regression Estimators Other than OLS

Under certain conditions, some regression estimators are more efficient than OLS.

The Weighted Least Squares Estimator

If the errors are heteroskedastic, then OLS is no longer BLUE. If the nature of the heteroskedastic is known—specifically, if the conditional variance of u_i given X_i is known up to a constant factor of proportionality—then it is possible to construct an estimator that has a smaller variance than the OLS estimator. This method, called **weighted least squares** (WLS), weights the ith observation by the inverse of the square root of the conditional variance of u_i given X_i. Because of this weighting, the errors in this weighted regression are homoskedastic, so OLS, when applied to the weighted data, is BLUE. Although theoretically elegant, the practical problem with weighted least squares is that you must know how the conditional variance of u_i depends on X_i—something that is rarely known in applications.

The Least Absolute Deviations Estimator

As discussed earlier, the OLS estimator can be sensitive to outliers. If extreme outliers are not rare, then other estimators can be more efficient than OLS and can produce inferences that are more reliable. One such estimator is the least absolute deviations (LAD) estimator, in which the regression coefficients β_0 and β_1 are obtained by solving a minimization like that in Equation (7.6), except that the absolute value of the prediction "mistake" is used instead of its square. That is, the least absolute deviations estimators of β_0 and β_1 are the values of b_0 and b_1 that minimize $\sum_{i=1}^{n}|Y_i - b_0 - b_1 X_i|$. In practice, this estimator is less sensitive to large outliers in u than is OLS.

In many economic data sets, severe outliers in u are rare, so use of the LAD estimator, or other estimators with reduced sensitivity to outliers, is uncommon in applications. Thus the treatment of linear regression throughout the remainder of this text focuses exclusively on least squares methods.

USING THE *t*-STATISTIC IN REGRESSION WHEN THE SAMPLE SIZE IS SMALL*

When the sample size is small, the exact distribution of the *t*-statistic is complicated and depends on the

---

* This section is optional and is not used in later chapters.

unknown population distribution of the data. If, however, the three least squares assumptions hold, the regression errors are homoskedastic, *and* the regression errors are normally distributed, then the OLS estimator is normally distributed and the homoskedasticity-only *t*-statistic has a Student *t* distribution. These five assumptions—the three least squares assumptions, that the errors are homoskedastic, and that the errors are normally distributed—are collectively called the **homoskedastic normal regression assumptions**.

The *t*-Statistic and the Student *t* Distribution

The Student *t* distribution with m degrees of freedom is defined to be the distribution of $Z/\sqrt{W/m}$, where Z is a random variable with a standard normal distribution, W is a random variable with a chi-squared distribution with m degrees of freedom, and Z and W are independent. Under the null hypothesis, the *t*-statistic computed using the homoskedasticity-only standard error can be written in this form.

The homoskedasticity-only *t*-statistic testing $\beta_1 = \beta_{1,0}$ is $\tilde{t} = (\hat{\beta}_1 - \beta_{1,0})/\tilde{\sigma}_{\hat{\beta}_1}$, where $\tilde{\sigma}_{\hat{\beta}_1}^2$ is defined in Equation (8.22). Under the homoskedastic normal regression assumptions, Y has a normal distribution, conditional on $X_1, \ldots, X_n$. As discussed previously, the OLS estimator is a weighted average of $Y_1, \ldots, Y_n$, where the weights depend on $X_1, \ldots, X_n$. Because a weighted average of independent normal random variables is normally distributed, $\hat{\beta}_1$ has a normal distribution, conditional on $X_1, \ldots, X_n$. Thus $(\hat{\beta}_1 - \beta_{1,0})$ has a normal distribution under the null hypothesis, conditional on $X_1, \ldots, X_n$. In addition, the (normalized) homoskedasticity-only variance estimator has a chi-squared distribution with $n - 2$ degrees of freedom, divided by $n - 2$, and $\tilde{\sigma}_{\hat{\beta}_1}^2$ and $\hat{\beta}_1$ are independently distributed. Consequently, the homoskedasticity-only *t*-statistic has a Student *t* distribution with $n - 2$ degrees of freedom.

This result is closely related to a result discussed in the context of testing for the equality of the means in two samples. In that problem, if the two population distributions are normal with the same variance and if the *t*-statistic is constructed using the pooled standard error formula, then the (pooled) *t*-statistic has a Student *t* distribution. When X is binary, the homoskedasticity-only standard error for $\hat{\beta}_1$ simplifies to the pooled standard error formula for the difference of means. It follows that the result is a special case of the result that, if the homoskedastic normal regression assumptions hold, then the homoskedasticity-only regression *t*-statistic has a Student *t* distribution.

Use of the Student *t* Distribution in Practice

If the regression errors are homoskedastic and normally distributed and if the homoskedasticity-only *t*-statistic is used, then critical values should be taken from the Student *t* distribution instead of the standard normal distribution. Because the difference between the Student *t* distribution and the normal distribution is negligible if *n* is moderate or large, this distinction is relevant only if the sample size is small.

In econometric applications, there is rarely a reason to believe that the errors are homoskedastic and normally distributed. Because sample sizes typically are large, however, inference can proceed as described earlier—that is, by first computing heteroskedasticity-robust standard errors, and then using the standard normal distribution to compute *p*-values, hypothesis tests, and confidence intervals.

CONCLUSION

Return for a moment to the problem that started Chapter 7: the superintendent who is considering hiring additional teachers to cut the student–teacher ratio. What have we learned that she might find useful?

Our regression analysis, based on the 420 observations for 1998 in the California test score data set, showed that there was a negative relationship between the student–teacher ratio and test scores: Districts with smaller classes have higher test scores. The coefficient is moderately large, in a practical sense: Districts with 2 fewer students per teacher have, on average, test scores that are 4.6 points higher. This corresponds to moving a district at the 50th percentile of the distribution of test scores to approximately the 60th percentile.

The coefficient on the student–teacher ratio is statistically significantly different from 0 at the 5% significance level. The population coefficient might be 0, and we might simply have estimated our negative coefficient by random sampling variation. However, the probability of doing so (and of obtaining a *t*-statistic on β_1 as large as we did) purely by random variation over potential samples is exceedingly small, approximately 0.001%. A 95% confidence interval for β_1 is $-3.30 \leq \beta_1 \leq -1.26$.

This represents considerable progress toward answering the superintendent's question. Yet, a nagging concern remains. There is a negative relationship between the student–teacher ratio and test scores, but is this relationship necessarily the *causal* one that the superintendent needs to make her decision? Districts with lower student–teacher ratios have, on average, higher test scores. But does this mean that reducing the student–teacher ratio will, in fact, increase scores?

There is, in fact, reason to worry that it might not. Hiring more teachers, after all, costs money, so wealthier school districts can better afford smaller classes. But students at wealthier schools also have other advantages over their poorer neighbors, including better facilities, newer books, and better-paid teachers. Moreover, students at wealthier schools tend themselves to come from more affluent families, and thus have other advantages not directly associated with their school. For example, California has a large immigrant community; these immigrants tend to be poorer than the overall population and, in many cases, their children are not native English speakers. It thus might be that our negative estimated relationship between test scores and the student–teacher ratio is a consequence of large classes being found in conjunction with many other factors that are, in fact, the real cause of the lower test scores.

These other factors, or "omitted variables," could mean that the OLS analysis done so far has little value to the superintendent. Indeed, it could be misleading: Changing the student–teacher ratio alone would not change these other factors that determine a child's performance at school. To address this problem, we need a method that will allow us to isolate the effect on test scores of changing the student–teacher ratio, *holding these other factors constant*. That method is multiple regression analysis, the topic of Chapters 9 and 10.

SUMMARY

1. Hypothesis testing for regression coefficients is analogous to hypothesis testing for the population mean: Use the t-statistic to calculate the p-values and either accept or reject the null hypothesis. Like a confidence interval for the population mean, a 95% confidence interval for a regression coefficient is computed as the estimator ± 1.96 standard errors.

2. When X is binary, the regression model can be used to estimate and test hypotheses about the difference between the population means of the "$X = 0$" group and the "$X = 1$" group.

3. In general the error u_i is heteroskedastic—that is, the variance of u_i at a given value of X_i, $\mathrm{VaR}(u_i | X_i = x)$ depends on x. A special case is when the error is homoskedastic, that is, $\mathrm{VaR}(u_i | X_i = x)$ is constant. Homoskedasticity-only standard errors do not produce valid statistical inferences when the errors are heteroskedastic, but heteroskedasticity-robust standard errors do.

4. If the three least squares assumption hold *and* if the regression errors are homoskedastic, then, as a result of the Gauss-Markov theorem, the OLS estimator is BLUE.

5. If the three least squares assumptions hold, if the regression errors are homoskedastic, *and* if the regression errors are normally distributed, then the OLS t-statistic computed using homoskedasticity-only standard errors has a Student t distribution when the null hypothesis is true. The difference between the Student t distribution and the normal distribution is negligible if the sample size is moderate or large.

Key Terms

APPENDIX

The Gauss-Markov Conditions and a Proof of the Gauss-Markov Theorem

As discussed earlier, the Gauss-Markov theorem states that if the Gauss-Markov conditions hold, then the OLS estimator is the best (most efficient) conditionally linear unbiased estimator (is BLUE). This appendix begins by stating the Gauss-Markov conditions and showing that they are implied by the three least squares condition plus homoskedasticity.

The Gauss-Markov Conditions

The three **Gauss-Markov conditions** are

(i) $E(u_i | X_1, \ldots, X_n) = 0$ $\qquad$ **(8.26)**

(ii) $\mathrm{var}(u_i | X_1, \ldots, X_n) = \sigma_u^2, \ 0 < \sigma_u^2 < \infty$

(iii) $E(u_i u_j | X_1, \ldots, X_n) = 0, i \neq j$

where the conditions hold for $i, j = 1, \ldots, n$. The three conditions, respectively, state that u_i has mean zero, that u_i has a constant variance, and that the errors are uncorrelated for different observations, where all these statements hold conditionally on all observed X's ($X_1, \ldots, X_n$).

The Gauss-Markov conditions are implied by the three least squares assumptions (Box 7-3), plus the additional assumptions that the errors are homoskedastic. Because the observations are i.i.d. (Assumption 2), $E(u_i | X_1, \ldots, X_n) = E(u_i | X_i)$, and by Assumption 1, $E(u_i | X_i) = 0$; thus condition (i) holds. Similarly, by Assumption 2, $\mathrm{VaR}(u_i | X_1, \ldots, X_n) = \mathrm{VaR}(u_i | X_i)$, and because the errors are assumed to be homoskedastic, $\mathrm{VaR}(u_i | X_i) = \sigma_u^2$, which is constant. Assumption 3 (nonzero finite fourth moments) ensures that $0 < \sigma_u^2 < \infty$, so condition (ii) holds.

To show that condition (iii) is implied by the least squares assumptions, note that $E(u_i u_j | X_1, \ldots, X_n) = E(u_i u_j | X_i, X_j)$ because (X_i, Y_i) are i.i.d. by Assumption 2. Assumption 2 also implies that $E(u_i u_j | X_i, X_j) = E(u_i | X_i) E(u_j | X_j)$ for $i \neq j$; because $E(u_i | X_i) = 0$ for all i, it follows that $E(u_i u_j | X_1, \ldots, X_n) = 0$ for all $i \neq j$, so condition (iii) holds. Thus, the least squares assumptions in Box 7-3, plus homoskedasticity of the errors, imply the Gauss-Markov conditions in Equation (8.26).

The Sample Average Is the Efficient Linear Estimator of $E(Y)$

An implication of the Gauss-Markov theorem is that the sample average, $\overline{Y}$, is the most efficient linear estimator of $E(Y_i)$ when $Y_i, \ldots, Y_n$ are i.i.d. To see this, consider the case of regression without an "X," so that the only regressor is the constant regressor $X_{0i} = 1$. Then the OLS estimator $\hat{\beta}_0 = \overline{Y}$. It follows that, under the Gauss-Markov assumptions, $\overline{Y}$ is BLUE. Note that the Gauss-Markov requirement that the error be homoskedastic is irrelevant in this case because there is no regressor, so it follows that $\overline{Y}$ is BLUE if $Y_1, \ldots, Y_n$ are i.i.d.

Linear Regression with Multiple Regressors

■ Learning Objectives

Candidates, after completing this reading, should be able to:

- Define and interpret omitted variable bias, and describe the methods for addressing this bias.
- Distinguish between single and multiple regression.
- Interpret the slope coefficient in a multiple regression.
- Describe homoskedasticity and heteroskedasticity in a multiple regression.

- Describe the OLS estimator in a multiple regression.
- Calculate and interpret measures of fit in multiple regression.
- Explain the assumptions of the multiple linear regression model.
- Explain the concept of imperfect and perfect multicollinearity and their implications.

Excerpt is Chapter 6 of Introduction to Econometrics, *Brief Edition, by James H. Stock and Mark W. Watson.*

Chapter 8 ended on a worried note. Although school districts with lower student–teacher ratios tend to have higher test scores in the California data set, perhaps students from districts with small classes have other advantages that help them perform well on standardized tests. Could this have produced misleading results and, if so, what can be done?

Omitted factors, such as student characteristics, can in fact make the ordinary least squares (OLS) estimator of the effect of class size on test scores misleading or, more precisely, biased. This chapter explains this "omitted variable bias" and introduces multiple regression, a method that can eliminate omitted variable bias. The key idea of multiple regression is that, if we have data on these omitted variables, then we can include them as additional regressors and thereby estimate the effect of one regressor (the student–teacher ratio) while holding constant the other variables (such as student characteristics).

This chapter explains how to estimate the coefficients of the multiple linear regression model. Many aspects of multiple regression parallel those of regression with a single regressor, studied in Chapters 7 and 8. The coefficients of the multiple regression model can be estimated from data using OLS; the OLS estimators in multiple regression are random variables because they depend on data from a random sample; and in large samples the sampling distributions of the OLS estimators are approximately normal.

OMITTED VARIABLE BIAS

By focusing only on the student–teacher ratio, the empirical analysis in Chapters 7 and 8 ignored some potentially important determinants of test scores by collecting their influences in the regression error term. These omitted factors include school characteristics, such as teacher quality and computer usage, and student characteristics, such as family background. We begin by considering an omitted student characteristic that is particularly relevant in California because of its large immigrant population: the prevalence in the school district of students who are still learning English.

By ignoring the percentage of English learners in the district, the OLS estimator of the slope in the regression of test scores on the student–teacher ratio could be biased; that is, the mean of the sampling distribution of the OLS estimator might not equal the true effect on test scores of a unit change in the student–teacher ratio. Here is the reasoning. Students who are still learning English might perform worse on standardized tests than native English speakers. If districts with large classes also have many students still learning English, then the OLS regression of test scores on the student–teacher ratio could erroneously find a correlation and produce a large estimated coefficient, when in fact the true causal effect of cutting class sizes on test scores is small, even zero. Accordingly, based on the analysis of Chapters 7 and 8, the superintendent might hire enough new teachers to reduce the student–teacher ratio by two, but her hoped-for improvement in test scores will fail to materialize if the true coefficient is small or zero.

A look at the California data lends credence to this concern. The correlation between the student–teacher ratio and the percentage of English learners (students who are not native English speakers and who have not yet mastered English) in the district is 0.19. This small but positive correlation suggests that districts with more English learners tend to have a higher student–teacher ratio (larger classes). If the student–teacher ratio were unrelated to the percentage of English learners, then it would be safe to ignore English proficiency in the regression of test scores against the student–teacher ratio. But because the student–teacher ratio and the percentage of English learners are correlated, it is possible that the OLS coefficient in the regression of test scores on the student–teacher ratio reflects that influence.

Definition of Omitted Variable Bias

If the regressor (the student–teacher ratio) is correlated with a variable that has been omitted from the analysis (the percentage of English learners) and that determines, in part, the dependent variable (test scores), then the OLS estimator will have **omitted variable bias**.

Omitted variable bias occurs when two conditions are true: (1) the omitted variable is correlated with the included regressor; and (2) the omitted variable is a determinant of the dependent variable. To illustrate these conditions, consider three examples of variables that are omitted from the regression of test scores on the student–teacher ratio.

Example #1: Percentage of English Learners

Because the percentage of English learners is correlated with the student–teacher ratio, the first condition for omitted variable bias holds. It is plausible that students who are still learning English will do worse on standardized tests than native English speakers, in which case the percentage of English learners is a determinant of test scores and the second condition for omitted variable bias holds. Thus, the OLS estimator in the regression of test scores on the student–teacher ratio could incorrectly reflect the influence of the omitted variable, the percentage of English learners. That is, omitting the percentage of English learners may introduce omitted variable bias.

Example #2: Time of Day of the Test

Another variable omitted from the analysis is the time of day that the test was administered. For this omitted variable, it is plausible that the first condition for omitted variable bias does not hold but the second condition does. For example, if the time of day of the test varies from one district to the next in a way that is unrelated to class size, then the time of day and class size would be uncorrelated so the first condition does not hold. Conversely, the time of day of the test could affect scores (alertness varies through the school day), so the second condition holds. However, because in this example the time that the test is administered is uncorrelated with the student–teacher ratio, the student–teacher ratio could not be incorrectly picking up the "time of day" effect. Thus omitting the time of day of the test does not result in omitted variable bias.

Example #3: Parking Lot Space per Pupil

Another omitted variable is parking lot space per pupil (the area of the teacher parking lot divided by the number of students). This variable satisfies the first but not the second condition for omitted variable bias. Specifically, schools with more teachers per pupil probably have more teacher parking space, so the first condition would be satisfied. However, under the assumption that learning takes place in the classroom, not the parking lot, parking lot space has no direct effect on learning; thus the second condition does not hold. Because parking lot space per pupil is not a determinant of test scores, omitting it from the analysis does not lead to omitted variable bias.

Omitted variable bias is summarized in Box 9-1.

> **BOX 9-1**   Omitted Variable Bias in Regression with a Single Regressor
>
> Omitted variable bias is the bias in the OLS estimator that arises when the regressor, X, is correlated with an omitted variable. For omitted variable bias to occur, two conditions must be true:
>
> 1. X is correlated with the omitted variable.
> 2. The omitted variable is a determinant of the dependent variable, Y.

Omitted Variable Bias and the First Least Squares Assumption

Omitted variable bias means that the first least squares assumption—that $E(u_i \mid X_i) = 0$, as listed in Box 7-3—is incorrect. To see why, recall that the error term u_i in the linear regression model with a single regressor represents all factors, other than X_i, that are determinants of Y_i. If one of these other factors is correlated with X_i, this means that the error term (which contains this factor) is correlated with X_i. In other words, if an omitted variable is a determinant of Y_i, then it is in the error term, and if it is correlated with X_i, then the error term is correlated with X_i. Because u_i and X_i are correlated, the conditional mean of u_i given X_i is nonzero. This correlation therefore violates the first least squares assumption, and the consequence is serious: The OLS estimator is biased. This bias does not vanish even in very large samples, and the OLS estimator is inconsistent.

A Formula for Omitted Variable Bias

The discussion of the previous section about omitted variable bias can be summarized mathematically by a formula for this bias. Let the correlation between X_i and u_i be $\text{corr}(X_i, u_i) = \rho_{Xu}$. Suppose that the second and third least squares assumptions hold, but the first does not because ρ_{Xu} is nonzero. Then the OLS estimator has the limit

$$\hat{\beta}_1 \xrightarrow{p} \beta_1 + \rho_{Xu} \frac{\sigma_u}{\sigma_X} \qquad (9.1)$$

That is, as the sample size increases, $\hat{\beta}_1$ is close to $\beta_1 + \rho_{Xu}(\sigma_u/\sigma_X)$ with increasingly high probability.

The Mozart Effect: Omitted Variable Bias?

A study published in *Nature* in 1993 (Rauscher, Shaw and Ky, 1993) suggested that listening to Mozart for 10-15 minutes could temporarily raise your IQ by 8 or 9 points. That study made big news—and politicians and parents saw an easy way to make their children smarter. For a while, the state of Georgia even distributed classical music CDs to all infants in the state.

What is the evidence for the "Mozart effect"? A review of dozens of studies found that students who take optional music or arts courses in high school do in fact have higher English and math test scores than those who don't.[1] A closer look at these studies, however, suggests that the real reason for the better test performance has little to do with those courses. Instead, the authors of the review suggested that the correlation between testing well and taking art or music could arise from any number of things. For example, the academically better students

might have more time to take optional music courses or more interest in doing so, or those schools with a deeper music curriculum might just be better schools across the board.

In the terminology of regression, the estimated relationship between test scores and taking optional music courses appears to have omitted variable bias. By omitting factors such as the student's innate ability or the overall quality of the school, studying music appears to have an effect on test scores when in fact it has none.

So is there a Mozart effect? One way to find out is to do a randomized controlled experiment. (As discussed in Chapter 7, randomized controlled experiments eliminate omitted variable bias by randomly assigning participants to "treatment" and "control" groups.) Taken together, the many controlled experiments on the Mozart effect fail to show that listening to Mozart improves IQ or general test performance. For reasons not fully understood, however, it seems that listening to classical music *does* help temporarily in one narrow area: folding paper and visualizing shapes. So the next time you cram for an origami exam, try to fit in a little Mozart, too.

[1] See the *Journal of Aesthetic Education* 34: 3-4 (Fall/Winter 2000), especially the article by Ellen Winner and Monica Cooper, (pp. 11-76) and the one by Lois Hetland (pp. 105-148).

The formula in Equation (9.1) summarizes several of the ideas discussed above about omitted variable bias:

1. Omitted variable bias is a problem whether the sample size is large or small. Because $\hat{\beta}_1$ does not converge in probability to the true value β_1, $\hat{\beta}_1$ is inconsistent; that is, $\hat{\beta}_1$ is not a consistent estimator of β_1 when there is omitted variable bias. The term $\rho_{Xu}(\sigma_u/\sigma_X)$ in Equation (9.1) is the bias in $\hat{\beta}_1$ that persists even in large samples.

2. Whether this bias is large or small in practice depends on the correlation ρ_{Xu} between the regressor and the error term. The larger is $|\rho_{Xu}|$, the larger is the bias.

3. The direction of the bias in $\hat{\beta}_1$ depends on whether X and u are positively or negatively correlated. For example, we speculated that the percentage of students learning English has a *negative* effect on district test scores (students still learning English have lower scores), so that the percentage of English learners enters the error term with a negative sign. In our data, the fraction of English learners is *positively* correlated with the student–teacher ratio (districts with more English learners have larger classes). Thus the student–teacher ratio (X) would be *negatively* correlated with

the error term (u), so $\rho_{Xu} < 0$ and the coefficient on the student–teacher ratio $\hat{\beta}_1$ would be biased toward a negative number. In other words, having a small percentage of English learners is associated both with *high* test scores and *low* student–teacher ratios, so one reason that the OLS estimator suggests that small classes improve test scores may be that the districts with small classes have fewer English learners.

Addressing Omitted Variable Bias by Dividing the Data into Groups

What can you do about omitted variable bias? Our superintendent is considering increasing the number of teachers in her district, but she has no control over the fraction of immigrants in her community. As a result, she is interested in the effect of the student–teacher ratio on test scores, *holding constant* other factors, including the percentage of English learners. This new way of posing her question suggests that, instead of using data for all districts, perhaps we should focus on districts with percentages of English learners comparable to hers. Among this subset of districts, do those with smaller classes do better on standardized tests?

TABLE 9-1 Differences in Test Scores for California School Districts with Low and High Student-Teacher Ratios, by the Percentage of English Learners in the District

	Student-Teacher Ratio < 20		Student-Teacher Ratio ≥ 20		Difference in Test Scores, Low vs. High STR	
	Average Test Score	*n*	Average Test Score	*n*	Difference	*t*-Statistic
All districts	657.4	238	650.0	182	7.4	4.04
Percentage of English learners						
< 1.9%	664.5	76	665.4	27	−0.9	−0.30
1.9−8.8%	665.2	64	661.8	44	3.3	1.13
8.8−23.0%	654.9	54	649.7	50	5.2	1.72
> 23.0%	636.7	44	634.8	61	1.9	0.68

Table 9-1 reports evidence on the relationship between class size and test scores within districts with comparable percentages of English learners. Districts are divided into eight groups. First, the districts are broken into four categories that correspond to the quartiles of the distribution of the percentage of English learners across districts. Second, within each of these four categories, districts are further broken down into two groups, depending on whether the student-teacher ratio is small ($STR < 20$) or large ($STR \geq 20$).

The first row in Table 9-1 reports the overall difference in average test scores between districts with low and high student-teacher ratios, that is, the difference in test scores between these two groups without breaking them down further into the quartiles of English learners. (Recall that this difference was previously reported in regression form in Equation (8.18) as the OLS estimate of the coefficient on D_i in the regression of *TestScore* on D_i, where D_i is a binary regressor that equals 1 if $STR_i < 20$ and equals 0 otherwise.) Over the full sample of 420 districts, the average test score is 7.4 points higher in districts with a low student-teacher ratio than a high one; the *t*-statistic is 4.04, so the null hypothesis that the mean test score is the same in the two groups is rejected at the 1% significance level.

The final four rows in Table 9-1 report the difference in test scores between districts with low and high student-teacher ratios, broken down by the quartile of the percentage of English learners. This evidence presents a different picture. Of the districts with the fewest English learners (< 1.9%), the average test score for those 76 with low student-teacher ratios is 664.5 and the average for the 27 with high student-teacher ratios is 665.4. Thus, for the districts with the fewest English learners, test scores were on average 0.9 points *lower* in the districts with low student-teacher ratios! In the second quartile, districts with low student-teacher ratios had test scores that averaged 3.3 points higher than those with high student-teacher ratios; this gap was 5.2 points for the third quartile and only 1.9 points for the quartile of districts with the most English learners. Once we hold the percentage of English learners constant, the difference in performance between districts with high and low student-teacher ratios is perhaps half (or less) of the overall estimate of 7.4 points.

At first this finding might seem puzzling. How can the overall effect of test scores be twice the effect of test scores within any quartile? The answer is that the districts with the most English learners tend to have *both* the highest student-teacher ratios *and* the lowest test scores. The difference in the average test score between districts in the lowest and highest quartile of the percentage of English learners is large, approximately 30 points. The districts with few English learners tend to have lower student-teacher ratios: 74% (76 of 103) of the districts in the first quartile of English learners have small classes ($STR < 20$), while only 42% (44 of 105) of the districts in the quartile with the most English learners have small classes. So, the districts with the most English learners have both lower test scores and higher student–teacher ratios than the other districts.

This analysis reinforces the superintendent's worry that omitted variable bias is present in the regression of test scores against the student–teacher ratio. By looking within quartiles of the percentage of English learners, the test score differences in the second part of Table 9-1 improve upon the simple difference-of-means analysis in the first line of Table 9-1. Still, this analysis does not yet provide the superintendent with a useful estimate of the effect on test scores of changing class size, holding constant the fraction of English learners. Such an estimate can be provided, however, using the method of multiple regression.

THE MULTIPLE REGRESSION MODEL

The **multiple regression model** extends the single variable regression model of Chapters 7 and 8 to include additional variables as regressors. This model permits estimating the effect on Y_i of changing one variable (X_{1i}) while holding the other regressors (X_{2i}, X_{3i}, and so forth) constant. In the class size problem, the multiple regression model provides a way to isolate the effect on test scores (Y_i) of the student–teacher ratio (X_{1i}) while holding constant the percentage of students in the district who are English learners (X_{2i}).

The Population Regression Line

Suppose for the moment that there are only two independent variables, X_{1i} and X_{2i}. In the linear multiple regression model, the average relationship between these two independent variables and the dependent variable, Y, is given by the linear function

$$E(Y_i \mid X_{1i} = x_1, X_{2i} = x_2) = \beta_0 + \beta_1 x_1 + \beta_2 x_2 \quad \textbf{(9.2)}$$

where $E(Y_i \mid X_{1i} = x_1, X_{2i} = x_2)$ is the conditional expectation of Y_i given that $X_{1i} = x_1$ and $X_{2i} = x_2$. That is, if the student–teacher ratio in the ith district (X_{1i}) equals some value x_1 and the percentage of English learners in the ith district (X_{2i}) equals x_2, then the expected value of Y_i given the student–teacher ratio and the percentage of English learners is given by Equation (9.2).

Equation (9.2) is the **population regression line** or **population regression function** in the multiple regression

model. The coefficient β_0 is the **intercept**, the coefficient β_1 is the **slope coefficient of X_{1i}** or, more simply, the **coefficient on X_{1i}**, and the coefficient β_2 is the **slope coefficient of X_{2i}** or, more simply, the **coefficient on X_{2i}**. One or more of the independent variables in the multiple regression model are sometimes referred to as **control variables**.

The interpretation of the coefficient β_1 in Equation (9.2) is different than it was when X_{1i} was the only regressor: In Equation (9.2), β_1 is the effect on Y of a unit change in X_1, **holding X_2 constant** or **controlling for X_2**.

This interpretation of β_1 follows from the definition that the expected effect on Y of a change in X_1, ΔX_1, holding X_2 constant, is the difference between the expected value of Y when the independent variables take on the values $X_1 + \Delta X_1$ and X_2 and the expected value of Y when the independent variables take on the values X_1 and X_2. Accordingly, write the population regression function in Equation (9.2) as $Y = \beta_0 + \beta_1 X_1 + \beta_2 X_2$, and imagine changing X_1 by the amount ΔX_1 while not changing X_2, that is, while holding X_2 constant. Because X_1 has changed, Y will change by some amount, say ΔY. After this change, the new value of Y, $Y + \Delta Y$, is

$$Y + \Delta Y = \beta_0 + \beta_1(X_1 + \Delta X_1) + \beta_2 X_2 \quad \textbf{(9.3)}$$

An equation for ΔY in terms of ΔX_1 is obtained by subtracting the equation $Y = \beta_0 + \beta_1 X_1 + \beta_2 X_2$ from Equation (9.3), yielding $\Delta Y = \beta_1 \Delta X_1$. That is,

$$\beta_1 = \frac{\Delta Y}{\Delta X_1}, \text{ holding } X_2 \text{ constant} \quad \textbf{(9.4)}$$

The coefficient β_1 is the effect on Y (the expected change in Y) of a unit change in X_1, holding X_2 fixed. Another phrase used to describe β_1 is the **partial effect** on Y of X_1, holding X_2 fixed.

The interpretation of the intercept in the multiple regression model, β_0, is similar to the interpretation of the intercept in the single-regressor model: It is the expected value of Y_i when X_{1i} and X_{2i} are zero. Simply put, the intercept β_0 determines how far up the Y axis the population regression line starts.

The Population Multiple Regression Model

The population regression line in Equation (9.2) is the relationship between Y and X_1 and X_2 that holds on average in the population. Just as in the case of regression with a single regressor, however, this relationship does not hold exactly because many other factors influence the dependent variable. In addition to the student–teacher ratio and the fraction of students still learning English, for example, test scores are influenced by school characteristics, other student characteristics, and luck. Thus the population regression function in Equation (9.2) needs to be augmented to incorporate these additional factors.

Just as in the case of regression with a single regressor, the factors that determine Y_i in addition to X_{1i} and X_{2i} are incorporated into Equation (9.2) as an "error" term u_i. This error term is the deviation of a particular observation (test scores in the ith district in our example) from the average population relationship. Accordingly, we have

$$Y_i = \beta_0 + \beta_1 X_{1i} + \beta_2 X_{2i} + u_i, i = 1, \ldots, n \qquad \textbf{(9.5)}$$

where the subscript i indicates the ith of the n observations (districts) in the sample.

Equation (9.5) is the **population multiple regression model** when there are two regressors, X_{1i} and X_{2i}.

In regression with binary regressors it can be useful to treat β_0 as the coefficient on a regressor that always equals 1; think of β_0 as the coefficient on X_{0i}, where $X_{0i} = 1$ for $i = 1, \ldots, n$. Accordingly, the population multiple regression model in Equation (9.5) can alternatively be written as

$$Y_i = \beta_0 X_{0i} + \beta_1 X_{1i} + \beta_2 X_{2i} + u_i \qquad \textbf{(9.6)}$$
$$\text{where } X_{0i} = 1, i = 1, \ldots, n$$

The variable X_{0i} is sometimes called the **constant regressor** because it takes on the same value—the value 1—for all observations. Similarly, the intercept, β_0, is sometimes called the **constant term** in the regression.

The two ways of writing the population regression model, Equations (9.5) and (9.6), are equivalent.

The discussion so far has focused on the case of a single additional variable, X_2. In practice, however, there might be multiple factors omitted from the single-regressor model. For example, ignoring the students' economic background might result in omitted variable bias, just as ignoring the fraction of English learners did. This reasoning leads us to consider a model with three regressors or, more generally, a model that includes k regressors. The multiple regression model with k regressors, $X_{1i}, X_{2i}, \ldots, X_{ki}$, is summarized as Box 9-2.

The definitions of homoskedasticity and heteroskedasticity in the multiple regression model are extensions of their definitions in the single-regressor model. The error term u_i in the multiple regression model is **homoskedastic** if the variance of the conditional distribution of u_i given $X_{1i}, \ldots, X_{ki}$, $\text{var}(u_i \mid X_{1i}, \ldots, X_{ki})$, is constant for $i = 1, \ldots, n$ and thus does not depend on the values of $X_{1i}, \ldots, X_{ki}$. Otherwise, the error term is **heteroskedastic**.

The multiple regression model holds out the promise of providing just what the superintendent wants to know: the effect of changing the student–teacher ratio, holding constant other factors that are beyond her control. These factors include not just the percentage of English learners, but other measurable factors that might affect test performance, including the economic background of the students. To be of practical help to the superintendent, however, we need to provide her with estimates of the unknown population coefficients $\beta_0, \ldots, \beta_k$ of the population regression model calculated using a sample of data. Fortunately, these coefficients can be estimated using ordinary least squares.

THE OLS ESTIMATOR IN MULTIPLE REGRESSION

This section describes how the coefficients of the multiple regression model can be estimated using OLS.

The OLS Estimator

Chapter 7 shows how to estimate the intercept and slope coefficients in the single-regressor model by applying OLS to a sample of observations of Y and X. The key idea is that these coefficients can be estimated by minimizing the sum of squared prediction mistakes, that is, by choosing the estimators b_0 and b_1 so as to minimize $\sum_{i=1}^{n} (Y_i - b_0 - b_1X_i)^2$. The estimators that do so are the OLS estimators, $\hat{\beta}_0$ and $\hat{\beta}_1$.

The method of OLS also can be used to estimate the coefficients $\beta_0, \beta_1, \ldots, \beta_k$ in the multiple regression model. Let $b_0, b_1, \ldots, b_k$ be estimators of $\beta_0, \beta_1, \ldots, \beta_k$. The predicted value of Y_i, calculated using these estimators, is $b_0 + b_1X_{1i} + \cdots + b_kX_{ki}$, and the mistake in predicting Y_i is $Y_i - (b_0 + b_1X_{1i} + \cdots + b_kX_{ki}) = Y_i - b_0 - b_1X_{1i} - \cdots - b_kX_{ki}$. The sum of these squared prediction mistakes over all n observations thus is

$$\sum_{i=1}^{n} (Y_i - b_0 - b_1X_{1i} - \cdots - b_kX_{ki})^2 \qquad \textbf{(9.8)}$$

The sum of the squared mistakes for the linear regression model in Equation (9.8) is the extension of the sum of the squared mistakes given in Equation (7.6) for the linear regression model with a single regressor.

The estimators of the coefficients $\beta_0, \beta_1, \ldots, \beta_k$ that minimize the sum of squared mistakes in Equation (9.8) are called the **ordinary least squares (OLS) estimators** of $\beta_0, \beta_1, \ldots, \beta_k$. The OLS estimators are denoted $\hat{\beta}_0, \hat{\beta}_1, \ldots, \hat{\beta}_k$.

The terminology of OLS in the linear multiple regression model is the same as in the linear regression model with a single regressor. The **OLS regression line** is the straight line constructed using the OLS estimators: $\hat{\beta}_0 + \hat{\beta}_1X_1 + \cdots + \hat{\beta}_kX_k$. The **predicted value** of Y_i given $X_{1i}, \ldots, X_{ki}$, based on the OLS regression line, is $\hat{Y}_i = \hat{\beta}_0 + \hat{\beta}_1X_{1i} + \cdots + \hat{\beta}_kX_{ki}$. The **OLS residual** for the ith observation is the difference between Y_i and its OLS predicted value, that is, the OLS residual is $\hat{u}_i = Y_i - \hat{Y}_i$.

The OLS estimators could be computed by trial and error, repeatedly trying different values of $b_0, \ldots, b_k$ until you

are satisfied that you have minimized the total sum of squares in Equation (9.8). It is far easier, however, to use explicit formulas for the OLS estimators that are derived using calculus. The formulas for the OLS estimators in the multiple regression model are similar to those in Box 7-2 for the single-regressor model. These formulas are incorporated into modern statistical software. In the multiple regression model, the formulas for general k are best expressed and discussed using matrix notation, so their presentation is omitted.

The definitions and terminology of OLS in multiple regression are summarized in Box 9-3.

Application to Test Scores and the Student–Teacher Ratio

Earlier, we used OLS to estimate the intercept and slope coefficient of the regression relating test scores (*TestScore*) to the student–teacher ratio (*STR*), using our 420 observations for California school districts; the estimated OLS regression line, reported in Equation (7.11), is

$$\widehat{TestScore} = 698.9 - 2.28 \times STR \qquad \textbf{(9.11)}$$

Our concern has been that this relationship is misleading because the student–teacher ratio might be picking up the effect of having many English learners in districts with large classes. That is, it is possible that the OLS estimator is subject to omitted variable bias.

We are now in a position to address this concern by using OLS to estimate a multiple regression in which the dependent variable is the test score (Y_i) and there are two regressors: the student–teacher ratio (X_{1i}) and the percentage of English learners in the school district (X_{2i}) for our 420 districts ($i = 1, \ldots, 420$). The estimated OLS regression line for this multiple regression is

$$\widehat{TestScore} = 686.0 - 1.10 \times STR - 0.65 \times PctEL \quad \textbf{(9.12)}$$

where *PctEL* is the percentage of students in the district who are English learners. The OLS estimate of the intercept ($\hat{\beta}_0$) is 686.0, the OLS estimate of the coefficient on the student–teacher ratio ($\hat{\beta}_1$) is −1.10, and the OLS estimate of the coefficient on the percentage English learners ($\hat{\beta}_2$) is −0.65.

The estimated effect on test scores of a change in the student–teacher ratio in the multiple regression is approximately half as large as when the student–teacher ratio is the only regressor: in the single-regressor equation [Equation (9.11)], a unit decrease in the *STR* is estimated to increase test scores by 2.28 points, but in the multiple regression equation [Equation (9.12)], it is estimated to increase test scores by only 1.10 points. This difference occurs because the coefficient on *STR* in the multiple regression is the effect of a change in *STR*, holding constant (or controlling for) *PctEL*, whereas in the single-regressor regression, *PctEL* is not held constant.

These two estimates can be reconciled by concluding that there is omitted variable bias in the estimate in the single-regressor model in Equation (9.11). Previously, we saw that districts with a high percentage of English learners tend to have not only low test scores but also a high student–teacher ratio. If the fraction of English learners is omitted from the regression, reducing the student–teacher ratio is estimated to have a larger effect on test scores, but this estimate reflects *both* the effect of a change in the student–teacher ratio *and* the omitted effect of having fewer English learners in the district.

We have reached the same conclusion that there is omitted variable bias in the relationship between test scores and the student–teacher ratio by two different paths: the tabular approach of dividing the data into groups and the multiple regression approach [Equation (9.12)]. Of these two methods, multiple regression has two important advantages. First, it provides a quantitative estimate of the effect of a unit decrease in the student–teacher ratio,

which is what the superintendent needs to make her decision. Second, it readily extends to more than two regressors, so that multiple regression can be used to control for measurable factors other than just the percentage of English learners.

The rest of this chapter is devoted to understanding and to using OLS in the multiple regression model. Much of what you learned about the OLS estimator with a single regressor carries over to multiple regression with few or no modifications, so we will focus on that which is new with multiple regression. We begin by discussing measures of fit for the multiple regression model.

MEASURES OF FIT IN MULTIPLE REGRESSION

Three commonly used summary statistics in multiple regression are the standard error of the regression, the regression R^2, and the adjusted R^2 (also known as $\overline{R}^2$). All three statistics measure how well the OLS estimate of the multiple regression line describes, or "fits," the data.

The Standard Error of the Regression (*SER*)

The standard error of the regression (*SER*) estimates the standard deviation of the error term u_i. Thus, the *SER* is a measure of the spread of the distribution of *Y* around the regression line. In multiple regression, the *SER* is

$$SER = s_{\hat{u}}, \text{ where } s_{\hat{u}}^2 = \frac{1}{n-k-1}\sum_{i=1}^{n}\hat{u}_i^2 = \frac{SSR}{n-k-1} \quad \textbf{(9.13)}$$

where the *SSR* is the sum of squared residuals, $SSR = \sum_{i=1}^{n}\hat{u}_i^2$.

The only difference between the definition in Equation (9.13) and the definition of the *SER* in Chapter 7 for the single-regressor model is that here the divisor is $n - k - 1$ rather than $n - 2$. In Chapter 7, the divisor $n - 2$ (rather than n) adjusts for the downward bias introduced by estimating two coefficients (the slope and intercept of the regression line). Here, the divisor $n - k - 1$ adjusts for the downward bias introduced by estimating $k + 1$ coefficients (the k slope coefficients plus the intercept). As in Chapter 7, using $n - k - 1$ rather than n is called a degrees-of-freedom adjustment. If there is a single regressor, then $k = 1$, so the formula in Chapter 7 is the same as in Equation (9.13). When n is large, the effect of the degrees-of-freedom adjustment is negligible.

The R^2

The regression **R^2** is the fraction of the sample variance of Y_i explained by (or predicted by) the regressors. Equivalently, the R^2 is 1 minus the fraction of the variance of Y_i *not* explained by the regressors.

The mathematical definition of the R^2 is the same as for regression with a single regressor:

$$R^2 = \frac{ESS}{TSS} = 1 - \frac{SSR}{TSS} \qquad \textbf{(9.14)}$$

where the explained sum of squares is $ESS = \sum_{i=1}^{n}(\hat{Y}_i - \overline{Y})^2$ and the total sum of squares is $TSS = \sum_{i=1}^{n}(Y_i - \overline{Y})^2$. In multiple regression, the R^2 increases whenever a regressor is added, unless the estimated coefficient on the added regressor is exactly zero. To see this, think about starting with one regressor and then adding a second. When you use OLS to estimate the model with both regressors, OLS finds the values of the coefficients that minimize the sum of squared residuals. If OLS happens to choose the coefficient on the new regressor to be exactly zero, then the SSR will be the same whether or not the second variable is included in the regression. But if OLS chooses any value other than zero, then it must be that this value reduced the SSR relative to the regression that excludes this regressor. In practice it is extremely unusual for an estimated coefficient to be exactly zero, so in general the SSR will decrease when a new regressor is added. But this means that the R^2 generally increases (and never decreases) when a new regressor is added.

The "Adjusted R^2"

Because the R^2 increases when a new variable is added, an increase in the R^2 does not mean that adding a variable actually improves the fit of the model. In this sense, the R^2 gives an inflated estimate of how well the regression fits the data. One way to correct for this is to deflate or reduce the R^2 by some factor, and this is what the adjusted R^2, or $\overline{R}^2$, does.

The **adjusted R^2**, or $\overline{R}^2$, is a modified version of the R^2 that does not necessarily increase when a new regressor is added. The $\overline{R}^2$ is

$$\overline{R}^2 = 1 - \frac{n-1}{n-k-1} \frac{SSR}{TSS} = 1 - \frac{s_{\hat{u}}^2}{s_Y^2} \qquad \textbf{(9.15)}$$

The difference between this formula and the second definition of the R^2 in Equation (9.14) is that the ratio of the sum of squared residuals to the total sum of squares is multiplied by the factor $(n-1)/(n-k-1)$. As the second expression in Equation (9.15) shows, this means that the adjusted R^2 is 1 minus the ratio of the sample variance of the OLS residuals [with the degrees-of-freedom correction in Equation (9.13)] to the sample variance of Y. There are three useful things to know about the $\overline{R}^2$. First, $(n-1)/(n-k-1)$ is always greater than 1, so $\overline{R}^2$ is always less than R^2.

Second, adding a regressor has two opposite effects on the $\overline{R}^2$. On the one hand, the SSR falls, which increases the $\overline{R}^2$. On the other hand, the factor $(n-1)/(n-k-1)$ increases. Whether the $\overline{R}^2$ increases or decreases depends on which of these two effects is stronger.

Third, the $\overline{R}^2$ can be negative. This happens when the regressors, taken together, reduce the sum of squared residuals by such a small amount that this reduction fails to offset the factor $(n-1)/(n-k-1)$.

Application to Test Scores

Equation (9.12) reports the estimated regression line for the multiple regression relating test scores (*TestScore*) to the student–teacher ratio (*STR*) and the percentage of English learners (*PctEL*). The R^2 for this regression line is $R^2 = 0.426$, the adjusted R^2 is $\overline{R}^2 = 0.424$, and the standard error of the regression is $SER = 14.5$.

Comparing these measures of fit with those for the regression in which *PctEL* is excluded [Equation (9.11)] shows that including *PctEL* in the regression increased the R^2 from 0.051 to 0.426. When the only regressor is *STR*, only a small fraction of the variation in *TestScore* is explained, however, when *PctEL* is added to the regression, more than two-fifths (42.6%) of the variation in test scores is explained. In this sense, including the percentage of English learners substantially improves the fit of the regression. Because n is large and only two regressors appear in Equation (9.12), the difference between R^2 and adjusted R^2 is very small ($R^2 = 0.426$ versus $\overline{R}^2 = 0.424$).

The *SER* for the regression excluding *PctEL* is 18.6; this value falls to 14.5 when *PctEL* is included as a second regressor. The units of the *SER* are points on the standardized test. The reduction in the *SER* tells us that predictions about standardized test scores are substantially more precise if they are made using the regression with both *STR* and *PctEL* than if they are made using the regression with only *STR* as a regressor.

Using the R^2 and Adjusted R^2

The $\bar{R}^2$ is useful because it quantifies the extent to which the regressors account for, or explain, the variation in the dependent variable. Nevertheless, heavy reliance on the $\bar{R}^2$ (or R^2) can be a trap. In applications, "maximize the $\bar{R}^2$" is rarely the answer to any economically or statistically meaningful question. Instead, the decision about whether to include a variable in a multiple regression should be based on whether including that variable allows you better to estimate the causal effect of interest. We return to the issue of how to decide which variables to include—and which to exclude—in Chapter 10. First, however, we need to develop methods for quantifying the sampling uncertainty of the OLS estimator. The starting point for doing so is extending the least squares assumptions of Chapter 7 to the case of multiple regressors.

THE LEAST SQUARES ASSUMPTIONS IN MULTIPLE REGRESSION

There are four least squares assumptions in the multiple regression model. The first three are those of Chapter 7 for the single regressor model (Box 7-3), extended to allow for multiple regressors, and these are discussed only briefly. The fourth assumption is new and is discussed in more detail.

Assumption #1: The Conditional Distribution of u_i Given $X_{1i}, X_{2i}, \ldots, X_{ki}$ Has a Mean of Zero

The first assumption is that the conditional distribution of u_i given $X_{1i}, \ldots, X_{ki}$ has a mean of zero. This assumption extends the first least squares assumption with a single regressor to multiple regressors. This assumption means that sometimes Y_i is above the population regression line and sometimes Y_i is below the population regression line, but on average over the population Y_i falls on the population regression line. Therefore, for any value of the regressors, the expected value of u_i is zero. As is the case for regression with a single regressor, this is the key assumption that makes the OLS estimators unbiased. We return to omitted variable bias in multiple regression in Chapter 10.

Assumption #2: $(X_{1i}, X_{2i}, \ldots, X_{ki}, Y_i)$, $i = 1, \ldots, n$ Are i.i.d.

The second assumption is that $(X_{1i}, \ldots, X_{ki}, Y_i)$, $i = 1, \ldots, n$ are independently and identically distributed (i.i.d.) random variables. This assumption holds automatically if the data are collected by simple random sampling. The comments on this assumption appearing in Chapter 7 for a single regressor also apply to multiple regressors.

Assumption #3: Large Outliers Are Unlikely

The third least squares assumption is that large outliers—that is, observations with values far outside the usual range of the data—are unlikely. This assumption serves as a reminder that, as in single-regressor case, the OLS estimator of the coefficients in the multiple regression model can be sensitive to large outliers.

The assumption that large outliers are unlikely is made mathematically precise by assuming that $X_{1i}, \ldots, X_{ki}$, and Y_i have nonzero finite fourth moments: $0 < E(X_{1i}^4) < \infty, \ldots, 0 < E(X_{ki}^4) < \infty$ and $0 < E(Y_i^4) < \infty$. Another way to state this assumption is that the dependent variable and regressors have finite kurtosis. This assumption is used to derive the properties of OLS regression statistics in large samples.

Assumption #4: No Perfect Multicollinearity

The fourth assumption is new to the multiple regression model. It rules out an inconvenient situation, called perfect multicollinearity, in which it is impossible to compute the OLS estimator. The regressors are said to be **perfectly multicollinear** (or to exhibit **perfect multicollinearity**) if one of the regressors is a perfect linear function of the other regressors. The fourth least squares assumption is that the regressors are not perfectly multicollinear.

Why does perfect multicollinearity make it impossible to compute the OLS estimator? Suppose you want to estimate the coefficient on *STR* in a regression of *TestScore*$_i$ on *STR*$_i$ and *PctEL*$_i$, except that you make a typographical error and accidentally type in *STR*$_i$ a second time instead of *PctEL*$_i$; that is, you regress *TestScore*$_i$ on *STR*$_i$ and *STR*$_i$. This is a case of perfect multicollinearity because one of the regressors (the first occurrence of *STR*) is a perfect linear function of another regressor (the second occurrence of *STR*). Depending on how your software package handles perfect multicollinearity, if you try to estimate this regression the software will do one of three things: (1) It will drop one of the occurrences of *STR*; (2) it will refuse to calculate the OLS estimates and give an error message; or (3) it will crash the computer. The mathematical reason for this failure is that perfect multicollinearity produces division by zero in the OLS formulas.

At an intuitive level, perfect multicollinearity is a problem because you are asking the regression to answer an illogical question. In multiple regression, the coefficient on one of the regressors is the effect of a change in that regressor, holding the other regressors constant. In the hypothetical regression of *TestScore* on *STR* and *STR*, the coefficient on the first occurrence of *STR* is the effect on test scores of a change in *STR*, holding constant *STR*. This makes no sense, and OLS cannot estimate this nonsensical partial effect.

The solution to perfect multicollinearity in this hypothetical regression is simply to correct the typo and to replace one of the occurrences of *STR* with the variable you originally wanted to include. This example is typical: When perfect multicollinearity occurs, it often reflects a logical mistake in choosing the regressors or some previously unrecognized feature of the data set. In general, the solution to perfect multicollinearity is to modify the regressors to eliminate the problem.

Additional examples of perfect multicollinearity are given later in this chapter, which also defines and discusses imperfect multicollinearity.

The least squares assumptions for the multiple regression model are summarized in Box 9-4.

BOX 9-4 The Least Squares Assumptions in the Multiple Regression Model

$Y_i = \beta_0 + \beta_1 X_{1i} + \beta_2 X_{2i} + \ldots + \beta_k X_{ki} + u_i$, $i = 1, \ldots, n$, where

1. u_i has conditional mean zero given $X_{1i}, X_{2i}, \ldots, X_{ki}$; that is,

$$E(u_i \mid X_{1i}, X_{2i}, \ldots, X_{ki}) = 0$$

2. $(X_{1i}, X_{2i}, \ldots, X_{ki}, Y_i)$, $i = 1, \ldots, n$ are independently and identically distributed (i.i.d.) draws from their joint distribution.

3. Large outliers are unlikely: $X_{1i}, \ldots, X_{ki}$ and Y_i have nonzero finite fourth moments.

4. There is no perfect multicollinearity.

THE DISTRIBUTION OF THE OLS ESTIMATORS IN MULTIPLE REGRESSION

Because the data differ from one sample to the next, different samples produce different values of the OLS estimators. This variation across possible samples gives rise to the uncertainty associated with the OLS estimators of the population regression coefficients, $\beta_0, \beta_1, \ldots, \beta_k$. Just as in the case of regression with a single regressor, this variation is summarized in the sampling distribution of the OLS estimators.

Recall from Chapter 7 that, under the least squares assumptions, the OLS estimators ($\hat{\beta}_0$ and $\hat{\beta}_1$) are unbiased and consistent estimators of the unknown coefficients (β_0 and β_1) in the linear regression model with a single regressor. In addition, in large samples, the sampling distribution of $\hat{\beta}_0$ and $\hat{\beta}_1$ is well approximated by a bivariate normal distribution.

These results carry over to multiple regression analysis. That is, under the least squares assumptions of Box 9-4, the OLS estimators $\hat{\beta}_0, \hat{\beta}_1, \ldots, \hat{\beta}_k$ are unbiased and consistent estimators of $\beta_0, \beta_1, \ldots, \beta_k$ in the linear multiple regression model. In large samples, the joint sampling distribution of $\hat{\beta}_0, \hat{\beta}_1, \ldots, \hat{\beta}_k$ is well approximated by a multivariate normal distribution, which is the extension of the bivariate normal distribution to the general case of two or more jointly normal random variables.

Although the algebra is more complicated when there are multiple regressors, the central limit theorem applies to the OLS estimators in the multiple regression model for the same reason that it applies to $\overline{Y}$ and to the OLS estimators when there is a single regressor: The OLS estimators $\hat{\beta}_0, \hat{\beta}_1, \ldots, \hat{\beta}_k$ are averages of the randomly sampled data, and if the sample size is sufficiently large the sampling distribution of those averages becomes normal. Because the multivariate normal distribution is best handled mathematically using matrix algebra, the expressions for the joint distribution of the OLS estimators are omitted.

Box 9-5 summarizes the result that, in large samples, the distribution of the OLS estimators in multiple regression is approximately jointly normal. In general, the OLS estimators are correlated; this correlation arises from the correlation between the regressors.

MULTICOLLINEARITY

As discussed previously, perfect multicollinearity arises when one of the regressors is a perfect linear combination of the other regressors. This section provides some examples of perfect multicollinearity and discusses how perfect multicollinearity can arise, and can be avoided, in regressions with multiple binary regressors. Imperfect multicollinearity arises when one of the regressors is very highly correlated—but not perfectly correlated—with the other regressors. Unlike perfect multicollinearity, imperfect multicollinearity does not prevent estimation of the regression, nor does it imply a logical problem with the choice of regressors. However, it does mean that one or more regression coefficients could be estimated imprecisely.

Examples of Perfect Multicollinearity

We continue the discussion of perfect multicollinearity by examining three additional hypothetical regressions. In each, a third regressor is added to the regression of *TestScore$_i$* on *STR$_i$* and *PctEL$_i$* in Equation (9.12).

Example #1: Fraction of English Learners

Let *FracEL$_i$* be the fraction of English learners in the ith district, which varies between 0 and 1. If the variable *FracEL$_i$* were included as a third regressor in addition to *STR$_i$* and *PctEL$_i$*, the regressors would be perfectly multicollinear. The reason is that *PctEL* is the *percentage* of English learners, so that $PctEL_i = 100 \times FracEL_i$ for every district. Thus one of the regressors (*PctEL$_i$*) can be written as a perfect linear function of another regressor (*FracEL$_i$*).

Because of this perfect multicollinearity, it is impossible to compute the OLS estimates of the regression of *TestScore$_i$* on *STR$_i$*, *PctEL$_i$*, and *FracEL$_i$*. At an intuitive level, OLS fails because you are asking, What is the effect of a unit change in the *percentage* of English learners, holding constant the *fraction* of English learners? Because the percentage of English learners and the fraction of English learners move together in a perfect linear relationship, this question makes no sense and OLS cannot answer it.

Example #2: "Not Very Small" Classes

Let *NVS$_i$* be a binary variable that equals 1 if the student-teacher ratio in the ith district is "not very small," specifically, *NVS$_i$* equals 1 if $STR_i \geq 12$ and equals 0 otherwise. This regression also exhibits perfect multicollinearity, but for a more subtle reason than the regression in the previous example. There are in fact no districts in our data set with $STR_i < 12$; as you can see in the scatterplot in Figure 7-2, the smallest value of *STR* is 14. Thus, $NVS_i = 1$ for all observations. Now recall that the linear regression model with an intercept can equivalently be thought of as including a regressor, X_{0i}, that equals 1 for all i, as is shown in Equation (9.6). Thus we can write $NVS_i = 1 \times X_{0i}$ for all the observations in our data set; that is, *NVS$_i$* can be written as a perfect linear combination of the regressors; specifically, it equals X_{0i}.

This illustrates two important points about perfect multicollinearity. First, when the regression includes an intercept, then one of the regressors that can be implicated in perfect multicollinearity is the constant regressor X_{0i}. Second, perfect multicollinearity is a statement about the data set you have on hand. While it is possible to imagine a school district with fewer than 12 students per teacher, there are no such districts in our data set so we cannot analyze them in our regression.

Example #3: Percentage of English Speakers

Let *PctES$_i$* be the percentage of "English speakers" in the ith district, defined to be the percentage of students who are not English learners. Again the regressors will be perfectly multicollinear. Like the previous example, the perfect linear relationship among the regressors involves the constant regressor X_{0i}: For every district, $PctES_i = 100 \times X_{0i} - PctEL_i$.

This example illustrates another point: perfect multicollinearity is a feature of the entire set of regressors. If either the intercept (i.e., the regressor X_{0i}) or *PctEL$_i$* were excluded from this regression, the regressors would not be perfectly multicollinear.

The Dummy Variable Trap

Another possible source of perfect multicollinearity arises when multiple binary, or dummy, variables are used as regressors. For example, suppose you have partitioned the school districts into three categories: rural, suburban, and urban. Each district falls into one (and only one) category. Let these binary variables be $Rural_i$, which equals 1 for a rural district and equals 0 otherwise; $Suburban_i$, and $Urban_i$. If you include all three binary variables in the regression along with a constant, the regressors will be perfect multicollinearity: Because each district belongs to one and only one category, $Rural_i + Suburban_i + Urban_i = 1 = X_{0i}$, where X_{0i} denotes the constant regressor introduced in Equation (9.6). Thus, to estimate the regression, you must exclude one of these four variables, either one of the binary indicators or the constant term. By convention, the constant term is retained, in which case one of the binary indicators is excluded. For example, if $Rural_i$ were excluded, then the coefficient on $Suburban_i$ would be the average difference between test scores in suburban and rural districts, holding constant the other variables in the regression.

In general, if there are G binary variables, if each observation falls into one and only one category, if there is an intercept in the regression, and if all G binary variables are included as regressors, then the regression will fail because of perfect multicollinearity. This situation is called the **dummy variable trap**. The usual way to avoid the dummy variable trap is to exclude one of the binary variables from the multiple regression, so only $G - 1$ of the G binary variables are included as regressors. In this case, the coefficients on the included binary variables represent the incremental effect of being in that category, relative to the base case of the omitted category, holding constant the other regressors. Alternatively, all G binary regressors can be included if the intercept is omitted from the regression.

Solutions to Perfect Multicollinearity

Perfect multicollinearity typically arises when a mistake has been made in specifying the regression. Sometimes the mistake is easy to spot (as in the first example) but sometimes it is not (as in the second example). In one way or another your software will let you know if you make such a mistake because it cannot compute the OLS estimator if you have.

When your software lets you know that you have perfect multicollinearity, it is important that you modify your regression to eliminate it. Some software is unreliable when there is perfect multicollinearity, and at a minimum you will be ceding control over your choice of regressors to your computer if your regressors are perfectly multicollinear.

Imperfect Multicollinearity

Despite its similar name, imperfect multicollinearity is conceptually quite different than perfect multicollinearity. **Imperfect multicollinearity** means that two or more of the regressors are highly correlated, in the sense that there is a linear function of the regressors that is highly correlated with another regressor. Imperfect multicollinearity does not pose any problems for the theory of the OLS estimators; indeed, a purpose of OLS is to sort out the independent influences of the various regressors when these regressors are potentially correlated.

If the regressors are imperfectly multicollinear, then the coefficients on at least one individual regressor will be imprecisely estimated. For example, consider the regression of *TestScore* on *STR* and *PctEL*. Suppose we were to add a third regressor, the percentage the district's residents who are first-generation immigrants. First-generation immigrants often speak English as a second language, so the variables *PctEL* and percentage immigrants will be highly correlated: Districts with many recent immigrants will tend to have many students who are still learning English. Because these two variables are highly correlated, it would be difficult to use these data to estimate the partial effect on test scores of an increase in *PctEL*, holding constant the percentage immigrants. In other words, the data set provides little information about what happens to test scores when the percentage of English learners is low but the fraction of immigrants is high, or vice versa. If the least squares assumptions hold, then the OLS estimator of the coefficient on *PctEL* in this regression will be unbiased; however, it will have a larger variance than if the regressors *PctEL* and percentage immigrants were uncorrelated.

The effect of imperfect multicollinearity on the variance of the OLS estimators can be seen mathematically by inspecting the variance of $\hat{\beta}_1$ in a multiple regression with two regressors (X_1 and X_2) for the special case of a homoskedastic error.[1] In this case, the variance of $\hat{\beta}_1$ is inversely

---

[1] $\sigma_{\hat{\beta}_1}^2 = \frac{1}{n} \left[\frac{1}{1 - \rho_{X_1, X_2}^2} \right] \frac{\sigma_u^2}{\sigma_{X_1}^2}$

proportional to $1 - \rho_{X_1,X_2}^2$, where ρ_{X_1,X_2} is the correlation between X_1 and X_2. The larger is the correlation between the two regressors, the closer is this term to zero and the larger is the variance of $\hat{\beta}_1$. More generally, when multiple regressors are imperfectly multicollinear, then the coefficients on one or more of these regressors will be imprecisely estimated—that is, they will have a large sampling variance.

Perfect multicollinearity is a problem that often signals the presence of a logical error. In contrast, imperfect multicollinearity is not necessarily an error, but rather just a feature of OLS, your data, and the question you are trying to answer. If the variables in your regression are the ones you meant to include—the ones you chose to address the potential for omitted variable bias—then imperfect multicollinearity implies that it will be difficult to estimate precisely one or more of the partial effects using the data at hand.

CONCLUSION

Regression with a single regressor is vulnerable to omitted variable bias: If an omitted variable is a determinant of the dependent variable and is correlated with the regressor, then the OLS estimator of the slope coefficient will be biased and will reflect both the effect of the regressor and the effect of the omitted variable. Multiple regression makes it possible to mitigate omitted variable bias by including the omitted variable in the regression. The coefficient on a regressor, X_1, in multiple regression is the partial effect of a change in X_1, holding constant the other included regressors. In the test score example, including the percentage of English learners as a regressor made it possible to estimate the effect on test scores of a change in the student–teacher ratio, holding constant the percentage of English learners. Doing so reduced by half the estimated effect on test scores of a change in the student–teacher ratio.

The statistical theory of multiple regression builds on the statistical theory of regression with a single regressor. The least squares assumptions for multiple regression are extensions of the three least squares assumptions for regression with a single regressor, plus a fourth assumption ruling out perfect multicollinearity. Because the regression coefficients are estimated using a single sample, the OLS estimators have a joint sampling distribution and, therefore, have sampling uncertainty. This sampling uncertainty must be quantified as part of an empirical study, and the ways to do so in the multiple regression model are the topic of the next chapter.

SUMMARY

1. Omitted variable bias occurs when an omitted variable (1) is correlated with an included regressor and (2) is a determinant of Y.

2. The multiple regression model is a linear regression model that includes multiple regressors, X_1, $X_2, \ldots, X_k$. Associated with each regressor is a regression coefficient, $\beta_1, \beta_2, \ldots, \beta_k$. The coefficient β_1 is the expected change in Y associated with a one-unit change in X_1, holding the other regressors constant. The other regression coefficients have an analogous interpretation.

3. The coefficients in multiple regression can be estimated by OLS. When the four least squares assumptions in Box 9-4 are satisfied, the OLS estimators are unbiased, consistent, and normally distributed in large samples.

4. Perfect multicollinearity, which occurs when one regressor is an exact linear function of the other regressors, usually arises from a mistake in choosing which regressors to include in a multiple regression. Solving perfect multicollinearity requires changing the set of regressors.

5. The standard error of the regression, the R^2, and the $\overline{R}^2$ are measures of fit for the multiple regression model.

Key Terms

omitted variable bias (120)
multiple regression model (124)
population regression line (124)
population regression function (124)
intercept (124)
slope coefficient of X_{1i} (124)
coefficient on X_{1i} (124)
slope coefficient of X_{2i} (124)
coefficient on X_{2i} (124)
control variable (124)
holding X_2 constant (124)
controlling for X_2 (124)
partial effect (124)

Hypothesis Tests and Confidence Intervals in Multiple Regression

10

Learning Objectives

Candidates, after completing this reading, should be able to:

- Construct, apply, and interpret hypothesis tests and confidence intervals for a single coefficient in a multiple regression.
- Construct, apply, and interpret joint hypothesis tests and confidence intervals for multiple coefficients in a multiple regression.
- Interpret the F-statistic.

- Interpret tests of a single restriction involving multiple coefficients.
- Interpret confidence sets for multiple coefficients.
- Identify examples of omitted variable bias in multiple regressions.
- Interpret the R^2 and adjusted-R^2 in a multiple regression.

Excerpt is Chapter 7 of Introduction to Econometrics, *Brief Edition, by James H. Stock and Mark W. Watson.*

As discussed in Chapter 9, multiple regression analysis provides a way to mitigate the problem of omitted variable bias by including additional regressors, thereby controlling for the effects of those additional regressors. The coefficients of the multiple regression model can be estimated by OLS. Like all estimators, the OLS estimator has sampling uncertainty because its value differs from one sample to the next.

This chapter presents methods for quantifying the sampling uncertainty of the OLS estimator through the use of standard errors, statistical hypothesis tests, and confidence intervals. One new possibility that arises in multiple regression is a hypothesis that simultaneously involves two or more regression coefficients. The general approach to testing such "joint" hypotheses involves a new test statistic, the F-statistic.

The first section extends the methods for statistical inference in regression with a single regressor to multiple regression. The next two sections show how to test hypotheses that involve two or more regression coefficients. Next the discussion extends the notion of confidence intervals for a single coefficient to confidence sets for multiple coefficients. Deciding which variables to include in a regression is an important practical issue, so the text includes ways to approach this problem. Finally, we apply multiple regression analysis to obtain improved estimates of the effect on test scores of a reduction in the student–teacher ratio using the California test score data set.

HYPOTHESIS TESTS AND CONFIDENCE INTERVALS FOR A SINGLE COEFFICIENT

This section describes how to compute the standard error, how to test hypotheses, and how to construct confidence intervals for a single coefficient in a multiple regression equation.

Standard Errors for the OLS Estimators

Recall that, in the case of a single regressor, it was possible to estimate the variance of the OLS estimator by substituting sample averages for expectations, which led to the estimator $\hat{\sigma}^2_{\hat{\beta}_1}$ given in Equation (8.4). Under the least squares assumptions, the law of large numbers implies that these sample averages converge to their population

counterparts, so for example $\hat{\sigma}^2_{\hat{\beta}_1}/\sigma^2_{\hat{\beta}_1} \xrightarrow{p} 1$. The square root of $\hat{\sigma}^2_{\hat{\beta}_1}$ is the standard error of $\hat{\beta}_1$, $SE(\hat{\beta}_1)$, an estimator of the standard deviation of the sampling distribution of $\hat{\beta}_1$.

All this extends directly to multiple regression. The OLS estimator $\hat{\beta}_j$ of the jth regression coefficient has a standard deviation, and this standard deviation is estimated by its standard error, $SE(\hat{\beta}_j)$. The formula for the standard error is most easily stated using matrices. The important point is that, as far as standard errors are concerned, there is nothing conceptually different between the single- or multiple-regressor cases. The key ideas—the large-sample normality of the estimators and the ability to estimate consistently the standard deviation of their sampling distribution—are the same whether one has one, two, or 12 regressors.

Hypothesis Tests for a Single Coefficient

Suppose that you want to test the hypothesis that a change in the student–teacher ratio has no effect on test scores, holding constant the percentage of English learners in the district. This corresponds to hypothesizing that the true coefficient β_1 on the student–teacher ratio is zero in the population regression of test scores on STR and $PctEL$. More generally, we might want to test the hypothesis that the true coefficient β_j on the jth regressor takes on some specific value, $\beta_{j,0}$. The null value $\beta_{j,0}$ comes either from economic theory or, as in the student–teacher ratio example, from the decision-making context of the application. If the alternative hypothesis is two-sided, then the two hypotheses can be written mathematically as

$$H_0: \beta_j = \beta_{j,0} \text{ vs. } H_1: \beta_j \neq \beta_{j,0} \quad \text{(two-sided alternative).} \quad \textbf{(10.1)}$$

For example, if the first regressor is STR, then the null hypothesis that changing the student–teacher ratio has no effect on class size corresponds to the null hypothesis that $\beta_1 = 0$ (so $\beta_{1,0} = 0$). Our task is to test the null hypothesis H_0 against the alternative H_1 using a sample of data.

Box 8-2 gives a procedure for testing this null hypothesis when there is a single regressor. The first step in this procedure is to calculate the standard error of the coefficient. The second step is to calculate the t-statistic using the general formula in Box 8-1. The third step is to compute the p-value of the test using the cumulative normal distribution in Appendix Table 1 on page 233 or, alternatively, to compare the t-statistic to the critical value corresponding

BOX 10-1   Testing the Hypothesis $\beta_j = \beta_{j,0}$ Against the Alternative $\beta_j \neq \beta_{j,0}$

1. Compute the standard error of $\hat{\beta}_j$, $SE(\hat{\beta}_j)$.

2. Compute the t-statistic,

$$t = \frac{\hat{\beta}_j - \beta_{j,0}}{SE(\hat{\beta}_j)} \qquad \textbf{(10.2)}$$

3. Compute the p-value,

$$p\text{-value} = 2\Phi(-|t^{act}|) \qquad \textbf{(10.3)}$$

where t^{act} is the value of the t-statistic actually computed. Reject the hypothesis at the 5% significance level if the p-value is less than 0.05 or, equivalently, if $|t^{act}| > 1.96$.

The standard error and (typically) the t-statistic and p-value testing $\beta_j = 0$ are computed automatically by regression software.

BOX 10-2   Confidence Intervals for a Single Coefficient in Multiple Regression

A 95% two-sided confidence interval for the coefficient β_j is an interval that contains the true value of β_j with a 95% probability; that is, it contains the true value of β_j in 95% of all possible randomly drawn samples. Equivalently, it is the set of values of β_j that cannot be rejected by a 5% two-sided hypothesis test. When the sample size is large, the 95% confidence interval is

$$\begin{aligned} &95\% \text{ confidence interval for } \beta_j \\ &= [\hat{\beta}_j - 1.96SE(\hat{\beta}_j), \ \hat{\beta}_j + 1.96SE(\hat{\beta}_j)]. \end{aligned} \qquad \textbf{(10.4)}$$

A 90% confidence interval is obtained by replacing 1.96 in Equation (10.4) with 1.645.

---

to the desired significance level of the test. The theoretical underpinning of this procedure is that the OLS estimator has a large-sample normal distribution which, under the null hypothesis, has as its mean the hypothesized true value, and that the variance of this distribution can be estimated consistently.

This underpinning is present in multiple regression as well. As stated in Box 9-5, the sampling distribution of $\hat{\beta}_j$ is approximately normal. Under the null hypothesis the mean of this distribution is $\beta_{j,0}$. The variance of this distribution can be estimated consistently. Therefore we can simply follow the same procedure as in the single-regressor case to test the null hypothesis in Equation (10.1).

The procedure for testing a hypothesis on a single coefficient in multiple regression is summarized as Box 10-1. The t-statistic actually computed is denoted t^{act} in this Box. However, it is customary to denote this simply as t.

Confidence Intervals for a Single Coefficient

The method for constructing a confidence interval in the multiple regression model is also the same as in the single-regressor model. This method is summarized as Box 10-2.

The method for conducting a hypothesis test in Box 10-1 and the method for constructing a confidence interval in

Box 10-2 rely on the large-sample normal approximation to the distribution of the OLS estimator $\hat{\beta}_j$. Accordingly, it should be kept in mind that these methods for quantifying the sampling uncertainty are only guaranteed to work in large samples.

Application to Test Scores and the Student–Teacher Ratio

Can we reject the null hypothesis that a change in the student–teacher ratio has no effect on test scores, once we control for the percentage of English learners in the district? What is a 95% confidence interval for the effect on test scores of a change in the student–teacher ratio, controlling for the percentage of English learners? We are now able to find out. The regression of test scores against STR and $PctEL$, estimated by OLS, was given in Equation (9.12) and is restated here with standard errors in parentheses below the coefficients:

$$\widehat{TestScore} = 686.0 - 1.10 \times STR - 0.650 \times PctEL \qquad \textbf{(10.5)}$$
$$\phantom{\widehat{TestScore} = } (8.7) \quad (0.43) \qquad\qquad (0.031)$$

To test the hypothesis that the true coefficient on STR is 0, we first need to compute the t-statistic in Equation (10.2). Because the null hypothesis says that the true value of this coefficient is zero, the t-statistic is $t = (-1.10 - 0)/0.43 = -2.54$. The associated p-value is $2\Phi(-2.54) = 1.1\%$; that is, the smallest significance level at which we can reject the null hypothesis is 1.1%. Because the p-value is less than 5%, the null hypothesis can be rejected at the 5% significance level (but not quite at the 1% significance level).

A 95% confidence interval for the population coefficient on STR is $-1.10 \pm 1.96 \times 0.43 = (-1.95, -0.26)$; that is, we can be 95% confident that the true value of the coefficient is between -1.95 and -0.26. Interpreted in the context of the superintendent's interest in decreasing the student–teacher ratio by 2, the 95% confidence interval for the effect on test scores of this reduction is $(-1.95 \times 2, -0.26 \times 2) = (-3.90, -0.52)$.

Adding Expenditures per Pupil to the Equation

Your analysis of the multiple regression in Equation (10.5) has persuaded the superintendent that, based on the evidence so far, reducing class size will help test scores in her district. Now, however, she moves on to a more nuanced question. If she is to hire more teachers, she can pay for those teachers either through cuts elsewhere in the budget (no new computers, reduced maintenance, and so on), or by asking for an increase in her budget, which taxpayers do not favor. What, she asks, is the effect on test scores of reducing the student–teacher ratio, holding expenditures per pupil (and the percentage of English learners) constant?

This question can be addressed by estimating a regression of test scores on the student–teacher ratio, total spending per pupil, and the percentage of English learners. The OLS regression line is

$$\widehat{TestScore} = 649.6 - 0.29 \times STR + 3.87$$
$$\quad\quad (15.5) \;\; (0.48) \quad\quad\quad (1.59)$$
$$\times Expn - 0.656 \times PctEL \quad\quad \textbf{(10.6)}$$
$$\quad (0.032)$$

where $Expn$ is total annual expenditures per pupil in the district in thousands of dollars.

The result is striking. Holding expenditures per pupil and the percentage of English learners constant, changing the student–teacher ratio is estimated to have a very small effect on test scores: The estimated coefficient on STR is -1.10 in Equation (10.5) but, after adding $Expn$ as a regressor in Equation (10.6), it is only -0.29. Moreover, the t-statistic for testing that the true value of the coefficient is zero is now $t = (-0.29 - 0)/0.48 = -0.60$, so the hypothesis that the population value of this coefficient is indeed zero cannot be rejected even at the 10% significance level ($|-0.60| < 1.645$). Thus Equation (10.6)

provides no evidence that hiring more teachers improves test scores if overall expenditures per pupil are held constant.

One interpretation of the regression in Equation (10.6) is that, in these California data, school administrators allocate their budgets efficiently. Suppose, counterfactually, that the coefficient on STR in Equation (10.6) were negative and large. If so, school districts could raise their test scores simply by decreasing funding for other purposes (textbooks, technology, sports, and so on) and transferring those funds to hire more teachers, thereby reducing class sizes while holding expenditures constant. However, the small and statistically insignificant coefficient on STR in Equation (10.6) indicates that this transfer would have little effect on test scores. Put differently, districts are already allocating their funds efficiently.

Note that the standard error on STR increased when $Expn$ was added, from 0.43 in Equation (10.5) to 0.48 in Equation (10.6). This illustrates the general point, introduced in Chapter 9 in the context of imperfect multicollinearity, that correlation between regressors (the correlation between STR and $Expn$ is -0.62) can make the OLS estimators less precise.

What about our angry taxpayer? He asserts that the population values of *both* the coefficient on the student–teacher ratio (β_1) *and* the coefficient on spending per pupil (β_2) are zero, that is, he hypothesizes that both $\beta_1 = 0$ and $\beta_2 = 0$. Although it might seem that we can reject this hypothesis because the t-statistic testing $\beta_2 = 0$ in Equation (10.6) is $t = 3.87/1.59 = 2.43$, this reasoning is flawed. The taxpayer's hypothesis is a joint hypothesis, and to test it we need a new tool, the F-statistic.

TESTS OF JOINT HYPOTHESES

This section describes how to formulate joint hypotheses on multiple regression coefficients and how to test them using an F-statistic.

Testing Hypotheses on Two or More Coefficients

Joint Null Hypotheses

Consider the regression in Equation (10.6) of the test score against the student–teacher ratio, expenditures per pupil, and the percentage of English learners. Our angry taxpayer hypothesizes that neither the student–teacher ratio nor expenditures per pupil have an effect on test scores, once we control for the percentage of English learners. Because *STR* is the first regressor in Equation (10.6) and *Expn* is the second, we can write this hypothesis mathematically as

$$H_0: \beta_1 = 0 \text{ and } \beta_2 = 0 \text{ vs. } H_1: \beta_1 \neq 0 \text{ and/or } \beta_2 \neq 0 \quad \textbf{(10.7)}$$

The hypothesis that *both* the coefficient on the student–teacher ratio (β_1) *and* the coefficient on expenditures per pupil (β_2) are zero is an example of a joint hypothesis on the coefficients in the multiple regression model. In this case, the null hypothesis restricts the value of two of the coefficients, so as a matter of terminology we can say that the null hypothesis in Equation (10.7) imposes two **restrictions** on the multiple regression model: $\beta_1 = 0$ *and* $\beta_2 = 0$.

In general, a **joint hypothesis** is a hypothesis that imposes two or more restrictions on the regression coefficients. We consider joint null and alternative hypotheses of the form

$$H_0: \beta_j = \beta_{j,0}, \beta_m = \beta_{m,0}, \ldots, \text{ for a total of } q \text{ restrictions, vs.}$$

$$H_1: \text{one or more of the } q \text{ restrictions under } H_0 \text{ does not hold,} \quad \textbf{(10.8)}$$

where $\beta_j, \beta_m, \ldots$, refer to different regression coefficients, and $\beta_{j,0}, \beta_{m,0}, \ldots$, refer to the values of these coefficients under the null hypothesis. The null hypothesis in Equation (10.7) is an example of Equation (10.8). Another example is that, in a regression with $k = 6$ regressors, the null hypothesis is that the coefficients on the 2nd, 4th, and 5th regressors are zero; that is, $\beta_2 = 0$, $\beta_4 = 0$, and $\beta_5 = 0$, so that there are $q = 3$ restrictions. In general, under the null hypothesis H_0 there are q such restrictions.

If any one (or more than one) of the equalities under the null hypothesis H_0 in Equation (10.8) is false, then the joint null hypothesis itself is false. Thus, the alternative hypothesis is that at least one of the equalities in the null hypothesis H_0 does not hold.

Why Can't I Just Test the Individual Coefficients One at a Time?

Although it seems it should be possible to test a joint hypothesis by using the usual *t*-statistics to test the restrictions one at a time, the following calculation shows that this approach is unreliable. Specifically, suppose that you are interested in testing the joint null hypothesis in Equation (10.6) that $\beta_1 = 0$ and $\beta_2 = 0$. Let t_1 be the

t-statistic for testing the null hypothesis that $\beta_1 = 0$, and let t_2 be the *t*-statistic for testing the null hypothesis that $\beta_2 = 0$. What happens when you use the "one at a time" testing procedure: Reject the joint null hypothesis if either t_1 or t_2 exceeds 1.96 in absolute value?

Because this question involves the two random variables t_1 and t_2, answering it requires characterizing the joint sampling distribution of t_1 and t_2. As mentioned previously, in large samples $\hat{\beta}_1$ and $\hat{\beta}_2$ have a joint normal distribution, so under the joint null hypothesis the *t*-statistics t_1 and t_2 have a bivariate normal distribution, where each *t*-statistic has mean equal to 0 and variance equal to 1.

First consider the special case in which the *t*-statistics are uncorrelated and thus are independent. What is the size of the "one at a time" testing procedure; that is, what is the probability that you will reject the null hypothesis when it is true? More than 5%! In this special case we can calculate the rejection probability of this method exactly. The null is *not* rejected only if both $|t_1| \leq 1.96$ and $|t_2| \leq 1.96$. Because the *t*-statistics are independent, $\Pr(|t_1| \leq 1.96 \text{ and } |t_2| \leq 1.96) = \Pr(|t_1| \leq 1.96) \times \Pr(|t_2| \leq 1.96) = 0.95^2 = 0.9025 = 90.25\%$. So the probability of rejecting the null hypothesis when it is true is $1 - 0.95^2 = 9.75\%$. This "one at a time" method rejects the null too often because it gives you too many chances: If you fail to reject using the first *t*-statistic, you get to try again using the second.

If the regressors are correlated, the situation is even more complicated. The size of the "one at a time" procedure depends on the value of the correlation between the regressors. Because the "one at a time" testing approach has the wrong size—that is, its rejection rate under the null hypothesis does not equal the desired significance level—a new approach is needed.

One approach is to modify the "one at a time" method so that it uses different critical values that ensure that its size equals its significance level. This method, called the Bonferroni method, is described in the Appendix. The advantage of the Bonferroni method is that it applies very generally. Its disadvantage is that it can have low power; it frequently fails to reject the null hypothesis when in fact the alternative hypothesis is true.

Fortunately, there is another approach to testing joint hypotheses that is more powerful, especially when the regressors are highly correlated. That approach is based on the *F*-statistic.

The *F*-Statistic

The **F-statistic** is used to test joint hypothesis about regression coefficients. The formulas for the *F*-statistic are integrated into modern regression software. We first discuss the case of two restrictions, then turn to the general case of q restrictions.

The F-*Statistic with* q = 2 *Restrictions*

When the joint null hypothesis has the two restrictions that $\beta_1 = 0$ and $\beta_2 = 0$, the *F*-statistic combines the two t-statistics t_1 and t_2 using the formula

$$F = \frac{1}{2}\left(\frac{t_1^2 + t_2^2 - 2\hat{\rho}_{t_1, t_2} t_1 t_2}{1 - \hat{\rho}_{t_1, t_2}^2}\right) \qquad \textbf{(10.9)}$$

where $\hat{\rho}_{t_1, t_2}$ is an estimator of the correlation between the two *t*-statistics.

To understand the *F*-statistic in Equation (10.9), first suppose that we know that the *t*-statistics are uncorrelated so we can drop the terms involving $\hat{\rho}_{t_1, t_2}$. If so, Equation (10.9) simplifies and $F = \frac{1}{2}(t_1^2 + t_2^2)$; that is, the *F*-statistic is the average of the squared *t*-statistics. Under the null hypothesis, t_1 and t_2 are independent standard normal random variables (because the *t*-statistics are uncorrelated by assumption), so under the null hypothesis F has an $F_{2,\infty}$ distribution. Under the alternative hypothesis that either β_1 is nonzero or β_2 is nonzero (or both), then either t_1^2 or t_2^2 (or both) will be large, leading the test to reject the null hypothesis.

In general the *t*-statistics are correlated, and the formula for the *F*-statistic in Equation (10.9) adjusts for this correlation. This adjustment is made so that, under the null hypothesis, the *F*-statistic has an $F_{2,\infty}$ distribution in large samples whether or not the *t*-statistics are correlated.

The F-*Statistic with* q *Restrictions*

The formula for the heteroskedasticity-robust *F*-statistic testing the q restrictions of the joint null hypothesis in Equation (10.8) is a matrix extension of the formula for the heteroskedasticity-robust *t*-statistic. This formula is incorporated into regression software, making the *F*-statistic easy to compute in practice.

Under the null hypothesis, the *F*-statistic has a sampling distribution that, in large samples, is given by the $F_{q,\infty}$ distribution. That is, in large samples, under the null hypothesis

the *F*-statistic is distributed $F_{q,\infty}$ **(10.10)**

Thus the critical values for the *F*-statistic can be obtained from the tables of the $F_{q,\infty}$ distribution for the appropriate value of q and the desired significance level.

Computing the Heteroskedasticity-Robust F-Statistic in Statistical Software

If the *F*-statistic is computed using the general heteroskedasticity-robust formula, its large-n distribution under the null hypothesis is $F_{q,\infty}$ regardless of whether the errors are homoskedastic or heteroskedastic. As discussed in Chapter 8, for historical reasons most statistical software computes homoskedasticity-only standard errors by default. Consequently, in some software packages you must select a "robust" option so that the *F*-statistic is computed using heteroskedasticity-robust standard errors (and, more generally, a heteroskedasticity-robust estimate of the "covariance matrix"). The homoskedasticity-only version of the *F*-statistic is discussed at the end of this section.

Computing the p-*Value Using the* F-*Statistic*

The *p*-value of the *F*-statistic can be computed using the large-sample $F_{q,\infty}$ approximation to its distribution. Let F^{act} denote the value of the *F*-statistic actually computed. Because the *F*-statistic has a large-sample $F_{q,\infty}$ distribution under the null hypothesis, the *p*-value is

$$p\text{-value} = \Pr[F_{q,\infty} > F^{act}] \qquad \textbf{(10.11)}$$

The *p*-value in Equation (10.11) can be evaluated using a table of the $F_{q,\infty}$ distribution (or, alternatively, a table of the χ_q^2 distribution, because a χ_q^2-distributed random variable is q times an $F_{q,\infty}$-distributed random variable). Alternatively, the *p*-value can be evaluated using a computer, because formulas for the cumulative chi-squared and F distributions have been incorporated into most modern statistical software.

The "Overall" Regression F-*Statistic*

The "overall" regression *F*-statistic tests the joint hypothesis that *all* the slope coefficients are zero. That is, the null and alternative hypotheses are

$$H_0: \beta_1 = 0, \beta_2 = 0, \ldots, \beta_k = 0 \text{ vs.}$$
$$H_1: \beta_j \neq 0, \text{ at least one } j, j = 1, \ldots, k \qquad \textbf{(10.12)}$$

Under this null hypothesis, none of the regressors explains any of the variation in Y_i, although the intercept (which under the null hypothesis is the mean of Y_i) can be nonzero. The null hypothesis in Equation (10.12) is a special case of the general null hypothesis in Equation (10.8), and the overall regression F-statistic is the F-statistic computed for the null hypothesis in Equation (10.12). In large samples, the overall regression F-statistic has an $F_{k,\infty}$ distribution when the null hypothesis is true.

The F-*Statistic when* q = 1

When $q = 1$, the F-statistic tests a single restriction. Then the joint null hypothesis reduces to the null hypothesis on a single regression coefficient, and the F-statistic is the square of the t-statistic.

Application to Test Scores and the Student–Teacher Ratio

We are now able to test the null hypothesis that the coefficients on *both* the student–teacher ratio *and* expenditures per pupil are zero, against the alternative that at least one coefficient is nonzero, controlling for the percentage of English learners in the district.

To test this hypothesis, we need to compute the heteroskedasticity-robust F-statistic of the test that $\beta_1 = 0$ and $\beta_2 = 0$ using the regression of *TestScore* on *STR*, *Expn*, and *PctEL* reported in Equation (10.6). This F-statistic is 5.43. Under the null hypothesis, in large samples this statistic has an $F_{2,\infty}$ distribution. The 5% critical value of the $F_{2,\infty}$ distribution is 3.00, and the 1% critical value is 4.61. The value of the F-statistic computed from the data, 5.43, exceeds 4.61, so the null hypothesis is rejected at the 1% level. It is very unlikely that we would have drawn a sample that produced an F-statistic as large as 5.43 if the null hypothesis really were true (the p-value is 0.005). Based on the evidence in Equation (10.6) as summarized in this F-statistic, we can reject the taxpayer's hypothesis that *neither* the student–teacher ratio *nor* expenditures per pupil have an effect on test scores (holding constant the percentage of English learners).

The Homoskedasticity-Only *F*-Statistic

One way to restate the question addressed by the F-statistic is to ask whether relaxing the q restrictions that constitute the null hypothesis improves the fit of the regression by enough that this improvement is unlikely to be the result merely of random sampling variation if the null hypothesis is true. This restatement suggests that there is a link between the F-statistic and

the regression R^2: A large F-statistic should, it seems, be associated with a substantial increase in the R^2. In fact, if the error u_i is homoskedastic, this intuition has an exact mathematical expression. That is, if the error term is homoskedastic, the F-statistic can be written in terms of the improvement in the fit of the regression as measured either by the sum of squared residuals or by the regression R^2. The resulting F-statistic is referred to as the homoskedasticity-only F-statistic, because it is valid only if the error term is homoskedastic. In contrast, the heteroskedasticity-robust F-statistic is valid whether the error term is homoskedastic or heteroskedastic. Despite this significant limitation of the homoskedasticity-only F-statistic, its simple formula sheds light on what the F-statistic is doing. In addition, the simple formula can be computed using standard regression output, such as might be reported in a table that includes regression R^2's but not F-statistics.

The homoskedasticity-only F-statistic is computed using a simple formula based on the sum of squared residuals from two regressions. In the first regression, called the **restricted regression**, the null hypothesis is forced to be true. When the null hypothesis is of the type in Equation (10.8), where all the hypothesized values are zero, the restricted regression is the regression in which those coefficients are set to zero, that is, the relevant regressors are excluded from the regression. In the second regression, called the **unrestricted regression**, the alternative hypothesis is allowed to be true. If the sum of squared residuals is sufficiently smaller in the unrestricted than the restricted regression, then the test rejects the null hypothesis.

The **homoskedasticity-only *F*-statistic** is given by the formula

$$F = \frac{(SSR_{restricted} - SSR_{unrestricted})/q}{SSR_{unrestricted}/(n - k_{unrestricted} - 1)} \tag{10.13}$$

where $SSR_{restricted}$ is the sum of squared residuals from the restricted regression, $SSR_{unrestricted}$ is the sum of squared residuals from the unrestricted regression, q is the number of restrictions under the null hypothesis, and $k_{unrestricted}$ is the number of regressors in the unrestricted regression. An alternative equivalent formula for the homoskedasticity-only F-statistic is based on the R^2 of the two regressions:

$$F = \frac{(R^2_{unrestricted} - R^2_{restricted})/q}{(1 - R^2_{unrestricted})/(n - k_{unrestricted} - 1)} \tag{10.14}$$

If the errors are homoskedastic, then the difference between the homoskedasticity-only F-statistic computed using Equation (10.13) or (10.14) and the heteroskedasticity-robust F-statistic vanishes as the sample size n increases. Thus, if the errors are homoskedastic, the sampling distribution of the rule-of-thumb F-statistic under the null hypothesis is, in large samples, $F_{q,\infty}$.

The formulas in Equations (10.13) and (10.14) are easy to compute and have an intuitive interpretation in terms of how well the unrestricted and restricted regressions fit the data. Unfortunately, they are valid only if the errors are homoskedastic. Because homoskedasticity is a special case that cannot be counted on in applications with economic data, or more generally with data sets typically found in the social sciences, in practice the homoskedasticity-only F-statistic is not a satisfactory substitute for the heteroskedasticity-robust F-statistic.

Using the Homoskedasticity-Only F-Statistic when n Is Small

If the errors are homoskedastic and are i.i.d. normally distributed, then the homoskedasticity-only F-statistic defined in Equations (10.13) and (10.14) has an $F_{q,n-k_{unrestricted}-1}$ distribution under the null hypothesis. Critical values for this distribution depend on both q and $n - k_{unrestricted} - 1$. As discussed, the $F_{q,n-k_{unrestricted}-1}$ distribution converges to the $F_{q,\infty}$ distribution as n increases; for large sample sizes, the differences between the two distributions are negligible. For small samples, however, the two sets of critical values differ.

Application to Test Scores and the Student–Teacher Ratio

To test the null hypothesis that the population coefficients on STR and $Expn$ are 0, controlling for $PctEL$, we need to compute the SSR (or R^2) for the restricted and unrestricted regression. The unrestricted regression has the regressors STR, $Expn$, and $PctEL$, and is given in Equation (10.6); its R^2 is 0.4366; that is, $R^2_{unrestricted} = 0.4366$. The restricted regression imposes the joint null hypothesis that the true coefficients on STR and $Expn$ are zero; that is, under the null hypothesis STR and $Expn$ do not enter the population regression, although $PctEL$ does (the null hypothesis does not restrict the coefficient on $PctEL$). The restricted regression, estimated by OLS, is

$$\widehat{TestScore} = 664.7 - 0.671 \times PctEL, R^2 = 0.4149$$
$$(1.0) \quad (0.032) \qquad\qquad\qquad \textbf{(10.15)}$$

so $R^2_{restricted} = 0.4149$. The number of restrictions is $q = 2$, the number of observations is $n = 420$, and the number of regressors in the unrestricted regression is $k = 3$. The homoskedasticity-only F-statistic, computed using Equation (10.14), is

$$F = [(0.4366 - 0.4149)/2]/[(1 - 0.4366)/$$
$$(420 - 3 - 1)] = 8.01$$

Because 8.01 exceeds the 1% critical value of 4.61, the hypothesis is rejected at the 1% level using this rule-of-thumb approach.

This example illustrates the advantages and disadvantages of the homoskedasticity-only F-statistic. Its advantage is that it can be computed using a calculator. Its disadvantage is that the values of the homoskedasticity-only and heteroskedasticity-robust F-statistics can be very different: The heteroskedasticity-robust F-statistic testing this joint hypothesis is 5.43, quite different from the less reliable homoskedasticity-only rule-of-thumb value of 8.01.

TESTING SINGLE RESTRICTIONS INVOLVING MULTIPLE COEFFICIENTS

Sometimes economic theory suggests a single restriction that involves two or more regression coefficients. For example, theory might suggest a null hypothesis of the form $\beta_1 = \beta_2$; that is, the effects of the first and second regressor are the same. In this case, the task is to test this null hypothesis against the alternative that the two coefficients differ:

$$H_0: \beta_1 = \beta_2 \text{ vs. } H_1: \beta_1 \neq \beta_2 \qquad \textbf{(10.16)}$$

This null hypothesis has a single restriction, so $q = 1$, but that restriction involves multiple coefficients (β_1 and β_2). We need to modify the methods presented so far to test this hypothesis. There are two approaches; which one will be easiest depends on your software.

Approach #1: Test the Restriction Directly

Some statistical packages have a specialized command designed to test restrictions like Equation (10.16) and the result is an F-statistic that, because $q = 1$, has an $F_{1,\infty}$ distribution under the null hypothesis. (Recall that the square of a standard normal random variable has an $F_{1,\infty}$ distribution, so the 95% percentile of the $F_{1,\infty}$ distribution is $1.96^2 = 3.84$.)

Approach #2: Transform the Regression

If your statistical package cannot test the restriction directly, the hypothesis in Equation (10.16) can be tested using a trick in which the original regression equation is rewritten to turn the restriction in Equation (10.16) into a restriction on a single regression coefficient. To be concrete, suppose there are only two regressors, X_{1i} and X_{2i} in the regression, so the population regression has the form

$$Y_i = \beta_0 + \beta_1 X_{1i} + \beta_2 X_{2i} + u_i \qquad \textbf{(10.17)}$$

Here is the trick: By subtracting and adding $\beta_2 X_{1i}$, we have that $\beta_1 X_{1i} + \beta_2 X_{2i} = \beta_1 X_{1i} - \beta_2 X_{1i} + \beta_2 X_{1i} + \beta_2 X_{2i} = (\beta_1 - \beta_2)X_{1i} + \beta_2(X_{1i} + X_{2i}) = \gamma_1 X_{1i} + \beta_2 W_i$, where $\gamma_1 = \beta_1 - \beta_2$ and $W_i = X_{1i} + X_{2i}$. Thus, the population regression in Equation (10.17) can be rewritten as

$$Y_i = \beta_0 + \gamma_1 X_{1i} + \beta_2 W_i + u_i \qquad \textbf{(10.18)}$$

Because the coefficient γ_1 in this equation is $\gamma_1 = \beta_1 - \beta_2$, under the null hypothesis in Equation (10.16), $\gamma_1 = 0$ while under the alternative, $\gamma_1 \neq 0$. Thus, by turning Equation (10.17) into Equation (10.18), we have turned a restriction on two regression coefficients into a restriction on a single regression coefficient.

Because the restriction now involves the single coefficient γ_1, the null hypothesis in Equation (10.16) can be tested using the t-statistic method explained earlier. In practice, this is done by first constructing the new regressor W_i as the sum of the two original regressors, then estimating the regression of Y_i on X_{1i} and W_i. A 95% confidence interval for the difference in the coefficients $\beta_1 - \beta_2$ can be calculated as $\hat{\gamma}_1 \pm 1.96 SE(\hat{\gamma}_1)$.

This method can be extended to other restrictions on regression equations using the same trick.

The two methods (Approaches #1 and #2) are equivalent, in the sense that the F-statistic from the first method equals the square of the t-statistic from the second method.

Extension to q > 1

In general it is possible to have q restrictions under the null hypothesis in which some or all of these restrictions involve multiple coefficients. The F-statistic from earlier extends to this type of joint hypothesis. The F-statistic can be computed by either of the two methods just discussed for $q = 1$. Precisely how best to do this in practice depends on the specific regression software being used.

CONFIDENCE SETS FOR MULTIPLE COEFFICIENTS

This section explains how to construct a confidence set for two or more regression coefficients. The method is conceptually similar to the method in the first section for constructing a confidence set for a single coefficient using the t-statistic, except that the confidence set for multiple coefficients is based on the F-statistic.

A **95% confidence set** for two or more coefficients is a set that contains the true population values of these coefficients in 95% of randomly drawn samples. Thus, a confidence set is the generalization to two or more coefficients of a confidence interval for a single coefficient.

Recall that a 95% confidence interval is computed by finding the set of values of the coefficients that are not rejected using a t-statistic at the 5% significance level. This approach can be extended to the case of multiple coefficients. To make this concrete, suppose you are interested in constructing a confidence set for two coefficients, β_1 and β_2. Previously we showed how to use the F-statistic to test a joint null hypothesis that $\beta_1 = \beta_{1,0}$ and $\beta_2 = \beta_{2,0}$. Suppose you were to test every possible value of $\beta_{1,0}$ and $\beta_{2,0}$ at the 5% level. For each pair of candidates $(\beta_{1,0}, \beta_{2,0})$, you construct the F-statistic and reject it if it exceeds the 5% critical value of 3.00. Because the test has a 5% significance level, the true population values of β_1 and β_2 will not be rejected in 95% of all samples. Thus, the set of values not rejected at the 5% level by this F-statistic constitutes a 95% confidence set for β_1 and β_2.

Although this method of trying all possible values of $\beta_{1,0}$ and $\beta_{2,0}$ works in theory, in practice it is much simpler to use an explicit formula for the confidence set. This formula for the confidence set for an arbitrary number of coefficients is based on the formula for the F-statistic. When there are two coefficients, the resulting confidence sets are ellipses.

As an illustration, Figure 10-1 shows a 95% confidence set (confidence ellipse) for the coefficients on the student–teacher ratio and expenditure per pupil, holding constant the percentage of English learners, based on the estimated regression in Equation (10.6). This ellipse does not include the point (0,0). This means that the null hypothesis that these two coefficients are both zero is rejected using the F-statistic at the 5% significance level, which we already knew from earlier. The confidence ellipse is a fat

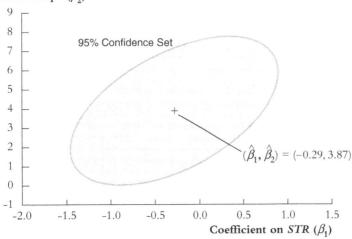

Coefficient on *Expn* (β_2)

FIGURE 10-1 95% confidence set for coefficients on *STR* and *Expn* from Equation (10.6).

The 95% confidence set for the coefficients on *STR* (β_1) and *Expn* (β_2) is an ellipse. The ellipse contains the pairs of values of β_1 and β_2 that cannot be rejected using the *F*-statistic at the 5% significance level.

sausage with the long part of the sausage oriented in the lower-left/upper-right direction. The reason for this orientation is that the estimated correlation between $\hat{\beta}_1$ and $\hat{\beta}_2$ is positive, which in turn arises because the correlation between the regressors *STR* and *Expn* is negative (schools that spend more per pupil tend to have fewer students per teacher).

MODEL SPECIFICATION FOR MULTIPLE REGRESSION

The job of determining which variables to include in multiple regression—that is, the problem of choosing a regression specification—can be quite challenging, and no single rule applies in all situations. But do not despair, because some useful guidelines are available. The starting point for choosing a regression specification is thinking through the possible sources of omitted variable bias. It is important to rely on your expert knowledge of the empirical problem and to focus on obtaining an unbiased estimate of the causal effect of interest; do not rely solely on purely statistical measures of fit such as the R^2 or $\overline{R}^2$.

Omitted Variable Bias in Multiple Regression

The OLS estimators of the coefficients in multiple regression will have omitted variable bias if an omitted determinant of Y_i is correlated with at least one of the regressors. For example, students from affluent families often have more learning opportunities than do their less affluent peers, which could lead to better test scores. Moreover, if the district is a wealthy one, then the schools will tend to have larger budgets and lower student-teacher ratios. If so, the affluence of the students and the student-teacher ratio would be negatively correlated, and the OLS estimate of the coefficient on the student-teacher ratio would pick up the effect of average district income, even after controlling for the percentage of English learners. In short, omitting the students' economic background could lead to omitted variable bias in the regression of test scores on the student-teacher ratio and the percentage of English learners.

The general conditions for omitted variable bias in multiple regression are similar to those for a single regressor: If an omitted variable is a determinant of Y_i and if it is correlated with at least one of the regressors, then the OLS estimators will have omitted variable bias. As was discussed previously, the OLS estimators are correlated, so in general the OLS estimators of all the coefficients will be biased. The two conditions for omitted variable bias in multiple regression are summarized in Box 10-3.

At a mathematical level, if the two conditions for omitted variable bias are satisfied, then at least one of the

---

BOX 10-3 Omitted Variable Bias in Multiple Regression

Omitted variable bias is the bias in the OLS estimator that arises when one or more included regressors are correlated with an omitted variable. For omitted variable bias to arise, two things must be true:

1. At least one of the included regressors must be correlated with the omitted variable.

2. The omitted variable must be a determinant of the dependent variable, *Y*.

---

regressors is correlated with the error term. This means that the conditional expectation of u_i given $X_{1i}, \ldots, X_{ki}$ is nonzero, so that the first least squares assumption is violated. As a result, the omitted variable bias persists even if the sample size is large, that is, omitted variable bias implies that the OLS estimators are inconsistent.

Model Specification in Theory and in Practice

In theory, when data are available on the omitted variable, the solution to omitted variable bias is to include the omitted variable in the regression. In practice, however, deciding whether to include a particular variable can be difficult and requires judgment.

Our approach to the challenge of potential omitted variable bias is twofold. First, a core or base set of regressors should be chosen using a combination of expert judgment, economic theory, and knowledge of how the data were collected; the regression using this base set of regressors is sometimes referred to as a **base specification**. This base specification should contain the variables of primary interest and the control variables suggested by expert judgment and economic theory. Expert judgment and economic theory are rarely decisive, however, and often the variables suggested by economic theory are not the ones on which you have data. Therefore the next step is to develop a list of candidate **alternative specifications**, that is, alternative sets of regressors. If the estimates of the coefficients of interest are numerically similar across the alternative specifications, then this provides evidence that the estimates from your base specification are reliable. If, on the other hand, the estimates of the coefficients of interest change substantially across specifications, this often provides evidence that the original specification had omitted variable bias.

Interpreting the R^2 and the Adjusted R^2 in Practice

An R^2 or an $\overline{R}^2$ near 1 means that the regressors are good at predicting the values of the dependent variable in the sample, and an R^2 or an $\overline{R}^2$ near 0 means they are not. This makes these statistics useful summaries of the predictive ability of the regression. However, it is easy to read more into them than they deserve.

There are four potential pitfalls to guard against when using the R^2 or $\overline{R}^2$:

1. ***An increase in the R^2 or $\overline{R}^2$ does not necessarily mean that an added variable is statistically significant.*** The R^2 increases whenever you add a regressor, whether or not it is statistically significant. The $\overline{R}^2$ does not always increase, but if it does this does not necessarily mean that the coefficient on that added regressor is statistically significant. To ascertain whether an added variable is statistically significant, you need to perform a hypothesis test using the t-statistic.

2. ***A high R^2 or $\overline{R}^2$ does not mean that the regressors are a true cause of the dependent variable.*** Imagine regressing test scores against parking lot area per pupil. Parking lot area is correlated with the student–teacher ratio, with whether the school is in a suburb or a city, and possibly with district income—all things that are correlated with test scores. Thus the regression of test scores on parking lot area per pupil could have a high R^2 and $\overline{R}^2$, but the relationship is not causal (try telling the superintendent that the way to increase test scores is to increase parking space!).

3. ***A high R^2 or $\overline{R}^2$ does not mean there is no omitted variable bias.*** Recall the discussion which concerned omitted variable bias in the regression of test scores on the student–teacher ratio. The R^2 of the regression never came up because it played no logical role in this discussion. Omitted variable bias can occur in regressions with a low R^2, a moderate R^2, or a high R^2. Conversely, a low R^2 does not imply that there necessarily is omitted variable bias.

4. ***A high R^2 or $\overline{R}^2$ does not necessarily mean you have the most appropriate set of regressors, nor does a low R^2 or $\overline{R}^2$ necessarily mean you have an inappropriate set of regressors.*** The question of what constitutes the right set of regressors in multiple regression is difficult and we return to it throughout this textbook. Decisions about the regressors must weigh issues of omitted variable bias, data availability, data quality, and, most importantly, economic theory and the nature of the substantive questions being addressed. None of these questions can be answered simply by having a high (or low) regression R^2 or $\overline{R}^2$.

These points are summarized in Box 10-4.

The R^2 and $\overline{R}^2$ tell you whether the regressors are good at predicting, or "explaining," the values of the dependent variable in the sample of data on hand. If the R^2 (or $\overline{R}^2$) is nearly 1, then the regressors produce good predictions of the dependent variable in that sample, in the sense that the variance of the OLS residual is small compared to the variance of the dependent variable. If the R^2 (or $\overline{R}^2$) is nearly 0, the opposite is true.

The R^2 and $\overline{R}^2$ do NOT tell you whether:

1. An included variable is statistically significant;
2. The regressors are a true cause of the movements in the dependent variable;
3. There is omitted variable bias; or
4. You have chosen the most appropriate set of regressors.

ANALYSIS OF THE TEST SCORE DATA SET

This section presents an analysis of the effect on test scores of the student–teacher ratio using the California data set. Our primary purpose is to provide an example in which multiple regression analysis is used to mitigate omitted variable bias. Our secondary purpose is to demonstrate how to use a table to summarize regression results.

Discussion of the Base and Alternative Specifications

This analysis focuses on estimating the effect on test scores of a change in the student–teacher ratio, holding constant student characteristics that the superintendent cannot control. Many factors potentially affect the average test score in a district. Some of the factors that could affect test scores are correlated with the student–teacher ratio, so omitting them from the regression will result in omitted variable bias. If data are available on these omitted variables, the solution to this problem is to include them as additional regressors in the multiple regression. When we do this, the coefficient on the student–teacher ratio is the effect of a change in the student–teacher ratio, holding constant these other factors.

Here we consider three variables that control for background characteristics of the students that could affect test scores. One of these control variables is the one we have used previously, the fraction of students who are still learning English. The two other variables are new and control for the economic background of the students. There is no perfect measure of economic background in the data set, so instead we use two imperfect indicators of low income in the district. The first new variable is the percentage of students who are eligible for receiving a subsidized or free lunch at school. Students are eligible for this program if their family income is less than a certain threshold (approximately 150% of the poverty line). The second new variable is the percentage of students in the district whose families qualify for a California income assistance program. Families are eligible for this income assistance program depending in part on their family income, but the threshold is lower (stricter) than the threshold for the subsidized lunch program. These two variables thus measure the fraction of economically disadvantaged children in the district; although they are related, they are not perfectly correlated (their correlation coefficient is 0.74). Although theory suggests that economic background could be an important omitted factor, theory and expert judgment do not really help us decide which of these two variables (percentage eligible for a subsidized lunch or percentage eligible for income assistance) is a better measure of background. For our base specification, we choose the percentage eligible for a subsidized lunch as the economic background variable, but we consider an alternative specification that includes the other variable as well.

Scatterplots of tests scores and these variables are presented in Figure 10-2. Each of these variables exhibits a negative correlation with test scores. The correlation between test scores and the percentage of English learners is −0.64; between test scores and the percentage eligible for a subsidized lunch is −0.87; and between test scores and the percentage qualifying for income assistance is −0.63.

What Scale Should We Use for the Regressors?

A practical question that arises in regression analysis is what scale you should use for the regressors. In Figure 10-2, the units of the variables are percent, so the maximum possible range of the data is 0 to 100. Alternatively, we could have defined these variables to be a

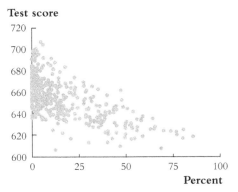

(a) Percentage of English language learners

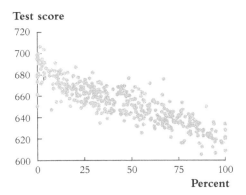

(b) Percentage qualifying for reduced price lunch

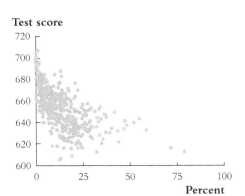

(c) Percentage qualifying for income assistance

FIGURE 10-2 Scatterplots of test scores vs. three student characteristics.

The scatterplots show a negative relationship between test scores and (a) the percentage of English learners (correlation = −0.64), (b) the percentage of students qualifying for a subsidized lunch (correlation = −0.87), and (c) the percentage qualifying for income assistance (correlation = −0.63).

R^2 and *SER*; however, the coefficient on *FracEL* would have been −65.0. In the specification with *PctEL*, the coefficient is the predicted change in test scores for a one-percentage-point increase in English learners, holding *STR* constant; in the specification with *FracEL*, the coefficient is the predicted change in test scores for an increase by 1 in the fraction of English learners—that is, for a 100-percentage-point-increase—holding *STR* constant. Although these two specifications are mathematically equivalent, for the purposes of interpretation the one with *PctEL* seems, to us, more natural.

Another consideration when deciding on a scale is to choose the units of the regressors so that the resulting regression coefficients are easy to read. For example, if a regressor is measured in dollars and has a coefficient of 0.00000356, it is easier to read if the regressor is converted to millions of dollars and the coefficient 3.56 is reported.

decimal fraction rather than a percent; for example, *PctEL* could be replaced by the *fraction* of English learners, *FracEL* (= *PctEL*/100), which would range between 0 and 1 instead of between 0 and 100. More generally, in regression analysis some decision usually needs to be made about the scale of both the dependent and independent variables. How, then, should you choose the scale, or units, of the variables?

The general answer to the question of choosing the scale of the variables is to make the regression results easy to read and to interpret. In the test score application, the natural unit for the dependent variable is the score of the test itself. In the regression of *TestScore* on *STR* and *PctEL* reported in Equation (10.5), the coefficient on *PctEL* is −0.650. If instead the regressor had been *FracEL*, the regression would have had an identical

Tabular Presentation of Result

We are now faced with a communication problem. What is the best way to show the results from several multiple regressions that contain different subsets of the possible regressors? So far, we have presented regression results by writing out the estimated regression equations, as in Equation (10.6). This works well when there are only a few regressors and only a few equations, but with more regressors and equations this method of presentation can be confusing. A better way to communicate the results of several regressions is in a table.

Table 10-1 summarizes the results of regressions of the test score on various sets of regressors. Each column summarizes a separate regression. Each regression has the same dependent variable, test score. The entries in the first five

TABLE 10-1 Results of Regressions of Test Scores on the Student–Teacher Ratio and Student Characteristic Control Variables Using California Elementary School Districts

Dependent Variable: Average Test Score in the District

Regressor	(1)	(2)	(3)	(4)	(5)
Student–teacher ratio (X_1)	−2.28** (0.52)	−1.10* (0.43)	−1.00** (0.27)	−1.31** (0.34)	−1.01** (0.27)
Percent English learners (X_2)		−0.650** (0.031)	−0.122** (0.033)	−0.488** (0.030)	−0.130** (0.036)
Percent eligible for subsidized lunch (X_3)			−0.547** (0.024)		−0.529** (0.038)
Percent on public income assistance (X_4)				−0.790** (0.068)	0.048 (0.059)
Intercept	698.9** (10.4)	686.0** (8.7)	700.2** (5.6)	698.0** (6.9)	700.4** (5.5)
Summary Statistics					
SER	18.58	14.46	9.08	11.65	9.08
$\overline{R}^2$	0.049	0.424	0.773	0.626	0.773
n	420	420	420	420	420

These regressions were estimated using the data on K–8 school districts in California, described in Appendix A in Chapter 7. Standard errors are given in parentheses under coefficients. The individual coefficient is statistically significant at the *5% level or **1% significance level using a two-sided test.

rows are the estimated regression coefficients, with their standard errors below them in parentheses. The asterisks indicate whether the t-statistics, testing the hypothesis that the relevant coefficient is zero, is significant at the 5% level (one asterisk) or the 1% level (two asterisks). The final three rows contain summary statistics for the regression (the standard error of the regression, SER, and the adjusted R^2, $\overline{R}^2$) and the sample size (which is the same for all of the regressions, 420 observations).

All the information that we have presented so far in equation format appears as a column of this table. For example, consider the regression of the test score against the student–teacher ratio, with no control variables. In equation form, this regression is

$$\widehat{TestScore} = 698.9 - 2.28 \times STR, \overline{R}^2 = 0.049,$$
$$(10.4)(0.52)$$
$$SER = 18.58, n = 420 \qquad \textbf{(10.19)}$$

All this information appears in column (1) of Table 10-1. The estimated coefficient on the student–teacher ratio

(−2.28) appears in the first row of numerical entries, and its standard error (0.52) appears in parentheses just below the estimated coefficient. The intercept (698.9) and its standard error (10.4) are given in the row labeled "Intercept." (Sometimes you will see this row labeled "constant" because, as discussed earlier, the intercept can be viewed as the coefficient on a regressor that is always equal to 1.) Similarly, the $\overline{R}^2$ (0.049), the SER (18.58), and the sample size n (420) appear in the final rows. The blank entries in the rows of the other regressors indicate that those regressors are not included in this regression.

Although the table does not report t-statistics, these can be computed from the information provided; for example, the t-statistic testing the hypothesis that the coefficient on the student–teacher ratio in column (1) is zero is −2.28/0.52 = −4.38. This hypothesis is rejected at the 1% level, which is indicated by the double asterisk next to the estimated coefficient in the table.

Regressions that include the control variables measuring student characteristics are reported in columns (2)–(5).

Column (2), which reports the regression of test scores on the student–teacher ratio and on the percentage of English learners, was previously stated as Equation (10.5).

Column (3) presents the base specification, in which the regressors are the student–teacher ratio and two control variables, the percentage of English learners and the percentage of students eligible for a free lunch.

Columns (4) and (5) present alternative specifications that examine the effect of changes in the way the economic background of the students is measured. In column (4), the percentage of students on income assistance is included as a regressor, and in column (5) both of the economic background variables are included.

Discussion of Empirical Results

These results suggest three conclusions:

1. Controlling for these student characteristics cuts the effect of the student–teacher ratio on test scores approximately in half. This estimated effect is not very sensitive to which specific control variables are included in the regression. In all cases the coefficient on the student–teacher ratio remains statistically significant at the 5% level. In the four specifications with control variables, regressions (2)–(5), reducing the student–teacher ratio by one student per teacher is estimated to increase average test scores by approximately one point, holding constant student characteristics.

2. The student characteristic variables are very useful predictors of test scores. The student–teacher ratio alone explains only a small fraction of the variation in test scores: The $\overline{R}^2$ in column (1) is 0.049. The $\overline{R}^2$ jumps, however, when the student characteristic variables are added. For example, the $\overline{R}^2$ in the base specification, regression (3), is 0.773. The signs of the coefficients on the student demographic variables are consistent with the patterns seen in Figure 10-2: Districts with many English learners and districts with many poor children have lower test scores.

3. The control variables are not always individually statistically significant: In specification (5), the hypothesis that the coefficient on the percentage qualifying for income assistance is zero is not rejected at the 5% level (the t-statistic is -0.82). Because adding this control variable to the base specification (3) has a negligible effect on the estimated coefficient for the student–teacher

ratio and its standard error, and because the coefficient on this control variable is not significant in specification (5), this additional control variable is redundant, at least for the purposes of this analysis.

CONCLUSION

Chapter 9 began with a concern: In the regression of test scores against the student–teacher ratio, omitted student characteristics that influence test scores might be correlated with the student–teacher ratio in the district, and if so the student–teacher ratio in the district would pick up the effect on test scores of these omitted student characteristics. Thus, the OLS estimator would have omitted variable bias. To mitigate this potential omitted variable bias, we augmented the regression by including variables that control for various student characteristics (the percentage of English learners and two measures of student economic background). Doing so cuts the estimated effect of a unit change in the student–teacher ratio in half, although it remains possible to reject the null hypothesis that the population effect on test scores, holding these control variables constant, is zero at the 5% significance level. Because they eliminate omitted variable bias arising from these student characteristics, these multiple regression estimates, hypothesis tests, and confidence intervals are much more useful for advising the superintendent than the single-regressor estimates of Chapters 7 and 8.

The analysis in this and the preceding chapter has presumed that the population regression function is linear in the regressors—that is, that the conditional expectation of Y_i given the regressors is a straight line. There is, however, no particular reason to think this is so. In fact, the effect of reducing the student–teacher ratio might be quite different in districts with large classes than in districts that already have small classes. If so, the population regression line is not linear in the X's but rather is a nonlinear function of the X's.

SUMMARY

1. Hypothesis tests and confidence intervals for a single regression coefficient are carried out using essentially the same procedures that were used in the

one-variable linear regression model of Chapter 8. For example, a 95% confidence interval for β_1 is given by $\hat{\beta}_1 \pm 1.96SE(\hat{\beta}_1)$.

2. Hypotheses involving more than one restriction on the coefficients are called joint hypotheses. Joint hypotheses can be tested using an F-statistic.

3. Regression specification proceeds by first determining a base specification chosen to address concern about omitted variable bias. The base specification can be modified by including additional regressors that address other potential sources of omitted variable bias. Simply choosing the specification with the highest R^2 can lead to regression models that do not estimate the causal effect of interest.

Key Terms

restrictions (141)
joint hypothesis (141)
F-statistic (142)
restricted regression (143)
unrestricted regression (143)
homoskedasticity-only F-statistic (143)
95% confidence set (145)
base specification (147)
alternative specifications (147)
Bonferroni test (152)

APPENDIX

The Bonferroni Test of a Joint Hypothesis

The method described in the second section of this chapter is the preferred way to test joint hypotheses in multiple regression. However, if the author of a study presents regression results but did not test a joint restriction in which you are interested, and you do not have the original data, then you will not be able to compute the F-statistic as shown earlier. This appendix describes a way to test joint hypotheses that can be used when you only have a table of regression results. This method is an application of a very general testing approach based on Bonferroni's inequality.

The Bonferroni test is a test of a joint hypothesis based on the t-statistics for the individual hypotheses; that is, the

Bonferroni test is the one-at-a-time t-statistic test done properly. The **Bonferroni test** of the joint null hypothesis $\beta_1 = \beta_{1,0}$ and $\beta_2 = \beta_{2,0}$ based on the critical value $c > 0$ uses the following rule:

Accept if $|t_1| \leq c$ and if $|t_2| \leq c$; otherwise reject

(Bonferroni one-at-a-time t-statistic test) **(10.20)**

where t_1 and t_2 are the t-statistics that test the restrictions on β_1 and β_2, respectfully.

The trick is to choose the critical value c in such a way that the probability that the one-at-a-time test rejects when the null hypothesis is true is no more than the desired significance level, say 5%. This is done by using Bonferroni's inequality to choose the critical value c to allow both for the fact that two restrictions are being tested and for any possible correlation between t_1 and t_2.

Bonferroni's Inequality

Bonferroni's inequality is a basic result of probability theory. Let A and B be events. Let $A \cap B$ be the event "both A and B" (the intersection of A and B), and let $A \cup B$ be the event "A or B or both" (the union of A and B). Then $\Pr(A \cup B) = \Pr(A) + \Pr(B) - \Pr(A \cap B)$. Because $\Pr(A \cap B) \geq 0$, it follows that $\Pr(A \cup B) \leq \Pr(A) + \Pr(B)$. This inequality in turn implies that $1 - \Pr(A \cup B) \geq 1 - [\Pr(A) + \Pr(B)]$. Let A^c and B^c be the complements of A and B, that is, the events "not A" and "not B." Because the complement of $A \cup B$ is $A^c \cap B^c$, $1 - \Pr(A \cup B) = \Pr(A^c \cap B^c)$, which yields Bonferroni's inequality, $\Pr(A^c \cap B^c) \geq 1 - [\Pr(A) + \Pr(B)]$.

Now let A be the event that $|t_1| > c$ and B be the event that $|t_2| > c$. Then the inequality $\Pr(A \cup B) \leq \Pr(A) + \Pr(B)$ yields

$$\Pr(|t_1| > c \text{ or } |t_2| > c \text{ or both})$$
$$\leq \Pr(|t_1| > c) + \Pr(|t_2| > c) \quad \textbf{(10.21)}$$

Bonferroni Tests

Because the event "$|t_1| > c$ or $|t_2| > c$ or both" is the rejection region of the one-at-a-time test, Equation (10.21) provides a way to choose the critical value c so that the "one at a time" t-statistic has the desired significance level in large samples. Under the null hypothesis in large samples, $\Pr(|t_1| > c) = \Pr(|t_2| > c) = \Pr(|Z| > c)$. Thus

TABLE 10-2 Bonferroni Critical Values c for the One-at-a-Time t-Statistic Test of a Joint Hypothesis

Number of Restrictions (q)	Significance Level		
	10%	5%	1%
2	1.960	2.241	2.807
3	2.128	2.394	2.935
4	2.241	2.498	3.023

Equation (10.21) implies that, in large samples, the probability that the one-at-a-time test rejects under the null is

$$Pr_{H_0}(\text{one-at-a-time test rejects}) \leq 2Pr(|Z| > c) \quad \textbf{(10.22)}$$

The inequality in Equation (10.22) provides a way to choose critical value c so that the probability of the rejection under the null hypothesis equals the desired significance level. The Bonferroni approach can be extended to more than two coefficients; if there are q restrictions under the null, the factor of 2 on the right-hand side in Equation (10.22) is replaced by q.

Table 10-2 presents critical values c for the one-at-a-time Bonferroni test for various significance levels and $q = 2, 3,$ and 4. For example, suppose the desired significance level is 5% and $q = 2$. According to Table 10-2, the critical value c is 2.241. This critical value is the 1.25% percentile of the

standard normal distribution, so $Pr(|Z| > 2.241) = 2.5\%$. Thus Equation (10.22) tells us that, in large samples, the one-at-a-time test in Equation (10.20) will reject at most 5% of the time under the null hypothesis.

The critical values in Table 10-2 are larger than the critical values for testing a single restriction. For example, with $q = 2$, the one-at-a-time test rejects if at least one t-statistic exceeds 2.241 in absolute value. This critical value is greater than 1.96 because it properly corrects for the fact that, by looking at two t-statistics, you get a second chance to reject the joint null hypothesis.

If the individual t-statistics are based on heteroskedasticity-robust standard errors, then the Bonferroni test is valid whether or not there is heteroskedasticity, but if the t-statistics are based on homoskedasticity-only standard errors, the Bonferroni test is valid only under homoskedasticity.

Application to Test Scores

The t-statistics testing the joint null hypothesis that the true coefficients on test scores and expenditures per pupil in Equation (10.6) are, respectively, $t_1 = -0.60$ and $t_2 = 2.43$. Although $|t_1| < 2.241$, because $|t_2| > 2.241$, we can reject the joint null hypothesis at the 5% significance level using the Bonferroni test. However, both t_1 and t_2 are less than 2.807 in absolute value, so we cannot reject the joint null hypothesis at the 1% significance level using the Bonferroni test. In contrast, using the F-statistic, we were able to reject this hypothesis at the 1% significance level.

Modeling and Forecasting Trend

Learning Objectives

Candidates, after completing this reading, should be able to:

- Define mean squared error (MSE) and explain the implications of MSE in model selection.
- Explain how to reduce the bias associated with MSE and similar measures.

- Compare and evaluate model selection criteria, including s^2, the Akaike information criterion (AIC), and the Schwarz information criterion (SIC).
- Explain the necessary conditions for a model selection criterion to demonstrate consistency.

Excerpt is Chapter 5, Section 5.4 of Elements of Forecasting, *Fourth Edition, by Francis X. Diebold.*

The series that we want to forecast vary over time, and we often mentally attribute that variation to unobserved underlying components, such as trends . . . and cycles. In this section we focus on trend. Trend is a slow, long-run evolution in the variables that we want to model and forecast. In business, finance, and economics, for example, trend is produced by slowly evolving preferences, technologies, institutions, and demographics. We'll focus here on models of deterministic trend, in which the trend evolves in a perfectly predictable way. Deterministic trend models are tremendously useful in practice.

Existence of trend is empirically obvious. Numerous series in diverse fields display trends. How do we select among trend models when fitting a trend to a specific series?

SELECTING FORECASTING MODELS USING THE AKAIKE AND SCHWARZ CRITERIA

How do we select among trend models when fitting a trend to a specific series? What are the consequences, for example, of fitting a number of trend models and selecting the model with highest R^2? Is there a better way? This issue of **model selection** is of tremendous importance in all of forecasting, so we introduce it now.

It turns out that model selection strategies such as selecting the model with highest R^2 do *not* produce good out-of-sample forecasting models. Fortunately, however, a number of powerful modern tools exist to assist with model selection. Here we digress to discuss some of the available methods, which will be immediately useful in selecting among alternative trend models, as well as many other situations.

Most model selection criteria attempt to find the model with the smallest out-of-sample 1-step-ahead mean squared prediction error. The criteria we examine fit this general approach; the differences among criteria amount to different penalties for the number of degrees of freedom used in estimating the model (that is, the number of parameters estimated). Because all of the criteria are effectively estimates of out-of-sample mean square prediction error, they have a negative orientation—the smaller, the better.

First, consider the **mean squared error** (MSE),

$$\text{MSE} = \frac{\sum_{t=1}^{T} e_t^2}{T},$$

where T is the sample size and

$$e_t = y_t - \hat{y}_t,$$

where

$$\hat{y}_t = \hat{\beta}_0 + \hat{\beta}_1 \text{TIME}_t.$$

MSE is intimately related to two other diagnostic statistics routinely computed by regression software, the sum of squared residuals and R^2. Looking at the MSE formula reveals that the model with the smallest MSE is also the model with smallest sum of squared residuals, because scaling the sum of squared residuals by $1/T$ doesn't change the ranking. So selecting the model with the smallest MSE is equivalent to selecting the model with the smallest sum of squared residuals. Similarly, recall the formula for R^2,

$$R^2 = 1 - \frac{\sum_{t=1}^{T} e_t^2}{\sum_{t=1}^{T} (y_t - \bar{y})^2}.$$

The denominator of the ratio that appears in the formula is just the sum of squared deviations of y from its sample mean (the so-called total sum of squares), which depends only on the data, not on the particular model fit. Thus, selecting the model that minimizes the sum of squared residuals—which, as we saw, is equivalent to selecting the model that minimizes MSE—is also equivalent to selecting the model that maximizes R^2.

Selecting forecasting models on the basis of MSE or any of the equivalent forms discussed—that is, using in-sample MSE to estimate the out-of-sample 1-step-ahead MSE—turns out to be a bad idea. In-sample MSE *can't* rise when more variables are added to a model, and typically it will fall continuously as more variables are added. To see why, consider the fitting of polynomial trend models. In that context, the number of variables in the model is linked to the degree of the polynomial (call it p):

$$T_t = \beta_0 + \beta_1 \text{TIME}_t + \beta_2 \text{TIME}_t^2 + \cdots + \beta_p \text{TIME}_t^p.$$

We've already considered the cases of $p = 1$ (linear trend) and $p = 2$ (quadratic trend), but there's nothing to stop us from fitting models with higher powers of time included. As we include higher powers of time, the sum of squared residuals *can't* rise, because the estimated parameters are explicitly chosen to *minimize* the sum of squared residuals. The last-included power of time could always wind up with an estimated coefficient of 0; to the extent that the estimate is anything else, the sum of squared residuals must have fallen. Thus, the more variables we include in a forecasting model, the lower the sum of squared residuals will be, and therefore the lower MSE will be, and the higher R^2 will be. The reduction in MSE as higher powers of time are included in the model occurs even if they are in fact of no use in forecasting the variable of interest. Again, the sum of squared residuals can't rise, and because of sampling error, it's very unlikely that we'd get a coefficient of exactly 0 on a newly included variable even if the coefficient is 0 in population.

The effects described here go under various names, including **in-sample overfitting** and **data mining**, reflecting the idea that including more variables in a forecasting model won't necessarily improve its out-of-sample forecasting performance, although it will improve the model's "fit" on historical data. The upshot is that MSE is a biased estimator of **out-of-sample 1-step-ahead prediction error variance**, and the size of the bias increases with the number of variables included in the model. The direction of the bias is downward—in-sample MSE provides an overly optimistic (that is, too small) assessment of out-of-sample prediction error variance.

To reduce the bias associated with MSE and its relatives, we need to penalize for degrees of freedom used. Thus, let's consider the mean squared error corrected for degrees of freedom,

$$s^2 = \frac{\sum_{t=1}^{T} e_t^2}{T - k},$$

where k is the number of degrees of freedom used in model fitting,[1] and s^2 is just the usual unbiased estimate of the regression disturbance variance. That is, it is the square of the usual standard error of the regression. So selecting the model that minimizes s^2 is also equivalent to selecting the model that minimizes the standard error of

the regression. Also, s^2 is intimately connected to the R^2 adjusted for degrees of freedom (the adjusted R^2, or $\bar{R}^2$). Recall that

$$\bar{R}^2 = 1 - \frac{\sum_{t=1}^{T} e_t^2 / (T - k)}{\sum_{t=1}^{T} (y_t - \bar{y})^2 / (T - 1)} = 1 - \frac{s^2}{\sum_{t=1}^{T} (y_t - \bar{y})^2 / (T - 1)}.$$

The denominator of the $\bar{R}^2$ expression depends only on the data, not the particular model fit, so the model that minimizes s^2 is also the model that maximizes $\bar{R}^2$. In short, the strategies of selecting the model that minimizes s^2, or the model that minimizes the standard error of the regression, or the model that maximizes $\bar{R}^2$, are equivalent, and they *do* penalize for degrees of freedom used.

To highlight the degree-of-freedom penalty, let's rewrite s^2 as a penalty factor times the MSE,

$$s^2 = \left(\frac{T}{T - k}\right) \frac{\sum_{t=1}^{T} e_t^2}{T}.$$

Note in particular that including more variables in a regression will not necessarily lower s^2 or raise $\bar{R}^2$—the MSE will fall, but the degrees-of-freedom penalty will rise, so the product could go either way.

As with s^2, many of the most important forecast model selection criteria are of the form "penalty factor times MSE." The idea is simply that if we want to get an accurate estimate of the 1-step-ahead out-of-sample prediction error variance, we need to penalize the in-sample residual variance (the MSE) to reflect the degrees of freedom used. Two very important such criteria are the Akaike information criterion (AIC) and the Schwarz information criterion (SIC). Their formulas are

$$AIC = e^{\left(\frac{2k}{T}\right)} \frac{\sum_{t=1}^{T} e_t^2}{T}$$

and

$$SIC = T^{\left(\frac{k}{T}\right)} \frac{\sum_{t=1}^{T} e_t^2}{T}.$$

How do the penalty factors associated with MSE, s^2, AIC, and SIC compare in terms of severity? All of the penalty factors are functions of k/T, the number of parameters

---

[1] The degrees of freedom used in model fitting is simply the number of parameters estimated.

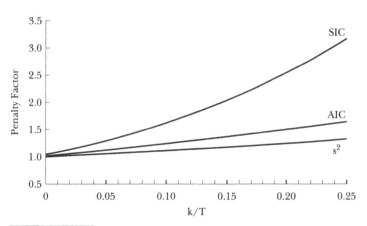

FIGURE 11-1 Degrees-of-freedom penalties, various model selection criteria.

estimated per sample observation, and we can compare the penalty factors graphically as k/T varies. In Figure 11-1, we show the penalties as k/T moves from 0 to 0.25, for a sample size of $T = 100$. The s^2 penalty is small and rises slowly with k/T; the AIC penalty is a bit larger and still rises only slowly with k/T. The SIC penalty, on the other hand, is substantially larger and rises at a slightly increasing rate with k/T.

It's clear that the different criteria penalize degrees of freedom differently. In addition, we could propose many other criteria by altering the penalty. How, then, do we select among the criteria? More generally, what properties might we expect a "good" model selection criterion to have? Are s^2, AIC, and SIC "good" model selection criteria?

We evaluate model selection criteria in terms of a key property called **consistency**. A model selection criterion is consistent if the following conditions are met:

a. when the true model—that is, the **data-generating process (DGP)**—is among the models considered, the probability of selecting the true DGP approaches 1 as the sample size gets large; and

b. when the true model is *not* among those considered, so that it's impossible to select the true DGP, the probability of selecting the best *approximation* to the true DGP approaches 1 as the sample size gets large.[2]

---

[2] Most model selection criteria—including all of those discussed here—assess goodness of approximation in terms of 1-step-ahead mean squared forecast error.

Consistency is, of course, desirable. If the DGP is among those considered, then we'd hope that as the sample size gets large, we'd eventually select it. Of course, all of our models are false—they're intentional simplifications of a much more complex reality. Thus, the second notion of consistency is the more compelling.

MSE is inconsistent, because it doesn't penalize for degrees of freedom; that's why it's unattractive. s^2 does penalize for degrees of freedom but, as it turns out, not enough to render it a consistent model selection procedure. The AIC penalizes degrees of freedom more heavily than s^2, but it, too, remains inconsistent; even as the sample size gets large, the AIC selects models that are too large ("overparameterized"). The SIC, which penalizes degrees of freedom most heavily, *is* consistent.

The discussion thus far conveys the impression that SIC is unambiguously superior to AIC for selecting forecasting models, but such is not the case. Until now, we've implicitly assumed that either the true DGP or the best approximation to the true DGP is in the fixed set of models considered. In that case, SIC is a superior model selection criterion. However, a potentially more compelling view for forecasters is that both the true DGP and the best approximation to it are much more complicated than any model we fit, in which case we may want to expand the set of models we entertain as the sample size grows. We're then led to a different optimality property, called **asymptotic efficiency.** An asymptotically efficient model selection criterion chooses a sequence of models, as the sample size gets large, whose 1-step-ahead forecast error variances approach the one that would be obtained using the true model with known parameters at a rate at least as fast as that of any other model selection criterion. The AIC, although inconsistent, is asymptotically efficient, whereas the SIC is not.

In practical forecasting, we usually report and examine both AIC and SIC. Most often they select the same model. When they don't, and in spite of the theoretical asymptotic efficiency property of AIC, I recommend use of the more parsimonious model selected by the SIC, other things being equal. This approach is in accord with the KISS principle and with the results of studies comparing out-of-sample forecasting performance of models selected by various criteria.

The AIC and SIC have enjoyed widespread popularity, but they are not universally applicable, and we're still learning about their performance in specific situations. However, the general principle that we need to correct somehow for degrees of freedom when estimating out-of-sample MSE on the basis of in-sample MSE *is* universally applicable. Judicious use of criteria like the AIC and SIC, in conjunction with knowledge about the nature of the system being forecast, is helpful in a variety of forecasting situations.

Bibliographical and Computational Notes

The AIC and SIC trace at least to Akaike (1974) and Schwarz (1978).

Concepts for Review

Model selection
Mean squared error
In-sample overfitting
Data mining
Out-of-sample 1-step-ahead prediction error variance
Consistency
Data-generating process (DGP)
Asymptotic efficiency

References and Additional Readings

Akaike, H. (1974). "A New Look at the Statistical Model Identification." *IEEE Transactions on Automatic Control*, AC-19, 716–723.

Schwarz, G. (1978). "Estimating the Dimension of a Model." *Annals of Statistics*, 6, 461–464.

Characterizing Cycles

12

Learning Objectives

Candidates, after completing this reading, should be able to:

- Define covariance stationary, autocovariance function, autocorrelation function, partial autocorrelation function, and autoregression.
- Describe the requirements for a series to be covariance stationary.
- Explain the implications of working with models that are not covariance stationary.
- Define white noise, and describe independent white noise and normal (Gaussian) white noise.
- Explain the characteristics of the dynamic structure of white noise.

- Explain how a lag operator works.
- Describe Wold's theorem.
- Define a general linear process.
- Relate rational distributed lags to Wold's theorem.
- Calculate the sample mean and sample autocorrelation, and describe the Box-Pierce Q-statistic and the Ljung-Box Q-statistic.
- Describe sample partial autocorrelation.

Excerpt is Chapter 7 of Elements of Forecasting, *Fourth Edition, by Francis X. Diebold.*

We've already built forecasting models with trend and seasonal components. In this chapter, as well as the next one, we consider a crucial third component, **cycles**. When you think of a "cycle," you probably think of the sort of rigid up-and-down pattern depicted in Figure 12-1. Such cycles can sometimes arise, but cyclical fluctuations in business, finance, economics, and government are typically much less rigid. In fact, when we speak of cycles, we have in mind a much more general, all-encompassing notion of cyclicality: any sort of dynamics not captured by trends or seasonals.

Cycles, according to our broad interpretation, may display the sort of back-and-forth movement characterized in Figure 12-1, but they don't have to. All we require is that there be some dynamics, some persistence, some way in which the present is linked to the past and the future to the present. Cycles are present in most of the series that concern us, and it's crucial that we know how to model and forecast them, because their history conveys information regarding their future.

Trend and seasonal dynamics are simple, so we can capture them with simple models. Cyclical dynamics, however, are more complicated. Because of the wide variety of cyclical patterns, the sorts of models we need are substantially more involved. Thus, we split the discussion into three parts. Here in Chapter 12 we develop methods for *characterizing* cycles and in Chapter 13 we discuss *models* of cycles. This material is crucial to a real understanding of forecasting and forecasting models, and it's also a bit difficult the first time around because it's unavoidably rather mathematical, so careful, systematic study is required.

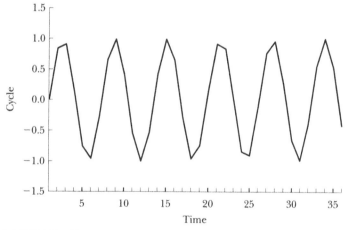

FIGURE 12-1 A rigid cyclical pattern.

COVARIANCE STATIONARY TIME SERIES

A **realization** of a time series is an ordered set, $\{\ldots, y_{-2}, y_{-1}, y_0, y_1, y_2, \ldots\}$. Typically the observations are ordered in time—hence the name **time series**—but they don't have to be. We could, for example, examine a spatial series, such as office space rental rates as we move along a line from a point in Midtown Manhattan to a point in the New York suburbs 30 miles away. But the most important case for forecasting, by far, involves observations ordered in time, so that's what we'll stress.

In theory, a time series realization begins in the infinite past and continues into the infinite future. This perspective may seem abstract and of limited practical applicability, but it will be useful in deriving certain very important properties of the forecasting models we'll be using soon. In practice, of course, the data we observe are just a finite subset of a realization, $\{y_1, \ldots, y_T\}$, called a **sample path**.

Shortly we'll be building forecasting models for cyclical time series. If the underlying probabilistic structure of the series were changing over time, we'd be doomed—there would be no way to predict the future accurately on the basis of the past, because the laws governing the future would differ from those governing the past. If we want to forecast a series, at a minimum we'd like its mean and its covariance structure (i.e., the covariances between current and past values) to be stable over time, in which case we say that the series is **covariance stationary**.

Let's discuss covariance stationarity in greater depth. The first requirement for a series to be covariance stationary is that the mean of the series be stable over time. The mean of the series at time t is

$$E(y_t) = \mu_t.$$

If the mean is stable over time, as required by covariance stationarity, then we can write

$$E(y_t) = \mu,$$

for all t. Because the mean is constant over time, there's no need to put a time subscript on it.

The second requirement for a series to be covariance stationary is that its covariance structure be stable over time. Quantifying stability of the covariance structure is a bit tricky, but tremendously important, and we do it using the **autocovariance function**. The autocovariance at displacement τ is just the covariance between y_t and $y_{t-\tau}$. It will of course depend on τ, and it may also depend on t, so in general we write

$$\gamma(t, \tau) = \text{cov}(y_t, y_{t-\tau}) = E(y_t - \mu)(y_{t-\tau} - \mu).$$

If the covariance structure is stable over time, as required by covariance stationarity, then the autocovariances depend only on displacement, τ, not on time, t, and we write

$$\gamma(t, \tau) = \gamma(\tau),$$

for all t.

The autocovariance function is important because it provides a basic summary of cyclical dynamics in a covariance stationary series. By examining the autocovariance structure of a series, we learn about its dynamic behavior. We graph and examine the autocovariances as a function of τ. Note that the autocovariance function is symmetric; that is,

$$\gamma(\tau) = \gamma(-\tau),$$

for all τ. Typically, we'll consider only nonnegative values of τ. Symmetry reflects the fact that the autocovariance of a covariance stationary series depends only on displacement; it doesn't matter whether we go forward or backward. Note also that

$$\gamma(0) = \text{cov}(y_t, y_t) = \text{var}(y_t).$$

There is one more technical requirement of covariance stationarity: We require that the variance of the series—the autocovariance at displacement 0, $\gamma(0)$—be finite. It can be shown that no autocovariance can be larger in absolute value than $\gamma(0)$, so if $\gamma(0) < \infty$, then so, too, are all the other autocovariances.

It may seem that the requirements for covariance stationarity are quite stringent, which would bode poorly for our forecasting models, almost all of which invoke covariance stationarity in one way or another. It is certainly true that many economic, business, financial, and government series are not covariance stationary. An upward trend, for example, corresponds to a steadily increasing mean, and seasonality corresponds to means that vary with the season, both of which are violations of covariance stationarity.

But appearances can be deceptive. Although many series are not covariance stationary, it is frequently possible to work with models that give special treatment to nonstationary components such as trend and seasonality, so that the cyclical component that's left over is likely to be covariance stationary. We'll often adopt that strategy. Alternatively, simple transformations often appear to transform nonstationary series to covariance stationarity. For example, many series that are clearly nonstationary in levels appear covariance stationary in growth rates.

In addition, note that although covariance stationarity requires means and covariances to be stable and finite, it places no restrictions on other aspects of the distribution of the series, such as skewness and kurtosis.[1] The upshot is simple: Whether we work directly in levels and include special components for the nonstationary elements of our models, or we work on transformed data such as growth rates, the covariance stationarity assumption is not as unrealistic as it may seem.

Recall that the correlation between two random variables x and y is defined by

$$\text{corr}(x, y) = \frac{\text{cov}(x, y)}{\sigma_x \sigma_y}.$$

That is, the correlation is simply the covariance, "normalized" or "standardized," by the product of the standard deviations of x and y. Both the correlation and the covariance are measures of linear association between two random variables. The correlation is often more informative and easily interpreted, however, because the construction of the correlation coefficient guarantees that $\text{corr}(x, y) \in [-1, 1]$, whereas the covariance between the same two random variables may take any value. The correlation, moreover, does not depend on the units in which x and y are measured, whereas the covariance does. Thus, for example, if x and y have a covariance of 10 million, they're not necessarily very strongly associated, whereas if they have a correlation of .95, it is unambiguously clear that they are very strongly associated.

In light of the superior interpretability of correlations as compared with covariances, we often work with the correlation, rather than the covariance, between y_t and $y_{t-\tau}$. That is, we work with the **autocorrelation function**, $\rho(\tau)$, rather than the autocovariance function, $\gamma(\tau)$. The autocorrelation function is obtained by dividing the autocovariance function by the variance,

$$\rho(\tau) = \frac{\gamma(\tau)}{\gamma(0)}, \quad \tau = 0, 1, 2, \ldots.$$

---

[1] For that reason, covariance stationarity is sometimes called **second-order stationarity** or **weak stationarity**.

The formula for the autocorrelation is just the usual correlation formula, specialized to the correlation between y_t and $y_{t-\tau}$. To see why, note that the variance of y_t is $\gamma(0)$, and by covariance stationarity, the variance of y at any other time $y_{t-\tau}$ is also $\gamma(0)$. Thus,

$$\rho(\tau) = \frac{\text{cov}(y_t, y_{t-\tau})}{\sqrt{\text{var}(y_t)}\sqrt{\text{var}(y_{t-\tau})}}$$

$$= \frac{\gamma(\tau)}{\sqrt{\gamma(0)}\sqrt{\gamma(0)}} = \frac{\gamma(\tau)}{\gamma(0)},$$

as claimed. Note that we always have $\rho(0) = \gamma(0)/\gamma(0) = 1$, because any series is perfectly correlated with itself. Thus, the autocorrelation at displacement 0 isn't of interest; rather, only the autocorrelations *beyond* displacement 0 inform us about a series' dynamic structure.

Finally, the **partial autocorrelation function**, $p(\tau)$, is sometimes useful. $p(\tau)$ is just the coefficient of $y_{t-\tau}$ in a population linear regression of y_t on $y_{t-1}, \ldots, y_{t-\tau}$.[2] We call such a regression an **autoregression**, because the variable is regressed on lagged values of itself. It's easy to see that the autocorrelations and partial autocorrelations, although related, differ in an important way. The autocorrelations are just the "simple" or "regular" correlations between y_t and $y_{t-\tau}$. The partial autocorrelations, on the other hand, measure the association between y_t and $y_{t-\tau}$ after *controlling* for the effects of $y_{t-1}, \ldots, y_{t-\tau+1}$; that is, they measure the partial correlation between y_t and $y_{t-\tau}$.

As with the autocorrelations, we often graph the partial autocorrelations as a function of τ and examine their qualitative shape, which we'll do soon. Like the autocorrelation function, the partial autocorrelation function provides a

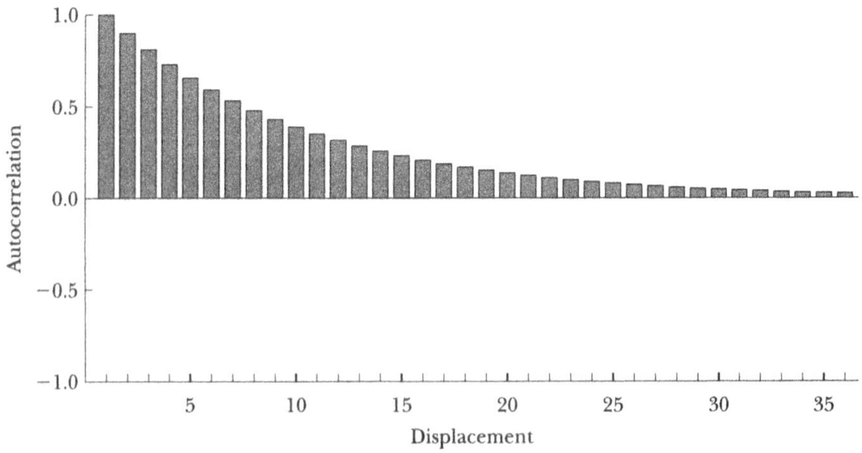

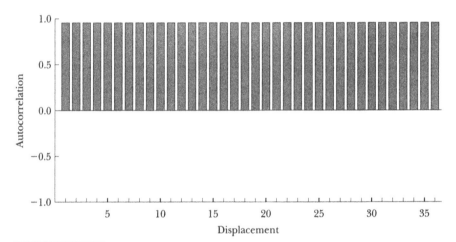

FIGURE 12-2 Autocorrelation function, one-sided gradual damping.

FIGURE 12-3 Autocorrelation function, nondamping.

summary of a series' dynamics, but as we'll see, it does so in a different way.[3]

All of the covariance stationary processes that we will study subsequently have autocorrelation and partial autocorrelation functions that approach 0, one way or another, as the displacement gets large. In Figure 12-2 we show an autocorrelation function that displays gradual one-sided damping, and in Figure 12-3 we show a

---

[2] To get a feel for what we mean by "population regression," imagine that we have an infinite sample of data at our disposal, so that the parameter estimates in the regression are not contaminated by sampling variation; that is, they're the true population values. The thought experiment just described is a **population regression**.

---

[3] Also in parallel to the autocorrelation function, the partial autocorrelation at displacement 0 is always 1 and is therefore uninformative and uninteresting. Thus, when we graph the autocorrelation and partial autocorrelation functions, we'll begin at displacement 1 rather than displacement 0.

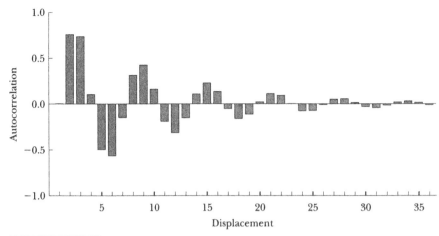

FIGURE 12-4 Autocorrelation function, gradual damped oscillation.

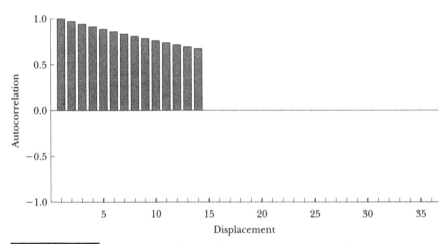

FIGURE 12-5 Autocorrelation function, sharp cutoff.

WHITE NOISE

In this section and throughout the next chapter, we'll study the population properties of certain time series models, or **time series processes**, which are very important for forecasting. Before we estimate time series forecasting models, we need to understand their population properties, assuming that the postulated model is true. The simplest of all such time series processes is the fundamental building block from which all others are constructed. In fact, it's so important that we introduce it now. We use y to denote the observed series of interest. Suppose that

$$y_t = \epsilon_t$$

$$\epsilon_t \sim (0, \sigma^2),$$

where the "shock," ϵ_t, is uncorrelated over time. We say that ϵ_t, and hence y_t, is **serially uncorrelated**. Throughout, unless explicitly stated otherwise, we assume that $\sigma^2 < \infty$. Such a process, with zero mean, constant variance, and no serial correlation, is called **zero-mean white noise**, or simply **white noise**.[4] Sometimes for short we write

$$\epsilon_t \sim WN(0, \sigma^2)$$

and hence

$$y_t \sim WN(0, \sigma^2).$$

Note that, although ϵ_t and hence y_t are serially uncorrelated, they are not necessarily serially independent, because they are not necessarily normally distributed.[5] If in addition to being serially uncorrelated, y is serially independent, then we say that y is **independent white noise**.[6] We write

$$y_t \stackrel{iid}{\sim} (0, \sigma^2),$$

constant autocorrelation function; the latter could not be the autocorrelation function of a stationary process, whose autocorrelation function must eventually decay. The precise decay patterns of autocorrelations and partial autocorrelations of a covariance stationary series, however, depend on the specifics of the series, as we'll see in detail in the next chapter. In Figure 12-4, for example, we show an autocorrelation function that displays damped oscillation—the autocorrelations are positive at first, then become negative for a while, then positive again, and so on, while continuously getting smaller in absolute value. Finally, in Figure 12-5 we show an autocorrelation function that differs in the way it approaches 0—the autocorrelations drop abruptly to 0 beyond a certain displacement.

[4] It's called white noise by analogy with white light, which is composed of all colors of the spectrum, in equal amounts. We can think of white noise as being composed of a wide variety of cycles of differing periodicities, in equal amounts.

[5] Recall that zero correlation implies independence only in the normal case.

[6] Another name for independent white noise is **strong white noise**, in contrast to standard serially uncorrelated **weak white noise**.

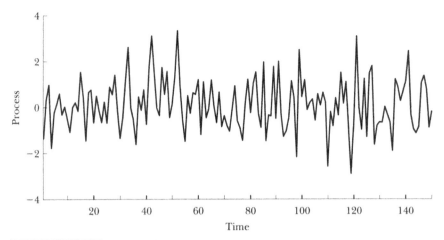

FIGURE 12-6 Realization of white noise process.

and we say that "y is independently and identically distributed with zero mean and constant variance." If y is serially uncorrelated and normally distributed, then it follows that y is also serially independent, and we say that y is **normal white noise** or **Gaussian white noise**.[7] We write

$$y_t \overset{iid}{\sim} N(0, \sigma^2).$$

We read "y is independently and identically distributed as normal, with zero mean and constant variance" or simply "y is Gaussian white noise." In Figure 12-6 we show a sample path of Gaussian white noise, of length $T = 150$, simulated on a computer. There are no patterns of any kind in the series due to the independence over time.

You're already familiar with white noise, although you may not realize it. Recall that the disturbance in a regression model is typically assumed to be white noise of one sort or another. There's a subtle difference here, however. Regression disturbances are not observable, whereas we're working with an observed series. Later, however, we'll see how all of our models for observed series can be used to model unobserved variables such as regression disturbances.

Let's characterize the dynamic stochastic structure of white noise, $y_t \sim WN(0, \sigma^2)$. By construction the unconditional mean of y is

$$E(y_t) = 0,$$

and the unconditional variance of y is

$$\text{var}(y_t) = \sigma^2.$$

Note that the unconditional mean and variance are constant. In fact, the unconditional mean and variance must be constant for any covariance stationary process. The reason is that constancy of the unconditional mean was our first explicit requirement of covariance stationarity and that constancy of the unconditional variance follows implicitly from the second requirement of covariance stationarity—that the autocovariances depend only on displacement, not on time.[8]

To understand fully the linear dynamic structure of a covariance stationary time series process, we need to compute and examine its mean and its autocovariance function. For white noise, we've already computed the mean and the variance, which is the autocovariance at displacement 0. We have yet to compute the rest of the autocovariance function; fortunately, however, it's very simple. Because white noise is, by definition, uncorrelated over time, all the autocovariances, and hence all the autocorrelations, are 0 beyond displacement 0.[9] Formally, then, the autocovariance function for a white noise process is

$$\gamma(\tau) = \begin{cases} \sigma^2, & \tau = 0 \\ 0, & \tau \geq 1, \end{cases}$$

and the autocorrelation function for a white noise process is

$$\rho(\tau) = \begin{cases} 1, & \tau = 0 \\ 0, & \tau \geq 1. \end{cases}$$

In Figure 12-7 we plot the white noise autocorrelation function.

Finally, consider the partial autocorrelation function for a white noise series. For the same reason that the autocorrelation at displacement 0 is always 1, so, too, is the partial autocorrelation at displacement 0. For a white noise process, all partial autocorrelations beyond displacement 0 are 0, which again follows from the fact that white noise, by construction, is serially uncorrelated. Population regressions of y_t on y_{t-1}, or on y_{t-1} and y_{t-2} or on any other lags, produce nothing but 0 coefficients, because the

---

[7] Karl Friedrich Gauss, one of the greatest mathematicians of all time, discovered the normal distribution some 200 years ago—hence the adjective *Gaussian*.

[8] Recall that $\sigma^2 = y(0)$.

[9] If the autocovariances are all 0, so are the autocorrelations, because the autocorrelations are proportional to the autocovariances.

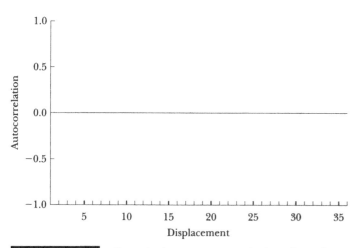

FIGURE 12-7 Population autocorrelation function, white noise process.

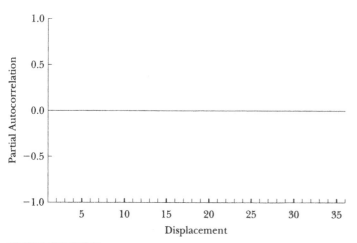

FIGURE 12-8 Population partial autocorrelation function, white noise process.

process is serially uncorrelated. Formally, the partial autocorrelation function of a white noise process is

$$\rho(\tau) = \begin{cases} 1, & \tau = 0 \\ 0, & \tau \geq 1. \end{cases}$$

We show the partial autocorrelation function of a white noise process in Figure 12-8. Again, it's degenerate and exactly the same as the autocorrelation function!

By now you've surely noticed that if you were assigned the task of forecasting independent white noise, you'd likely be doomed to failure. What happens to a white noise series at any time is uncorrelated with anything in the past; similarly, what happens in the future is uncorrelated with anything in the present or past. But understanding white noise is tremendously important for at

least two reasons. First, as already mentioned, processes with much richer dynamics are built up by taking simple transformations of white noise. Second, 1-step-ahead forecast errors from good models should be white noise. After all, if such forecast errors aren't white noise, then they're serially correlated, which means that they're forecastable; and if forecast errors are forecastable, then the forecast can't be very good. Thus, it's important that we understand and be able to recognize white noise.

Thus far we've characterized white noise in terms of its mean, variance, autocorrelation function, and partial autocorrelation function. Another characterization of dynamics, with important implications for forecasting, involves the mean and variance of a process, *conditional* on its past. In particular, we often gain insight into the dynamics in a process by examining its conditional mean, which is a key object for forecasting.[10] In fact, throughout our study of time series, we'll be interested in computing and contrasting the **unconditional mean and variance** and the **conditional mean and variance** of various processes of interest. Means and variances, which convey information about location and scale of random variables, are examples of what statisticians call **moments**. For the most part, our comparisons of the conditional and unconditional moment structure of time series processes will focus on means and variances (they're the most important moments), but sometimes we'll be interested in higher-order moments, which are related to properties such as skewness and kurtosis.

For comparing conditional and unconditional means and variances, it will simplify our story to consider independent white noise, $y_t \overset{iid}{\sim} (0, \sigma^2)$. By the same arguments as before, the unconditional mean of y is 0, and the unconditional variance is σ^2. Now consider the conditional mean and variance, where the information set Ω_{t-1} on which we condition contains either the past history of the observed series, $\Omega_{t-1} = \{y_{t-1}, y_{t-2}, \ldots\}$, or the past history of the shocks, $\Omega_{t-1} = \{\epsilon_{t-1}, \epsilon_{t-2}, \ldots\}$. (They're the same in the white noise case.) In contrast to the unconditional mean and variance, which must be constant by covariance stationarity, the conditional mean and variance need not be constant, and in general we'd expect them *not* to be constant. The unconditionally expected growth of laptop

---

[10] If you need to refresh your memory on conditional means, consult any good introductory statistics book, such as Wonnacott and Wonnacott (1990).

computer sales next quarter may be 10%, but expected sales growth may be much higher, *conditional* on knowledge that sales grew this quarter by 20%. For the independent white noise process, the conditional mean is

$$E(y_t \mid \Omega_{t-1}) = 0,$$

and the conditional variance is

$$\text{var}(y_t \mid \Omega_{t-1}) = E((y_t - E(y_t \mid \Omega_{t-1}))^2 \mid \Omega_{t-1}) = \sigma^2.$$

Conditional and unconditional means and variances are identical for an independent white noise series; there are no dynamics in the process and hence no dynamics in the conditional moments to exploit for forecasting.

THE LAG OPERATOR

The **lag operator** and related constructs are the natural language in which forecasting models are expressed. If you want to understand and manipulate forecasting models—indeed, even if you simply want to be able to read the software manuals—you have to be comfortable with the lag operator. The lag operator, L, is very simple: It "operates" on a series by lagging it. Hence,

$$Ly_t = y_{t-1}.$$

Similarly,

$$L^2y_t = L(L(y_t)) = L(y_{t-1}) = y_{t-2},$$

and so on. Typically we'll operate on a series not with the lag operator but with a **polynomial in the lag operator**. A lag operator polynomial of degree m is just a linear function of powers of L, up through the mth power,

$$B(L) = b_0 + b_1L + b_2L^2 + \cdots b_mL^m.$$

To take a very simple example of a lag operator polynomial operating on a series, consider the mth-order lag operator polynomial L^m, for which

$$L^my_t = y_{t-m}.$$

A well-known operator, the first-difference operator Δ, is actually a first-order polynomial in the lag operator; you can readily verify that

$$\Delta y_t = (1 - L)y_t = y_t - y_{t-1}.$$

As a final example, consider the second-order lag operator polynomial $(1 + 0.9L + 0.6L^2)$ operating on y_t. We have

$$(1 + 0.9L + 0.6L^2)y_t = y_t + 0.9y_{t-1} + 0.6y_{t-2},$$

which is a weighted sum, or **distributed lag**, of current and past values. All forecasting models, one way or another, must contain such distributed lags, because they've got to quantify how the past evolves into the present and future; hence, lag operator notation is a useful shorthand for stating and manipulating forecasting models.

Thus far, we've considered only finite-order polynomials in the lag operator; it turns out that infinite-order polynomials are also of great interest. We write the infinite-order lag operator polynomial as

$$B(L) = b_0 + b_1L + b_2L^2 + \cdots = \sum_{i=0}^{\infty} b_iL^i.$$

Thus, for example, to denote an infinite distributed lag of current and past shocks, we might write

$$B(L)\epsilon_t = b_0\epsilon_t + b_1\epsilon_{t-1} + b_2\epsilon_{t-2} + \cdots = \sum_{i=0}^{\infty} b_i\epsilon_{t-i}.$$

At first sight, infinite distributed lags may seem esoteric and of limited practical interest, because models with infinite distributed lags have infinitely many parameters (b_0, b_1, b_2, ...) and therefore can't be estimated with a finite sample of data. On the contrary, and surprisingly, it turns out that models involving infinite distributed lags are central to time series modeling and forecasting. Wold's theorem, to which we now turn, establishes that centrality.

WOLD'S THEOREM, THE GENERAL LINEAR PROCESS, AND RATIONAL DISTRIBUTED LAGS[11]

Wold's Theorem

Many different dynamic patterns are consistent with covariance stationarity. Thus, if we know only that a series is covariance stationary, it's not at all clear what sort of model we might fit to describe its evolution. The trend and seasonal models that we've studied aren't of use; they're models of specific nonstationary

---

[11] This section is a bit more abstract than others, but don't be put off. On the contrary, you may want to read it several times. The material in it is crucially important for time series modeling and forecasting and is therefore central to our concerns.

components. Effectively, what we need now is an appropriate model for what's left after fitting the trend and seasonal components—a model for a covariance stationary residual. **Wold's representation theorem** points to the appropriate model.

Theorem

Let $\{y_t\}$ be any zero-mean covariance-stationary process.[12] Then we can write it as

$$y_t = B(L)\epsilon_t = \sum_{i=0}^{\infty} b_i \epsilon_{t-i}$$

$$\epsilon_t \sim WN(0, \sigma^2),$$

where $b_0 = 1$ and $\sum_{i=0}^{\infty} b_i^2 < \infty$. In short, the correct "model" for any covariance stationary series is some infinite distributed lag of white noise, called the **Wold representation**. The ϵ_t's are often called **innovations**, because they correspond to the 1-step-ahead forecast errors that we'd make if we were to use a particularly good forecast. That is, the ϵ_t's represent that part of the evolution of y that's linearly unpredictable on the basis of the past of y. Note also that the ϵ_t's, although uncorrelated, are not necessarily independent. Again, it's only for Gaussian random variables that lack of correlation implies independence, and the innovations are not necessarily Gaussian.

In our statement of Wold's theorem we assumed a zero mean. That may seem restrictive, but it's not. Rather, whenever you see y_t just read $y_t - \mu$, so that the process is expressed in deviations from its mean. The deviation from the mean has a zero mean, by construction. Working with zero-mean processes therefore involves no loss of generality while facilitating notational economy. We'll use this device frequently.

The General Linear Process

Wold's theorem tells us that when formulating forecasting models for covariance stationary time series, we need only consider models of the form

$$y_t = B(L)\epsilon_t = \sum_{i=0}^{\infty} b_i \epsilon_{t-i}$$

$$\epsilon_t \sim WN(0, \sigma^2),$$

---

[12] Moreover, we require that the covariance stationary processes don't contain any deterministic components.

where the b_i are coefficients with $b_0 = 1$ and $\sum_{i=0}^{\infty} b_i^2 < \infty$. We call this the **general linear process**, "general" because any covariance stationary series can be written that way, and "linear" because the Wold representation expresses the series as a linear function of its innovations.

The general linear process is so important that it's worth examining its unconditional and conditional moment structure in some detail. Taking means and variances, we obtain the unconditional moments

$$E(y_t) = E\left(\sum_{i=0}^{\infty} b_i \epsilon_{t-i}\right) = \sum_{i=0}^{\infty} b_i E(\epsilon_{t-i}) = \sum_{i=0}^{\infty} b_i \cdot 0 = 0$$

and

$$\text{var}(y_t) = \text{var}\left(\sum_{i=0}^{\infty} b_i \epsilon_{t-i}\right) = \sum_{i=0}^{\infty} b_i^2 \text{var}(\epsilon_{t-i}) = \sum_{i=0}^{\infty} b_i^2 \sigma^2 = \sigma^2 \sum_{i=0}^{\infty} b_i^2.$$

At this point, in parallel to our discussion of white noise, we could compute and examine the autocovariance and autocorrelation functions of the general linear process. Those calculations, however, are rather involved, and not particularly revealing, so we'll proceed instead to examine the conditional mean and variance, where the information set Ω_{t-1} on which we condition contains past innovations; that is, $\Omega_{t-1} = \{\epsilon_{t-1}, \epsilon_{t-2}, \ldots\}$. In this manner, we can see how dynamics are modeled via conditional moments.[13] The conditional mean is

$$E(y_t \mid \Omega_{t-1}) = E(\epsilon_t \mid \Omega_{t-1}) + b_1 E(\epsilon_{t-1} \mid \Omega_{t-1}) + b_2 E(\epsilon_{t-2} \mid \Omega_{t-1}) + \ldots$$

$$= 0 + b_1 \epsilon_{t-1} + b_2 \epsilon_{t-2} + \cdots = \sum_{i=1}^{\infty} b_i \epsilon_{t-i},$$

and the conditional variance is

$$\text{var}(y_t \mid \Omega_{t-1}) = E((y_t - E(y_t \mid \Omega_{t-1}))^2 \mid \Omega_{t-1}) = E(\epsilon_t^2 \mid \Omega_{t-1})$$

$$= E(\epsilon_t^2) = \sigma^2.$$

The key insight is that the conditional mean *moves* over time in response to the evolving information set. The model captures the dynamics of the process, and the evolving conditional mean is one crucial way of summarizing them. An important goal of time series modeling,

---

[13] Although Wold's theorem guarantees only serially uncorrelated white noise innovations, we shall sometimes make a stronger assumption of independent white noise innovations to focus the discussion. We do so, for example, in the following characterization of the conditional moment structure of the general linear process.

especially for forecasters, is capturing such conditional mean dynamics—the unconditional mean is constant (a requirement of stationarity), but the conditional mean varies in response to the evolving information set.[14]

Rational Distributed Lags

As we've seen, the Wold representation points to the crucial importance of models with infinite distributed lags. Infinite distributed lag models, in turn, are stated in terms of infinite polynomials in the lag operator, which are therefore very important as well. Infinite distributed lag models are not of immediate practical use, however, because they contain infinitely many parameters, which certainly inhibits practical application! Fortunately, infinite polynomials in the lag operator needn't contain infinitely many free parameters. The infinite polynomial $B(L)$ may, for example, be a ratio of finite-order (and perhaps very low-order) polynomials. Such polynomials are called **rational polynomials,** and distributed lags constructed from them are called **rational distributed lags.**

Suppose, for example, that

$$B(L) = \frac{\Theta(L)}{\Phi(L)},$$

where the numerator polynomial is of degree q,

$$\Theta(L) = \sum_{i=0}^{q} \theta_i L^i,$$

and the denominator polynomial is of degree p,

$$\Phi(L) = \sum_{i=0}^{p} \varphi_i L^i.$$

There are *not* infinitely many free parameters in the $B(L)$ polynomial; instead, there are only $p + q$ parameters (the θ's and the φ's). If p and q are small—say, 0, 1, or 2—then what seems like a hopeless task—estimation of $B(L)$—may actually be easy.

More realistically, suppose that $B(L)$ is not exactly rational but is approximately rational,

$$B(L) \approx \frac{\Theta(L)}{\Phi(L)}.$$

---

[14] Note, however, an embarrassing asymmetry: the conditional variance, like the unconditional variance, is a fixed constant. However, models that allow the conditional variance to change with the information set have been developed recently.

Then we can find an **approximation of the Wold representation** using a rational distributed lag. Rational distributed lags produce models of cycles that economize on parameters (they're **parsimonious**), while nevertheless providing accurate approximations to the Wold representation. The popular ARMA and ARIMA forecasting models, which we'll study shortly, are simply rational approximations to the Wold representation.

ESTIMATION AND INFERENCE FOR THE MEAN, AUTOCORRELATION, AND PARTIAL AUTOCORRELATION FUNCTIONS

Now suppose we have a sample of data on a time series, and we don't know the true model that generated the data, or the mean, autocorrelation function, or partial autocorrelation function associated with that true model. Instead, we want to use the data to *estimate* the mean, autocorrelation function, and partial autocorrelation function, which we might then use to help us learn about the underlying dynamics and to decide on a suitable model or set of models to fit to the data.

Sample Mean

The mean of a covariance stationary series is $\mu = Ey_t$. A fundamental principle of estimation, called the **analog principle**, suggests that we develop estimators by replacing expectations with sample averages. Thus, our estimator for the population mean, given a sample of size T, is the **sample mean,**

$$\bar{y} = \frac{1}{T}\sum_{t=1}^{T} y_t.$$

Typically we're not directly interested in the estimate of the mean, but it's needed for estimation of the autocorrelation function.

Sample Autocorrelations

The autocorrelation at displacement τ for the covariance stationary series y is

$$\rho(\tau) = \frac{E((y_t - \mu)(y_{t-\tau} - \mu))}{E((y_t - \mu)^2)}.$$

Application of the analog principle yields a natural estimator,

$$\hat{\rho}(\tau) = \frac{\frac{1}{T}\sum_{t=\tau+1}^{T}((y_t - \bar{y})(y_{t-\tau} - \bar{y}))}{\frac{1}{T}\sum_{t=1}^{T}(y_t - \bar{y})^2} = \frac{\sum_{t=\tau+1}^{T}((y_t - \bar{y})(y_{t-\tau} - \bar{y}))}{\sum_{t=1}^{T}(y_t - \bar{y})^2}$$

This estimator, viewed as a function of τ, is called the **sample autocorrelation function** or correlogram. Note that some of the summations begin at $t = \tau + 1$, not at $t = 1$; this is necessary because of the appearance of $y_{t-\tau}$ in the sum. Note that we divide those same sums by T, even though only $(T - \tau)$ terms appear in the sum. When T is large relative to τ (which is the relevant case), division by T or by $T - \tau$ will yield approximately the same result, so it won't make much difference for practical purposes; moreover, there are good mathematical reasons for preferring division by T.

It's often of interest to assess whether a series is reasonably approximated as white noise, which is to say whether all its autocorrelations are 0 in population. A key result, which we simply assert, is that if a series is white noise, then the distribution of the sample autocorrelations in large samples is

$$\hat{\rho}(\tau) \sim N\left(0, \frac{1}{T}\right).$$

Note how simple the result is. The sample autocorrelations of a white noise series are approximately normally distributed, and the normal is always a convenient distribution to work with. Their mean is 0, which is to say the sample autocorrelations are unbiased estimators of the true autocorrelations, which are in fact 0. Finally, the variance of the sample autocorrelations is approximately $1/T$ (equivalently, the standard deviation is $1/\sqrt{T}$), which is easy to construct and remember. Under normality, taking plus or minus two standard errors yields an approximate 95% confidence interval. Thus, if the series is white noise, then approximately 95% of the sample autocorrelations should fall in the interval $\pm 2/\sqrt{T}$. In practice, when we plot the sample autocorrelations for a sample of data, we typically include the "two-standard-error bands," which are useful for making informal graphical assessments of whether and how the series deviates from white noise.

The two-standard-error bands, although very useful, only provide 95% bounds for the sample autocorrelations taken one at a time. Ultimately, we're often interested in whether a series is white noise—that is, whether *all* its autocorrelations are *jointly* 0. A simple extension lets us test that hypothesis. Rewrite the expression

as

$$\hat{\rho}(\tau) \sim N\left(0, \frac{1}{T}\right)$$

$$\sqrt{T}\hat{\rho}(\tau) \sim N(0, 1).$$

Squaring both sides yields[15]

$$T\hat{\rho}^2(\tau) \sim \chi_1^2.$$

It can be shown that, in addition to being approximately normally distributed, the sample autocorrelations at various displacements are approximately independent of one another. Recalling that the sum of independent χ^2 variables is also χ^2 with degrees of freedom equal to the sum of the degrees of freedom of the variables summed, we have shown that the **Box-Pierce Q-statistic**,

$$Q_{BP} = T\sum_{\tau=1}^{m}\hat{\rho}^2(\tau),$$

is approximately distributed as a χ_m^2 random variable under the null hypothesis that y is white noise.[16] A slight modification of this, designed to follow more closely the χ^2 distribution in small samples, is

$$Q_{LB} = T(T + 2)\sum_{\tau=1}^{m}\left(\frac{1}{T - \tau}\right)\hat{\rho}^2(\tau).$$

Under the null hypothesis that y is white noise, Q_{LB} is approximately distributed as a χ_m^2 random variable. Note that the **Ljung-Box Q-statistic** is the same as the Box-Pierce Q-statistic, except that the sum of squared autocorrelations is replaced by a weighted sum of squared autocorrelations, where the weights are $(T + 2)/(T - \tau)$. For moderate and large T, the weights are approximately 1, so that the Ljung-Box statistic differs little from the Box-Pierce statistic.

Selection of m is done to balance competing criteria. On the one hand, we don't want m too small, because, after all, we're trying to do a joint test on a large part of the autocorrelation function. On the other hand, as m grows relative to T, the quality of the distributional

---

[15] Recall that the square of a standard normal random variable is a χ^2 random variable with 1 degree of freedom. We square the sample autocorrelations $\hat{\rho}(\tau)$ so that positive and negative values don't cancel when we sum across various values of τ, as we will soon do.

[16] m is a maximum displacement selected by the user. Shortly we'll discuss how to choose it.

approximately we've invoked deteriorates. In practice, focusing on m in the neighborhood of $\sqrt{T}$ is often reasonable.

Sample Partial Autocorrelations

Recall that the partial autocorrelations are obtained from population linear regressions, which correspond to a thought experiment involving linear regression using an infinite sample of data. The sample partial autocorrelations correspond to the same thought experiment, except that the linear regression is now done on the (feasible) sample of size T. If the fitted regression is

$$\hat{y}_t = \hat{c} + \hat{\beta}_1 y_{t-1} + \cdots + \hat{\beta}_\tau y_{t-\tau},$$

then the **sample partial autocorrelation** at displacement τ is

$$\hat{p}(\tau) \equiv \hat{\beta}_\tau.$$

Distributional results identical to those we discussed for the sample autocorrelations hold as well for the sample *partial* autocorrelations. That is, if the series is white noise, approximately 95% of the sample partial autocorrelations should fall in the interval $\pm 2/\sqrt{T}$. As with the sample autocorrelations, we typically plot the sample partial autocorrelations along with their two-standard-error bands.

APPLICATION: CHARACTERIZING CANADIAN EMPLOYMENT DYNAMICS

To illustrate the ideas we've introduced, we examine a quarterly, seasonally adjusted index of Canadian employment, 1962.1–1993.4, which we plot in Figure 12-9. The series displays no trend, and of course it displays no

TABLE 12-1   Canadian Employment Index, Correlogram

Sample: 1962:1–1993:4
Included observations: 128

	Acorr.	P. Acorr.	Std. Error	Ljung-Box	*p*-value
1	0.949	0.949	.088	118.07	0.000
2	0.877	−0.244	.088	219.66	0.000
3	0.795	−0.101	.088	303.72	0.000
4	0.707	−0.070	.088	370.82	0.000
5	0.617	−0.063	.088	422.27	0.000
6	0.526	−0.048	.088	460.00	0.000
7	0.438	−0.033	.088	486.32	0.000
8	0.351	−0.049	.088	503.41	0.000
9	0.258	−0.149	.088	512.70	0.000
10	0.163	−0.070	.088	516.43	0.000
11	0.073	−0.011	.088	517.20	0.000
12	−0.005	0.016	.088	517.21	0.000

seasonality because it's seasonally adjusted. It does, however, appear highly serially correlated. It evolves in a slow, persistent fashion—high in business cycle booms and low in recessions.

To get a feel for the dynamics operating in the employment series, we perform a correlogram analysis.[17] The results appear in Table 12-1. Consider first the Q-statistic.[18] We compute the Q-statistic and its *p*-value under the null hypothesis of white noise for values of m (the number of terms in the sum that underlies the Q-statistic) ranging from 1 through 12. The *p*-value is consistently 0 to four decimal places, so the null hypothesis of white noise is decisively rejected.

---

[17] A **correlogram analysis** simply means examination of the sample autocorrelation and partial autocorrelation functions (with two-standard-error bands), together with related diagnostics, such as Q-statistics.

[18] We show the Ljung-Box version of the Q-statistic.

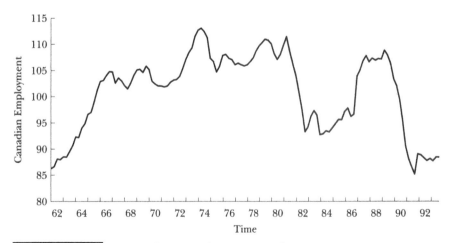

FIGURE 12-9   Canadian employment index.

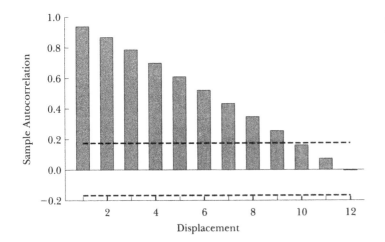

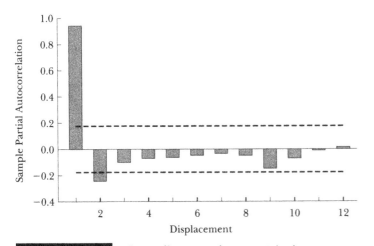

FIGURE 12-10   Canadian employment index: sample autocorrelation and partial autocorrelation functions, with plus or minus two-standard-error bands.

Now we examine the sample autocorrelations and partial autocorrelations. The sample autocorrelations are very large relative to their standard errors and display slow one-sided decay.[19] The sample partial autocorrelations, in contrast, are large relative to their standard errors at first (particularly for the one-quarter displacement) but are statistically negligible beyond displacement 2.[20] In Figure 12-10 we plot the sample

---

[19] We don't show the sample autocorrelation or partial autocorrelation at displacement 0, because as we mentioned earlier, they equal 1.0, by construction, and therefore convey no useful information. We'll adopt this convention throughout.

[20] Note that the sample autocorrelation and partial autocorrelation are identical at displacement 1. That's because at displacement 1, there are no earlier lags to control for when computing the sample partial autocorrelation, so it equals the sample autocorrelation. At higher displacements, of course, the two diverge.

autocorrelations and partial autocorrelations along with their two-standard-error bands.

It's clear that employment has a strong cyclical component; all diagnostics reject the white noise hypothesis immediately. Moreover, the sample autocorrelation and partial autocorrelation functions have particular shapes—the autocorrelation function displays slow one-sided damping, while the partial autocorrelation function cuts off at displacement 2. You might guess that such patterns, which summarize the dynamics in the series, might be useful for suggesting candidate forecasting models. Such is indeed the case, as we'll see in the next chapter.

Bibliographical and Computational Notes

Wold's theorem was originally proved in a 1938 monograph, later revised as Wold (1954). Rational distributed lags have long been used in engineering, and their use in econometric modeling dates at least to Jorgenson (1966).

Bartlett (1946) derived the standard errors of the sample autocorrelations and partial autocorrelations of white noise. In fact, the plus-or-minus two-standard-error bands are often called the "**Bartlett bands**."

The two variants of the Q-statistic that we introduced were developed in the 1970s by Box and Pierce (1970) and by Ljung and Box (1978). Some packages compute both variants, and some compute only one (typically Ljung-Box, because it's designed to be more accurate in small samples). In practice, the Box-Pierce and Ljung-Box statistics usually lead to the same conclusions.

For concise and insightful discussion of random number generation, as well as a variety of numerical and computational techniques, see Press *et. al.* (1992).

Concepts for Review

Cycle
Realization
Sample path
Covariance stationarity
Autocovariance function
Second-order stationarity
Weak stationarity
Autocorrelation function
Partial autocorrelation function

Population regression
Autoregression
Time series process
Serially uncorrelated
Zero-mean white noise
White noise
Independent white noise
Strong white noise
Weak white noise
Normal white noise
Gaussian white noise
Unconditional mean and variance
Conditional mean and variance
Moments
Lag operator
Polynomial in the lag operator
Distributed lag
Wold's representation theorem
Wold representation
Innovation
General linear process
Rational polynomial
Rational distributed lag
Approximation of the Wold representation
Parsimonious
Analog principle
Sample mean
Sample autocorrelation function
Box-Pierce Q-statistic
Ljung-Box Q-statistic

Sample partial autocorrelation
Correlogram analysis
Bartlett bands

References and Additional Readings

Bartlett, M. (1946). "On the Theoretical Specification of Sampling Properties of Autocorrelated Time Series."*Journal of the Royal Statistical Society* B, 8, 27–41.

Box, G. E. P., and Pierce, D. A. (1970). "Distribution of Residual Autocorrelations in ARIMA Time-Series Models." *Journal of the American Statistical Association*, 65, 1509–1526.

Jorgenson, D. (1966). "Rational Distributed Lag Functions." *Econometrica*, 34, 135–149.

Ljung, G. M., and G. E. P. Box (1978). "On a Measure of Lack of Fit in Time-Series Models." *Biometrika*, 65, 297–303.

Press, W. H., et. al. (1992). *Numerical Recipes: The Art of Scientific Computing.* Cambridge: Cambridge University Press.

Wold, H. O. (1954). *A Study in the Analysis of Stationary Time Series.* 2nd ed. Uppsala, Sweden: Almquist and Wicksell.

Wonnacott, T. H., and Wonnacott, R. J. (1990). *Introductory Statistics.* 5th ed. New York: Wiley.

Modeling Cycles: MA, AR, and ARMA Models

13

■ Learning Objectives

Candidates, after completing this reading, should be able to:

- Describe the properties of the first-order moving average (MA(1)) process, and distinguish between autoregressive representation and moving average representation.
- Describe the properties of a general finite-order process of order q (MA(q)) process.
- Describe the properties of the first-order autoregressive (AR(1)) process, and define and explain the Yule-Walker equation.

- Describe the properties of a general pth order autoregressive (AR(p)) process.
- Define and describe the properties of the autoregressive moving average (ARMA) process.
- Describe the application of AR and ARMA processes.

Excerpt is Chapter 8 of Elements of Forecasting, *Fourth Edition, by Francis X. Diebold.*

When building forecasting models, we don't want to pretend that the model we fit is true. Instead, we want to be aware that we're *approximating* a more complex reality. That's the modern view, and it has important implications for forecasting. In particular, we've seen that the key to successful time series modeling and forecasting is parsimonious, yet accurate, approximation of the Wold representation. In this chapter, we consider three approximations: **moving average (MA) models, autoregressive (AR) models**, and **autoregressive moving average (ARMA) models**. The three models vary in their specifics and have different strengths in capturing different sorts of autocorrelation behavior.

We begin by characterizing the autocorrelation functions and related quantities associated with each model, under the assumption that the model is "true." We do this separately for MA, AR, and ARMA models.[1] These characterizations have nothing to do with data or estimation, but they're crucial for developing a basic understanding of the properties of the models, which is necessary to perform intelligent modeling and forecasting. They enable us to make statements such as "If the data were really generated by an autoregressive process, then we'd expect its autocorrelation function to have property x." Armed with that knowledge, we use the *sample* autocorrelations and partial autocorrelations, in conjunction with the AIC and the SIC, to suggest candidate forecasting models, which we then estimate.

MOVING AVERAGE (MA) MODELS

The finite-order moving average process is a natural and obvious approximation to the Wold representation, which is an infinite-order moving average process. Finite-order moving average processes also have direct motivation. The fact that all variation in time series, one way or another, is driven by shocks of various sorts suggests the possibility of modeling time series

directly as distributed lags of current and past shocks—that is, as moving average processes.[2]

The MA(1) Process

The first-order moving average process, or **MA(1) process**, is

$$y_t = \epsilon_t + \theta\epsilon_{t-1} = (1 + \theta L)\epsilon_t$$

$$\epsilon_t \sim WN(0, \sigma^2).$$

The defining characteristic of the MA process in general, and the MA(1) in particular, is that the current value of the observed series is expressed as a function of current and lagged unobservable shocks. Think of it as a regression model with nothing but current and lagged disturbances on the right-hand side.

To help develop a feel for the behavior of the MA(1) process, we show two simulated realizations of length 150 in Figure 13-1. The processes are

$$y_t = \epsilon_t + 0.4\epsilon_{t-1}$$

and

$$y_t = \epsilon_t + 0.95\epsilon_{t-1},$$

where in each case $\epsilon_t \overset{iid}{\sim} N(0, 1)$. To construct the realizations, we used the same series of underlying white noise shocks; the only difference in the realizations comes from the different coefficients. Past shocks feed *positively* into the current value of the series, with a small weight of $\theta = 0.4$ in one case and a large weight of $\theta = 0.95$ in the other. You might think that $\theta = 0.95$ would induce much more persistence than $\theta = 0.4$, but it doesn't. The structure of the MA(1) process, in which only the first lag of the

---

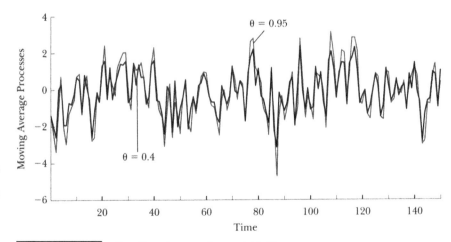

FIGURE 13-1   Realizations of two MA(1) processes.

shock appears on the right, forces it to have a very short memory, and hence weak dynamics, regardless of the parameter value.

The unconditional mean and variance are

$$E(y_t) = E(\epsilon_t) + \theta E(\epsilon_{t-1}) = 0$$

and

$$\text{var}\,(y_t) = \text{var}\,(\epsilon_t) + \theta^2\text{var}(\epsilon_{t-1}) = \sigma^2 + \theta^2\sigma^2 = \sigma^2(1 + \theta^2).$$

Note that for a fixed value of σ, as θ increases in absolute value, so, too, does the unconditional variance. That's why the MA(1) process with parameter $\theta = 0.95$ varies a bit more than the process with a parameter of $\theta = 0.4$.

The conditional mean and variance of an MA(1), where the conditioning information set is $\Omega_{t-1} = \{\epsilon_{t-1}, \epsilon_{t-2}, \ldots\}$, are

$$E(y_t \mid \Omega_{t-1}) = E(\epsilon_t + \theta\epsilon_{t-1} \mid \Omega_{t-1}) = E(\epsilon_t \mid \Omega_{t-1})$$
$$+ \theta E(\epsilon_{t-1} \mid \Omega_{t-1}) = \theta\epsilon_{t-1}$$

and

$$\text{var}(y_t \mid \Omega_{t-1}) = E((y_i - E(y_t \mid \Omega_{t-1}))^2 \mid \Omega_{t-1})$$
$$= E(\epsilon_t^2 \mid \Omega_{t-1}) = E(\epsilon_t^2) = \sigma^2.$$

The conditional mean explicitly adapts to the information set, in contrast to the unconditional mean, which is constant. Note, however, that only the first lag of the shock enters the conditional mean—more distant shocks have no effect on the current conditional expectation. This is indicative of the one-period memory of MA(1) processes, which we'll now characterize in terms of the autocorrelation function.

To compute the autocorrelation function for the MA(1) process, we must first compute the autocovariance function. We have

$$\gamma(\tau) = E(y_t y_{t-\tau}) = E((\epsilon_t + \theta\epsilon_{t-1})(\epsilon_{t-\tau} + \theta\epsilon_{t-\tau-1}))$$
$$= \begin{cases} \theta\sigma^2, & \tau = 1 \\ 0, & \text{otherwise.} \end{cases}$$

The autocorrelation function is just the autocovariance function scaled by the variance,

$$\rho(\tau) = \frac{\gamma(\tau)}{\gamma(0)} = \begin{cases} \dfrac{\theta}{1 + \theta^2}, & \tau = 1 \\ 0, & \text{otherwise.} \end{cases}$$

The key feature here is the sharp **cutoff in the autocorrelation function**. All autocorrelations are 0 beyond displacement 1, the order of the MA process. In Figures 13-2 and 13-3, we show the autocorrelation functions for our two MA(1) processes with parameters $\theta = 0.4$ and $\theta = 0.95$. At displacement 1, the process with parameter

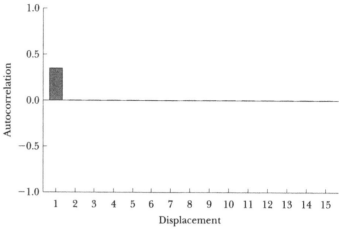

FIGURE 13-2 Population autocorrelation function, MA(1) process, $\theta = 0.4$.

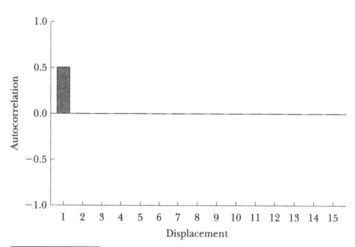

FIGURE 13-3 Population autocorrelation function, MA(1) process, $\theta = 0.95$.

$\theta = 0.4$ has a smaller autocorrelation (0.34) than the process with parameter $\theta = 0.95$ (0.50), but both drop to 0 beyond displacement 1.

Note that the requirements of covariance stationarity (constant unconditional mean, constant and finite unconditional variance, autocorrelation dependent only on displacement) are met for any MA(1) process, *regardless* of the values of its parameters. If, moreover, $|\theta| < 1$, then we say that the MA(1) process is **invertible**. In that case, we can "invert" the MA(1) process and express the current value of the series not in terms of a current shock and a lagged shock but rather in terms of a current shock *and lagged values of the series*. That's called an **autoregressive representation**. An autoregressive representation has a current shock and lagged observable values of the series on the right, whereas a moving average representation has a current shock and lagged unobservable shocks on the right.

Let's compute the autoregressive representation. The process is

$$y_t = \epsilon_t + \theta\epsilon_{t-1}$$

$$\epsilon_t \sim WN(0, \sigma^2).$$

Thus, we can solve for the innovation as

$$\epsilon_t = y_t - \theta\epsilon_{t-1}.$$

Lagging by successively more periods gives expressions for the innovations at various dates,

$$\epsilon_{t-1} = y_{t-1} - \theta\epsilon_{t-2}$$

$$\epsilon_{t-2} = y_{t-2} - \theta\epsilon_{t-3}$$

$$\epsilon_{t-3} = y_{t-3} - \theta\epsilon_{t-4},$$

and so forth. Making use of these expressions for lagged innovations, we can substitute backward in the MA(1) process, yielding

$$y_t = \epsilon_t + \theta y_{t-1} - \theta^2 y_{t-2} + \theta^3 y_{t-3} - \cdots.$$

In lag operator notation, we write the infinite autoregressive representation as

$$\frac{1}{1+\theta L} y_t = \epsilon_t.$$

Note that the back substitution used to obtain the autoregressive representation only makes sense, and in fact a convergent autoregressive representation only exists, if $|\theta| < 1$, because in the back substitution we raise θ to progressively higher powers.

We can restate the invertibility condition in another way: The inverse of the root of the moving average lag operator polynomial $(1 + \theta L)$ must be less than 1 in absolute value. Recall that a polynomial of degree m has m roots. Thus, the MA(1) lag operator polynomial has one root, which is the solution to

$$1 + \theta L = 0.$$

The root is $L = -1/\theta$, so its inverse will be less than 1 in absolute value if $|\theta| < 1$, and the two invertibility conditions are equivalent. The "inverse root" way of stating invertibility conditions seems tedious, but it turns out to be of greater applicability than the $|\theta| < 1$ condition, as we'll see shortly.

Autoregressive representations are appealing to forecasters, because one way or another, if a model is to be used for real-world forecasting, it must link the present observables to the past history of observables, so that we can extrapolate to form a forecast of future observables based on present and past observables. Superficially, moving average models don't seem to meet that requirement, because the current value of a series is expressed in terms of current and lagged unobservable shocks, not observable variables. But under the invertibility conditions that we've described, moving average processes have equivalent autoregressive representations. Thus, although we want autoregressive representations for forecasting, we don't have to start with an autoregressive model. However, we typically restrict ourselves to invertible processes, because for forecasting purposes we want to be able to express current observables as functions of past observables.

Finally, let's consider the partial autocorrelation function for the MA(1) process. From the infinite autoregressive representation of the MA(1) process, we see that the partial autocorrelation function will decay gradually to 0. As we discussed in Chapter 12, the partial autocorrelations are just the coefficients on the last included lag in a sequence of progressively higher-order autoregressive approximations. If $\theta > 0$, then the pattern of decay will be one of damped oscillation; otherwise, the decay will be one-sided.

In Figures 13-4 and 13-5 we show the partial autocorrelation functions for our example MA(1) processes. For each process, $|\theta| < 1$, so that an autoregressive representation

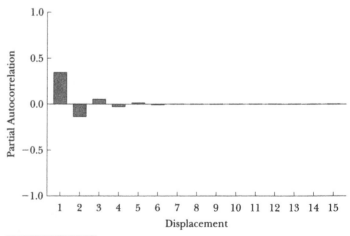

FIGURE 13-4 Population partial autocorrelation function, MA(1) process, $\theta = 0.4$.

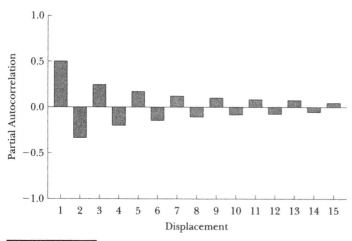

FIGURE 13-5 Population partial autocorrelation function, MA(1) process, $\theta = 0.95$.

exists, and $\theta > 0$, so that the coefficients in the autoregressive representations alternate in sign. Specifically, we showed the general autoregressive representation to be

$$y_t = \epsilon_t + \theta y_{t-1} - \theta^2 y_{t-2} + \theta^3 y_{t-3} - \cdots,$$

so the autoregressive representation for the process with $\theta = 0.4$ is

$$\begin{aligned} y_t &= \epsilon_t + 0.4y_{t-1} - 0.4^2 y_{t-2} + \cdots \\ &= \epsilon_t + 0.4y_{t-1} - 0.16y_{t-2} + \cdots, \end{aligned}$$

and the autoregressive representation for the process with $\theta = 0.95$ is

$$\begin{aligned} y_t &= \epsilon_t + 0.95y_{t-1} - 0.95^2 y_{t-2} + \cdots \\ &= \epsilon_t + 0.95y_{t-1} - 0.9025y_{t-2} + \cdots. \end{aligned}$$

The partial autocorrelations display a similar damped oscillation.[3] The decay, however, is slower for the $\theta = 0.95$ case.

The MA(q) Process

Now consider the general finite-order moving average process of order q, or MA(q) for short,

$$y_t = \epsilon_t + \theta_1 \epsilon_{t-1} + \cdots + \theta_q \epsilon_{t-q} = \Theta(L)\epsilon_t$$

$$\epsilon_t \sim WN(0, \sigma^2),$$

where

$$\Theta(L) = 1 + \theta_1 L + \cdots + \theta_q L^q$$

_____

[3] Note, however, that the partial autocorrelations are *not* the successive coefficients in the infinite autoregressive representation. Rather, they are the coefficients on the last included lag in sequence of progressively longer autoregressions. The two are related but distinct.

is a qth-order lag operator polynomial. The **MA(q) process** is a natural generalization of the MA(1). By allowing for more lags of the shock on the right side of the equation, the MA(q) process can capture richer dynamic patterns, which we can potentially exploit for improved forecasting. The MA(1) process is of course a special case of the MA(q), corresponding to $q = 1$.

The properties of the MA(q) processes parallel those of the MA(1) process in all respects, so in what follows we'll refrain from grinding through the mathematical derivations. Instead, we'll focus on the key features of practical importance. Just as the MA(1) process was covariance stationary for any value of its parameters, so, too, is the finite-order MA(q) process. As with the MA(1) process, the MA(q) process is *invertible* only if a root condition is satisfied. The MA(q) lag operator polynomial has q roots; when $q > 1$, the possibility of **complex roots** arises. The **condition for invertibility of the MA(q) process** is that the inverses of all of the roots must be inside the unit circle, in which case we have the convergent autoregressive representation,

$$\frac{1}{\Theta(L)} y_t = \epsilon_t.$$

The conditional mean of the MA(q) process evolves with the information set, in contrast to the unconditional moments, which are fixed. In contrast to the MA(1) case, in which the conditional mean depends on only the first lag of the innovation, in the MA(q) case the conditional mean depends on q lags of the innovation. Thus, the MA(q) process has the potential for longer memory.

The potentially longer memory of the MA(q) process emerges clearly in its autocorrelation function. In the MA(1) case, all autocorrelations beyond displacement 1 are 0; in the MA(q) case, all autocorrelations beyond displacement q are 0. This autocorrelation cutoff is a distinctive property of moving average processes. The partial autocorrelation function of the MA(q) process, in contrast, decays gradually, in accord with the infinite autoregressive representation, in either an oscillating or a one-sided fashion, depending on the parameters of the process.

In closing this section, let's step back for a moment and consider in greater detail the precise way in which finite-order moving average processes approximate the Wold representation. The Wold representation is

$$y_t = B(L)\epsilon_t,$$

where $B(L)$ is of infinite order. The MA(1), in contrast, is simply a first-order moving average, in which a series is expressed as a one-period moving average of current and past innovations. Thus, when we fit an MA(1) model, we're using the first-order polynomial $1 + \theta L$ to approximate the infinite-order polynomial $B(L)$. Note that $1 + \theta L$ is a rational polynomial with numerator polynomial of degree 1 and degenerate denominator polynomial (degree 0).

MA(q) processes have the potential to deliver better approximations to the Wold representation, at the cost of more parameters to be estimated. The Wold representation involves an infinite moving average; the MA(q) process approximates the infinite moving average with a *finite-order* moving average,

$$y_t = \Theta(L)\epsilon_t,$$

whereas the MA(1) process approximates the infinite moving average with only a *first-order* moving average, which can sometimes be very restrictive.

AUTOREGRESSIVE (AR) MODELS

The autoregressive process is also a natural approximation to the Wold representation. We've seen, in fact, that under certain conditions a moving average process has an autoregressive representation, so an autoregressive process is in a sense the same as a moving average process. Like the moving average process, the autoregressive process has direct motivation; it's simply a *stochastic difference equation*, a simple mathematical model in which the current value of a series is linearly related to its past values, plus an additive stochastic shock. Stochastic difference equations are a natural vehicle for discrete-time stochastic dynamic modeling.

The AR(1) Process

The first-order autoregressive process, AR(1) for short, is

$$y_t = \varphi y_{t-1} + \epsilon_t$$

$$\epsilon_t \sim WN(0, \sigma^2).$$

In lag operator form, we write

$$(1 - \varphi L)y_t = \epsilon_t.$$

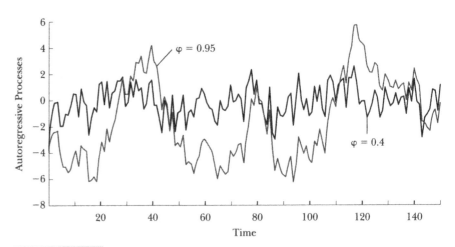

FIGURE 13-6 Realizations of two AR(1) processes.

In Figure 13-6 we show simulated realizations of length 150 of two AR(1) processes; the first is

$$y_t = 0.4y_{t-1} + \epsilon_t,$$

and the second is

$$y_t = 0.95y_{t-1} + \epsilon_t,$$

where in each case $\epsilon_t \overset{iid}{\sim} N(0, 1)$, and the same innovation sequence underlies each realization. The fluctuations in the AR(1) with parameter $\varphi = 0.95$ appear much more persistent than those of the AR(1) with parameter $\varphi = 0.4$. This contrasts sharply with the MA(1) process, which has a very short memory regardless of parameter value. Thus, the AR(1) model is capable of capturing much more persistent dynamics than is the MA(1).

Recall that a finite-order moving average process is always covariance stationary but that certain conditions must be satisfied for invertibility, in which case an autoregressive representation exists. For autoregressive processes, the situation is precisely the reverse. Autoregressive processes are always invertible—in fact, invertibility isn't even an issue, as finite-order autoregressive processes *already are* in autoregressive form—but certain conditions must be satisfied for an autoregressive process to be covariance stationary.

If we begin with the AR(1) process,

$$y_t = \varphi y_{t-1} + \epsilon_t,$$

and substitute backward for lagged y's on the right side, we obtain

$$y_t = \epsilon_t + \varphi\epsilon_{t-1} + \varphi^2\epsilon_{t-2} + \cdots.$$

In lag operator form, we write

$$y_t = \frac{1}{1 - \varphi L} \epsilon_t.$$

This moving average representation for y is convergent if and only if $|\varphi| < 1$; thus, $|\varphi| < 1$ is the condition for covariance stationarity in the AR(1) case. Equivalently, the condition for covariance stationarity is that the inverse of the root of the autoregressive lag operator polynomial be less than 1 in absolute value.

From the moving average representation of the covariance stationary AR(1) process, we can compute the unconditional mean and variance,

$$E(y_t) = E(\epsilon_t + \varphi\epsilon_{t-1} + \varphi^2\epsilon_{t-2} + \cdots)$$

$$= E(\epsilon_t) + \varphi E(\epsilon_{t-1}) + \varphi^2 E(\epsilon_{t-2}) + \cdots$$

$$= 0$$

and

$$\mathrm{var}(y_t) = \mathrm{var}(\epsilon_t + \varphi\epsilon_{t-1} + \varphi^2\epsilon_{t-2} + \cdots)$$

$$= \sigma^2 + \varphi^2\sigma^2 + \varphi^4\sigma^2 + \cdots$$

$$= \sigma^2 \sum_{i=0}^{\infty} \varphi^{2i}$$

$$= \frac{\sigma^2}{1 - \varphi^2}.$$

The conditional moments, in contrast, are

$$E(y_t \mid y_{t-1}) = E(\varphi y_{t-1} + \epsilon_t \mid y_{t-1})$$

$$= \varphi E(y_{t-1} \mid y_{t-1}) + E(\epsilon_t \mid y_{t-1})$$

$$= \varphi y_{t-1} + 0$$

$$= \varphi y_{t-1}$$

and

$$\mathrm{var}(y_t \mid y_{t-1}) = \mathrm{var}(\varphi y_{t-1} + \epsilon_t \mid y_{t-1})$$

$$= \varphi^2 \mathrm{var}(y_{t-1} \mid y_{t-1}) + \mathrm{var}(\epsilon_t \mid y_{t-1})$$

$$= 0 + \sigma^2$$

$$= \sigma^2.$$

Note in particular the simple way in which the conditional mean adapts to the changing information set as the process evolves.

To find the autocovariances, we proceed as follows. The process is

$$y_t = \varphi y_{t-1} + \epsilon_t,$$

so that, multiplying both sides of the equation by $y_{t-\tau}$ we obtain

$$y_t y_{t-\tau} = \varphi y_{t-1} y_{t-\tau} + \epsilon_t y_{t-\tau}.$$

For $\tau \geq 1$, taking expectations of both sides gives

$$\gamma(\tau) = \varphi \gamma(\tau - 1).$$

This is called the **Yule-Walker equation**. It is a recursive equation; that is, given $\gamma(\tau)$, for any τ, the Yule-Walker equation immediately tells us how to get $\gamma(\tau + 1)$. If we knew $\gamma(0)$ to start things off (an "initial condition"), we could use the Yule-Walker equation to determine the entire autocovariance sequence. And we *do* know $\gamma(0)$; it's just the variance of the process, which we already showed to be $\gamma(0) = \sigma^2/1 - \varphi^2$. Thus, we have

$$\gamma(0) = \frac{\sigma^2}{1 - \varphi^2}$$

$$\gamma(1) = \varphi \frac{\sigma^2}{1 - \varphi^2}$$

$$\gamma(2) = \varphi^2 \frac{\sigma^2}{1 - \varphi^2},$$

and so on. In general, then,

$$\gamma(\tau) = \varphi^\tau \frac{\sigma^2}{1 - \varphi^2}, \quad \tau = 0, 1, 2, \ldots.$$

Dividing through by $\gamma(0)$ gives the autocorrelations,

$$\rho(\tau) = \varphi^\tau, \quad \tau = 0, 1, 2, \ldots.$$

Note the gradual autocorrelation decay, which is typical of autoregressive processes. The autocorrelations approach 0, but only in the limit as the displacement approaches infinity. In particular, they don't cut off to 0, as is the case for moving average processes. If φ is positive, the autocorrelation decay is one-sided. If φ is negative, the decay involves back-and-forth oscillations. The relevant case in business and economics is $\varphi > 0$, but either way, the autocorrelations damp gradually, not abruptly. In Figures 13-7 and 13-8, we show the autocorrelation functions for AR(1) processes with parameters $\varphi = 0.4$ and $\varphi = 0.95$. The persistence is much stronger when $\varphi = 0.95$, in contrast to the MA(1) case, in which the persistence was weak regardless of the parameter.

Finally, the partial autocorrelation function for the AR(1) process cuts off abruptly; specifically,

$$p(\tau) = \begin{cases} \varphi, & \tau = 1 \\ 0, & \tau > 1 \end{cases}$$

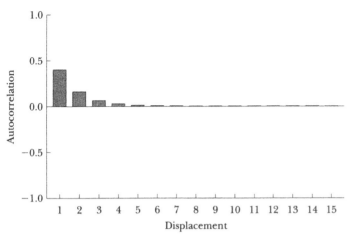

FIGURE 13-7 Population autocorrelation function, AR(1) process, $\varphi = 0.4$.

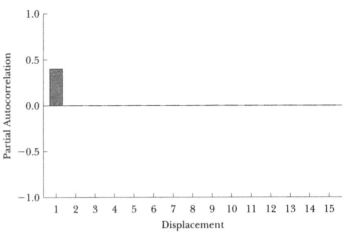

FIGURE 13-9 Population partial autocorrelation function, AR(1) process, $\varphi = 0.4$.

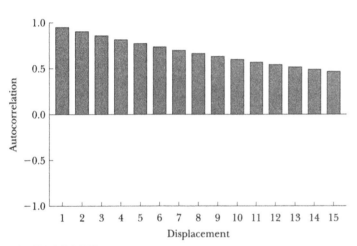

FIGURE 13-8 Population autocorrelation function, AR(1) process, $\varphi = 0.95$.

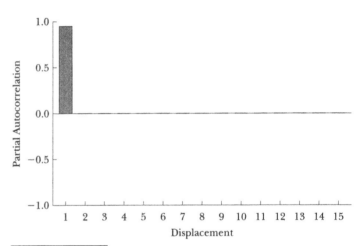

FIGURE 13-10 Population partial autocorrelation function, AR(1) process, $\varphi = 0.95$.

It's easy to see why. The partial autocorrelations are just the last coefficients in a sequence of successively longer population autoregressions. If the true process is in fact an AR(1), the first partial autocorrelation is just the autoregressive coefficient, and coefficients on all longer lags are 0.

In Figures 13-9 and 13-10 we show the partial autocorrelation functions for our two AR(1) processes. At displacement 1, the partial autocorrelations are simply the parameters of the process (0.4 and 0.95, respectively), and at longer displacements, the partial autocorrelations are 0.

The AR(*p*) Process

The general *p*th order autoregressive process, or AR(*p*) for short, is

$$y_t = \varphi_1 y_{t-1} + \varphi_2 y_{t-2} + \cdots + \varphi_p y_{t-p} + \epsilon_t$$
$$\epsilon_t \sim WN(0, \sigma^2).$$

In lag operator form, we write

$$\Phi(L)y_t = (1 - \varphi_1 L - \varphi_2 L^2 - \cdots - \varphi_p L^p)y_t = \epsilon_t.$$

As with our discussion of the MA(*q*) process, in our discussion of the **AR(*p*) process**, we dispense here with mathematical derivations and instead rely on parallels with the AR(1) case to establish intuition for its key properties.

An AR(*p*) process is covariance stationary if and only if the inverses of all roots of the autoregressive lag operator polynomial $\Phi(L)$ are inside the unit circle.[4] In the covariance stationary case, we can write the process in the convergent infinite moving average form

$$y_t = \frac{1}{\Phi(L)}\epsilon_t.$$

The autocorrelation function for the general AR(p) process, as with that of the AR(1) process, decays gradually with displacement. Finally, the AR(p) partial autocorrelation function has a sharp cutoff at displacement p, for the same reason that the AR(1) partial autocorrelation function has a sharp cutoff at displacement 1.

Let's discuss the AR(p) autocorrelation function in a bit greater depth. The key insight is that, in spite of the fact that its qualitative behavior (gradual damping) matches that of the AR(1) autocorrelation function, it can nevertheless display a richer variety of patterns, depending on the order and parameters of the process. It can, for example, have damped monotonic decay, as in the AR(1) case with a positive coefficient, but it can also have damped oscillation in ways that AR(1) can't have. In the AR(1) case, the only possible oscillation occurs when the coefficient is negative, in which case the autocorrelations switch signs at each successively longer displacement. In higher-order autoregressive models, however, the autocorrelations can oscillate with much richer patterns reminiscent of cycles in the more traditional sense. This occurs when some roots of the autoregressive lag operator polynomial are complex.[5]

Consider, for example, the AR(2) process,

$$y_t = 1.5y_{t-1} - 0.9y_{t-2} + \epsilon_t.$$

The corresponding lag operator polynomial is $1 - 1.5L + 0.9L^2$, with two complex conjugate roots, $0.83 \pm 0.65i$. The inverse roots are $0.75 \pm 0.58i$, both of which are close to, but inside, the unit circle; thus, the process is covariance stationary. It can be shown that the autocorrelation function for an AR(2) process is

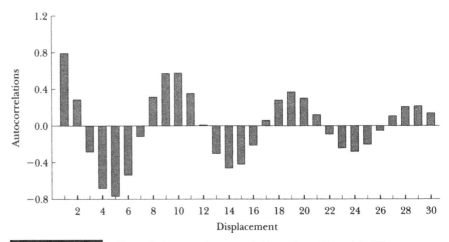

FIGURE 13-11 Population autocorrelation function AR(2) process with complex roots.

$$\rho(0) = 1$$

$$\rho(1) = \frac{\varphi_1}{1 - \varphi_2}$$

$$\rho(\tau) = \varphi_1\rho(\tau - 1) + \varphi_2\rho(\tau - 2), \quad \tau = 2, 3, \ldots.$$

Using this formula, we can evaluate the autocorrelation function for the process at hand; we plot it in Figure 13-11. Because the roots are complex, the autocorrelation function oscillates, and because the roots are close to the unit circle, the oscillation damps slowly.

Finally, let's step back once again to consider in greater detail the precise way that finite-order autoregressive processes approximate the Wold representation. As always, the Wold representation is

$$y_t = B(L)\epsilon_t,$$

where $B(L)$ is of infinite order. The AR(1), as compared to the MA(1), is simply a different approximation to the Wold representation. The moving average representation associated with the AR(1) process is

$$y_t = \frac{1}{1 - \varphi L}\epsilon_t.$$

Thus, when we fit an AR(1) model, we're using $1/1 - \varphi L$, a rational polynomial with degenerate numerator polynomial (degree 0) and denominator polynomial of degree 1, to approximate $B(L)$. The moving average representation associated with the AR(1) process is of infinite order, as is the Wold representation, but it does not have infinitely many free coefficients. In fact, only one parameter, φ, underlies it.

---

[4] A necessary **condition for covariance stationarity**, which is often useful as a quick check, is $\sum_{i=1}^{p} \varphi_i < 1$. If the condition is satisfied, the process mayor may not be stationary; but if the condition is violated, the process can't be stationary.

[5] Note that complex roots can't occur in the AR(1) case.

The AR(p) is an obvious generalization of the AR(1) strategy for approximating the Wold representation. The moving average representation associated with the AR(p) process is

$$y_t = \frac{1}{\Phi(L)} \epsilon_t.$$

When we fit an AR(p) model to approximate the Wold representation we're still using a rational polynomial with degenerate numerator polynomial (degree 0), but the denominator polynomial is of higher degree.

AUTOREGRESSIVE MOVING AVERAGE (ARMA) MODELS

Autoregressive and moving average models are often combined in attempts to obtain better and more par-simonious approximations to the Wold representation, yielding the autoregressive moving average process, **ARMA(p, q) process** for short. As with moving average and autoregressive processes, ARMA processes also have direct motivation.[6] First, if the random shock that drives an autoregressive process is itself a moving average process, then it can be shown that we obtain an ARMA process. Second, ARMA processes can arise from aggregation. For example, sums of AR processes, or sums of AR and MA processes, can be shown to be ARMA processes. Finally, AR processes observed subject to measurement error also turn out to be ARMA processes.

The simplest ARMA process that's not a pure autoregression or pure moving average is the ARMA(1, 1), given by

$$y_t = \varphi y_{t-1} + \epsilon_t + \theta \epsilon_{t-1}$$

$$\epsilon_t \sim WN(0, \sigma^2),$$

or, in lag operator form,

$$(1 - \varphi L) y_t = (1 + \theta L) \epsilon_t,$$

where $|\theta| < 1$ is required for stationarity and $|\theta| < 1$ is required for invertibility.[7] If the covariance stationarity condition is satisfied, then we have the moving average representation

$$y_t = \frac{(1 + \theta L)}{(1 - \varphi L)} \epsilon_t,$$

which is an infinite distributed lag of current and past innovations. Similarly, if the invertibility condition is satisfied, then we have the infinite autoregressive representation,

$$\frac{(1 - \varphi L)}{(1 + \theta L)} y_t = \epsilon_t.$$

The ARMA(p, q) process is a natural generalization of the ARMA(1, 1) that allows for multiple moving average and autoregressive lags. We write

$$y_t = \varphi_1 y_{t-1} + \cdots + \varphi_p y_{t-p} + \epsilon_t + \theta_1 \epsilon_{t-1} + \cdots + \theta_q \epsilon_{t-q}$$

$$\epsilon_t \sim WN(0, \sigma^2),$$

or

$$\Phi(L) y_t = \Theta(L) \epsilon_t,$$

where

$$\Phi(L) = 1 - \varphi_1 L - \varphi_2 L^2 - \cdots - \varphi_p L^p$$

and

$$\Theta(L) = 1 + \theta_1 L + \theta_2 L^2 + \cdots + \theta_q L^q.$$

If the inverses of all roots of $\Phi(L)$ are inside the unit circle, then the process is covariance stationary and has convergent infinite moving average representation

$$y_t = \frac{\Theta(L)}{\Phi(L)} \epsilon_t.$$

If the inverses of all roots of $\Theta(L)$ are inside the unit circle, then the process is invertible and has convergent infinite autoregressive representation

$$\frac{\Phi(L)}{\Theta(L)} y_t = \epsilon_t.$$

As with autoregressions and moving averages, ARMA processes have a fixed unconditional mean but a time-varying conditional mean. In contrast to pure moving average or pure autoregressive processes, however, neither the auto-correlation nor partial autocorrelation functions of ARMA processes cut off at any particular displacement. Instead, each damps gradually, with the precise pattern depending on the process.

ARMA models approximate the Wold representation by a ratio of two finite-order lag operator polynomials, neither of which is degenerate. Thus, ARMA models use ratios of full-fledged polynomials in the lag operator to approximate the Wold representation,

$$y_t = \frac{\Theta(L)}{\Phi(L)} \epsilon_t.$$

---

[6] For more extensive discussion, see Granger and Newbold (1986).

[7] Both stationarity and invertibility need to be checked in the ARMA case, because both autoregressive and moving average components are present.

ARMA models, by allowing for both moving average and autoregressive components, often provide accurate approximations to the Wold representation that nevertheless have just a few parameters. That is, ARMA models are often both highly accurate and highly parsimonious. In a particular situation, for example, it might take an AR(5) to get the same approximation accuracy as could be obtained with an ARMA(2, 1), but the AR(5) has five parameters to be estimated, whereas the ARMA(2, 1) has only three.

APPLICATION: SPECIFYING AND ESTIMATING MODELS FOR EMPLOYMENT FORECASTING

In Chapter 12, we examined the correlogram for the Canadian employment series, and we saw that the sample autocorrelations damp slowly and the sample partial autocorrelations cut off, just the opposite of what's expected for a moving average. Thus, the correlogram indicates that a finite-order moving average process would not provide a good approximation to employment dynamics. Nevertheless, nothing stops us from fitting moving average models, so let's fit them and use the AIC and the SIC to guide model selection.

Moving average models are nonlinear in the parameters; thus, estimation proceeds by nonlinear least squares (numerical minimization). The idea is the same as when we encountered nonlinear least squares in our study of nonlinear trends—pick the parameters to minimize the sum of squared residuals—but finding an expression for the residual is a little bit trickier. To understand why moving average models are nonlinear in the parameters, and to get a feel for how they're estimated, consider an invertible MA(1) model, with a nonzero mean explicitly included for added realism,

$$y_t = \mu + \epsilon_t + \theta\epsilon_{t-1}.$$

Substitute backward m times to obtain the autoregressive approximation

$$y_t \approx \frac{\mu}{1+\theta} + \theta y_{t-1} - \theta^2 y_{t-2} + \cdots + (-1)^{m+1}\theta^m y_{t-m} + \epsilon_t.$$

Thus, an invertible moving average can be approximated as a finite-order autoregression. The larger is m, the better the approximation. This lets us (approximately) express the residual in terms of observed data, after which we can use a computer to solve for the parameters that minimize the sum of squared residuals,

$$\hat{\mu}, \hat{\theta} = \underset{\mu,\theta}{\operatorname{argmin}} \sum_{t=1}^{T}\left(y_t - \left(\frac{\mu}{1+\theta} + \theta y_{t-1} - \theta^2 y_{t-2} + \cdots + (-1)^{m+1}\theta^m y_{t-m}\right)\right)^2$$

$$\hat{\sigma}^2 = \frac{1}{T}\sum_{t=1}^{T}\left(y_t - \left(\frac{\hat{\mu}}{1+\hat{\theta}} + \hat{\theta} y_{t-1} - \hat{\theta}^2 y_{t-2} + \cdots + (-1)^{m+1}\hat{\theta}^m y_{t-m}\right)\right)^2.$$

The parameter estimates must be found using numerical optimization methods, because the parameters of the autoregressive approximation are restricted. The coefficient of the second lag of y is the square of the coefficient on the first lag of y, and so on. The parameter restrictions must be imposed in estimation, which is why we can't simply run an ordinary least-squares regression of y on lags of itself.

The next step would be to estimate MA(q) models, $q = 1$, 2, 3, 4. Both the AIC and the SIC suggest that the MA(4) is best. To save space, we report only the results of MA(4) estimation in Table 13-1. The results of the MA(4) estimation, although better than lower-order MAs, are nevertheless poor. The R^2 of 0.84 is rather low, for example, and the Durbin-Watson statistic indicates that the MA(4) model fails to account for all the serial correlation in employment. The residual plot, which we show in Figure 13-12, clearly indicates a neglected cycle, an impression confirmed by the residual correlogram (Table 13-2 and Figure 13-13).

If we insist on using a moving average model, we'd want to explore orders greater than 4, but all the results thus far indicate that moving average processes don't provide good approximations to employment dynamics. Thus, let's consider alternative approximations, such as autoregressions. Autoregressions can be conveniently estimated by ordinary least-squares regression. Consider, for example, the AR(1) model,

$$(y_t - \mu) = \varphi(y_{t-1} - \mu) + \epsilon_t$$

$$\epsilon_t \sim WN(0, \sigma^2).$$

We can write it as

$$y_t = c + \varphi y_{t-1} + \epsilon_t,$$

where $c = \mu(1 - \varphi)$. The least-squares estimators are

$$\hat{c}, \hat{\varphi} = \underset{c,\varphi}{\operatorname{argmin}} \sum_{t=1}^{T}(y_t - c - \varphi y_{t-1})^2$$

$$\hat{\sigma}^2 = \frac{1}{T}\sum_{t=1}^{T}(y_t - \hat{c} - \hat{\varphi} y_{t-1})^2.$$

TABLE 13-1 Employment MA(4) Model

LS // Dependent variable is CANEMP.
Sample: 1962:1 1993:4
Included observations: 128
Convergence achieved after 49 iterations

Variable	Coefficient	Std. Error	*t*-Statistic	Prob.
C	100.5438	0.843322	119.2234	0.0000
MA(1)	1.587641	0.063908	24.84246	0.0000
MA(2)	0.994369	0.089995	11.04917	0.0000
MA(3)	−0.020305	0.046550	−0.436189	0.6635
MA(4)	−0.298387	0.020489	−14.56311	0.0000

R^2	0.849951	Mean dependent var.		101.0176
Adjusted R^2	0.845071	SD dependent var.		7.499163
SE of regression	2.951747	Akaike info criterion		2.203073
Sum squared resid.	1071.676	Schwarz criterion		2.314481
Log likelihood	−317.6208	F-statistic		174.1826
Durbin-Watson stat.	1.246600	Prob(F-statistic)		0.000000
Inverted MA roots	.41	−.56 + .72i	−.56 − .72i	−.87

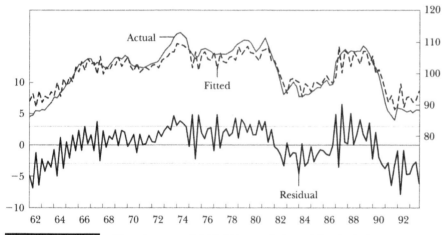

FIGURE 13-12 Employment MA(4) model, residual plot.

The implied estimate of μ is $\hat{\mu} = \hat{c}/(1 − \hat{\phi})$. Unlike the moving average case, for which the sum-of-squares function is nonlinear in the parameters, requiring the use of numerical minimization methods, the sum of squares function for autoregressive processes is linear in the parameters, so that estimation is particularly stable and easy. In the AR(1) case, we simply run an ordinary least-squares regression of y on one lag of y; in the AR(p) case, we regress y on p lags of y.

We estimate AR(p) models, (p) = 1, 2, 3, 4. Both the AIC and the SIC suggest that the AR(2) is best. To save space, we report only the results of AR(2) estimation in Table 13-3. The estimation results look good, and the residuals (Figure 13-14) look like white noise. The residual correlogram (Table 13-4 and Figure 13-15) supports that conclusion.

Finally, we consider ARMA(p, q) approximations to the Wold representation. ARMA models are estimated in a fashion similar to moving average models; they have autoregressive approximations with nonlinear restrictions on the parameters, which we impose when doing a numerical sum of squares minimization. We examine all ARMA(p, q) models with p and q less than or equal to 4; the SIC and AIC values appear in Tables 13-5 and 13-6. The SIC selects the AR(2) (an ARMA(2, 0)), which we've already discussed. The AIC, which penalizes degrees of freedom less harshly, selects an ARMA(3, 1) model. The ARMA(3, 1) model looks good; the estimation results appear in Table 13-7, the residual plot in Figure 13-16, and the residual correlogram in Table 13-8 and Figure 13-17.

Although the ARMA(3, 1) looks good, apart from its lower AIC, it looks no better than the AR(2), which basically seemed perfect. In fact, there are at least three reasons to prefer the AR(2). First, when the AIC and the SIC disagree, we recommend using the more parsimonious model selected by the SIC. Second, if we consider a model selection strategy involving examination of not just the AIC and SIC but also autocorrelations and partial autocorrelations, which we advocate, we're led to the AR(2). Finally, and importantly, the impression that the ARMA(3, 1) provides a richer approximation to employment dynamics is likely spurious in this case. The ARMA(3, 1) has an inverse autoregressive root of −0.94 and an inverse moving average root of −0.97. Those roots are of course just *estimates,* subject to sampling uncertainty, and are likely to be statistically indistinguishable from one another, in which case we can *cancel*

TABLE 13-2 Employment MA(4) Model, Residual Correlogram

Sample: 1962:1 1993:4
Included observations: 128
Q-statistic probabilities adjusted for 4 ARMA term(s)

	Acorr.	P. Acorr.	Std. Error	Ljung-Box	p-Value
1	0.345	0.345	.088	15.614	
2	0.660	0.614	.088	73.089	
3	0.534	0.426	.088	111.01	
4	0.427	−0.042	.088	135.49	
5	0.347	−0.398	.088	151.79	0.000
6	0.484	0.145	.088	183.70	0.000
7	0.121	−0.118	.088	185.71	0.000
8	0.348	−0.048	.088	202.46	0.000
9	0.148	−0.019	.088	205.50	0.000
10	0.102	−0.066	.088	206.96	0.000
11	0.081	−0.098	.088	207.89	0.000
12	0.029	−0.113	.088	208.01	0.000

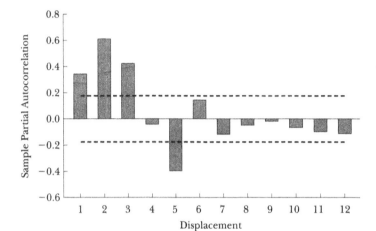

FIGURE 13-13 Employment MA(4) model: residual sample autocorrelation functions, with plus or minus two-standard-error bands.

TABLE 13-3 Employment AR(2) Model

LS//Dependent variable is CANEMP.
Sample: 1962:1 1993:4
Included observations: 128
Convergence achieved after 3 iterations

Variable	Coefficient	Std. Error	t-Statistic	Prob.
C	101.2413	3.399620	29.78017	0.0000
AR(1)	1.438810	0.078487	18.33188	0.0000
AR(2)	−0.476451	0.077902	−6.116042	0.0000
R^2	0.963372		Mean dependent var.	101.0176
Adjusted R^2	0.962786		SD dependent var.	7.499163
SE of regression	1.446663		Akaike info criterion	0.761677
Sum squared resid.	261.6041		Schwarz criterion	0.828522
Log likelihood	−227.3715		F-statistic	1643.837
Durbin-Watson stat.	2.067024		Prob(F-statistic)	0.000000
Inverted AR roots	.92		.52	

them, which brings us down to an ARMA(2, 0), or AR(2), model with roots virtually indistinguishable from those of our earlier-estimated AR(2) process! We refer to this situation as one of **common factors** in an ARMA model. Be on the lookout for such situations, which arise frequently and can lead to substantial model simplification.

Thus, we arrive at an AR(2) model for employment.

Bibliographical and Computational Notes

Characterization of time series by means of autoregressive, moving average, or ARMA

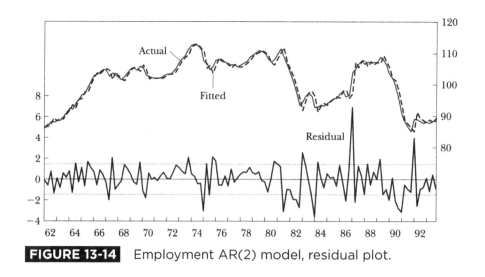

FIGURE 13-14 Employment AR(2) model, residual plot.

TABLE 13-4 Employment AR(2) Model, Residual Correlogram

Sample: 1962:1 1993:4
Included observations: 128
Q-statistic probabilities adjusted for 2 ARMA term(s)

	Acorr.	P. Accor.	Std. Error	Ljung-Box	p-Value
1	−0.035	−0.035	.088	0.1606	
2	0.044	0.042	.088	0.4115	
3	0.011	0.014	.088	0.4291	0.512
4	0.051	0.050	.088	0.7786	0.678
5	0.002	0.004	.088	0.7790	0.854
6	0.019	0.015	.088	0.8272	0.935
7	−0.024	−0.024	.088	0.9036	0.970
8	0.078	0.072	.088	1.7382	0.942
9	0.080	0.087	.088	2.6236	0.918
10	0.050	0.050	.088	2.9727	0.936
11	−0.023	−0.027	.088	3.0504	0.962
12	−0.129	−0.148	.088	5.4385	0.860

TABLE 13-5 Employment AIC Values, Various ARMA Models

		MA Order				
		0	1	2	3	4
	0		2.86	2.32	2.47	2.20
AR Order	1	1.01	0.83	0.79	0.80	0.81
	2	0.762	0.77	0.78	0.80	0.80
	3	0.77	0.761	0.77	0.78	0.79
	4	0.79	0.79	0.77	0.79	0.80

TABLE 13-6 Employment SIC Values, Various ARMA Models

		MA Order				
		0	1	2	3	4
	0		2.91	2.38	2.56	2.31
AR Order	1	1.05	0.90	0.88	0.91	0.94
	2	0.83	0.86	0.89	0.92	0.96
	3	0.86	0.87	0.90	0.94	0.96
	4	0.90	0.92	0.93	0.97	1.00

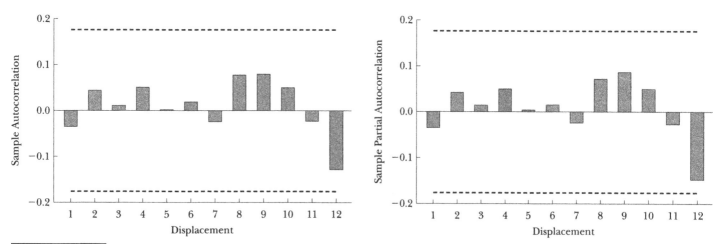

FIGURE 13-15 Employment AR(2) model: residual sample autocorrelation and partial autocorrelation functions, with plus or minus two-standard-error bands.

TABLE 13-7 Employment ARMA (3, 1) Model

LS//Dependent variable is CANEMP.
Sample: 1962:1 1993:4
Included observations: 128
Convergence achieved after 17 iterations

Variable	Coefficient	Std. Error	t-Statistic	Prob.
C	101.1378	3.538602	28.58130	0.0000
AR(1)	0.500493	0.087503	5.719732	0.0000
AR(2)	0.872194	0.067096	12.99917	0.0000
AR(3)	−0.443355	0.080970	−5.475560	0.0000
MA(1)	0.970952	0.035015	27.72924	0.0000

R^2	0.964535	Mean dependent var.	101.0176
Adjusted R^2	0.963381	SD dependent var.	7.499163
SE of regression	1.435043	Akaike info criterion	0.760668
Sum squared resid.	253.2997	Schwarz criterion	0.872076
Log likelihood	−225.3069	F-statistic	836.2912
Durbin-Watson stat.	2.057302	Prob(F-statistic)	0.000000
Inverted AR roots	.93	.51	−.94
Inverted MA roots	−.97		

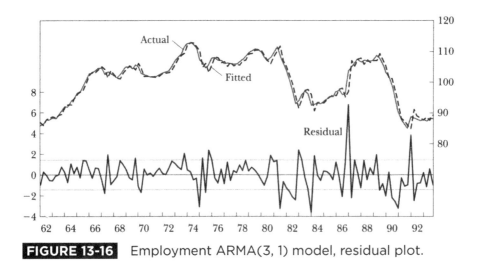

FIGURE 13-16 Employment ARMA(3, 1) model, residual plot.

TABLE 13-8 Employment ARMA(3, 1) Model, Residual Correlogram

Sample: 1962:1 1993:4
Included observations: 128
Q-statistic probabilities adjusted for four ARMA term(s)

	Acorr.	P. Acorr.	Std. Error	Ljung-Box	p-value
1	−0.032	−0.032	.09	0.1376	
2	0.041	0.040	.09	0.3643	
3	0.014	0.017	.09	0.3904	
4	0.048	0.047	.09	0.6970	
5	0.006	0.007	.09	0.7013	0.402
6	0.013	0.009	.09	0.7246	0.696
7	−0.017	−0.019	.09	0.7650	0.858
8	0.064	0.060	.09	1.3384	0.855
9	0.092	0.097	.09	2.5182	0.774
10	0.039	0.040	.09	2.7276	0.842
11	−0.016	−0.022	.09	2.7659	0.906
12	−0.137	−0.153	.09	5.4415	0.710

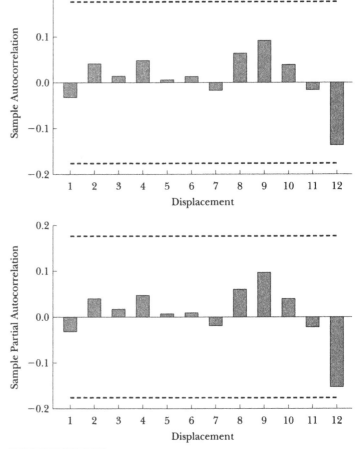

FIGURE 13-17 Employment ARMA(3, 1) model: residual sample autocorrelation and partial autocorrelation functions, with plus or minus two-standard-error bands.

models was suggested, more or less simultaneously, by the Russian statistician and economist E. Slutsky and the British statistician G. U. Yule. Slutsky (1927) remains a classic. The Slutsky-Yule framework was modernized, extended, and made part of an innovative and operational modeling and forecasting paradigm in a more recent classic, a 1970 book by Box and Jenkins, the latest edition of which is Box, Jenkins, and Reinsel (1994). In fact, ARMA and related models are often called **Box-Jenkins models**.

Granger and Newbold (1986) contains more detailed discussion of a number of topics that arose in this chapter, including the idea of moving average processes as describing economic equilibrium disturbed by transient shocks, the Yule-Walker equation, and the insight that aggregation and measurement error lead naturally to ARMA processes.

The sample autocorrelations and partial autocorrelations, together with related diagnostics, provide graphical aids to model selection that complement the Akaike and Schwarz information criteria introduced earlier. Not long ago, the sample autocorrelation and partial autocorrelation functions were often used *alone* to guide forecast model selection, a tricky business that was more art than science. Use of the Akaike and Schwarz criteria results in more systematic and replicable model selection, but the sample autocorrelation and partial autocorrelation functions nevertheless remain important as basic graphical summaries of dynamics in time series data. The two approaches are complements, not substitutes.

Our discussion of estimation was a bit fragmented; we discussed estimation of moving average and ARMA models using nonlinear least squares, whereas we discussed estimation of autoregressive models using ordinary least squares. A more unified approach proceeds by writing each model as a regression on an intercept, with a serially correlated disturbance. Thus, the moving average model is

$$y_t = \mu + \epsilon_t$$
$$\epsilon_t = \Theta(L)v_t$$
$$v_t \sim WN(0, \sigma^2),$$

the autoregressive model is

$$y_t = \mu + \epsilon_t$$
$$\Phi(L)\epsilon_t = v_t$$
$$v_t \sim WN(0, \sigma^2),$$

and the ARMA model is

$$y_t = \mu + \epsilon_t$$
$$\Phi(L)\epsilon_t = \Theta(L)v_t$$
$$v_t \sim WN(0, \sigma^2).$$

We can estimate each model in identical fashion using nonlinear least squares. Eviews and other forecasting packages proceed in precisely that way.[8]

This framework—regression on a constant with serially correlated disturbances—has a number of attractive features. First, the mean of the process is the regression constant term.[9] Second, it leads us naturally toward regression on more than just a constant, as other right-hand-side variables can be added as desired. Finally, it exploits the fact that because autoregressive and moving average models are special cases of the ARMA model, their estimation is also a special case of estimation of the ARMA model.

Our description of estimating ARMA models—compute the autoregressive representation, truncate it, and estimate the resulting approximate model by nonlinear least squares—is conceptually correct but intentionally simplified. The actual estimation methods implemented in modern software are more sophisticated, and the precise implementations vary across software packages. Beneath it all, however, all estimation methods are closely related to our discussion, whether implicitly or explicitly. You should consult your software manual for details. (Hopefully they're provided!)

Pesaran, Pierse, and Kumar (1989) and Granger (1990) study the question of top-down versus bottom-up forecasting. For a comparative analysis in the context of forecasting Euro-area macroeconomic activity, see Stock and Watson (2003).

Our discussion of regime-switching models draws heavily on Diebold and Rudebusch (1996). Tong (1983) is a key reference on observable-state threshold models, as is Hamilton (1989) for latent-state threshold models. There are a number of extensions of those basic regime-switching models of potential interest for forecasters, such as allowing for smooth as opposed to abrupt transitions

---

[8] That's why, for example, information on the number of iterations required for convergence is presented even for estimation of the autoregressive model.

[9] Hence the notation "μ" for the intercept.

in threshold models with observed states (Granger and Terasvirta, 1993) and allowing for time-varying transition probabilities in threshold models with latent states (Diebold, Lee, and Weinbach, 1994).

Concepts for Review

Moving Average (MA) model
Autoregressive (AR) model
Autoregressive moving average (ARMA) model
Stochastic process
MA(1) process
Cutoff in the autocorrelation function
Invertibility
Autoregressive representation
MA(q) process
Complex roots
Condition for invertibility of the MA(q) process
Yule-Walker equation
AR(p) process
Condition for covariance stationarity
ARMA(p, q) process
Common factors
Box-Jenkins model

References and Additional Readings

Bollerslev, T. (1986). "Generalized Autoregressive Conditional Heteroskedasticity." *Journal of Econometrics*, 31, 307–327.

Bollerslev, T., Chou, R. Y, and Kroner, K. F. (1992). "ARCH Modeling in Finance: A Selective Review of the Theory and Empirical Evidence."*Journal of Econometrics,* 52, 5–59.

Box, G. E. P., Jenkins, G. W., and Reinsel, G. (1994). *Time Series Analysis, Forecasting and Control.* 3rd ed. Englewood Cliffs, N.J.: Prentice Hall.

Burns, A. F., and Mitchell, W. C. (1946). *Measuring Business Cycles.* New York: National Bureau of Economic Research.

Diebold, F. X., Lee, J.-H., and Weinbach, G. (1994). "Regime Switching with Time-Varying Transition Probabilities." In C. Hargreaves (ed.), *Nonstationary Time Series Analysis and Cointegration.* Oxford: Oxford University Press, 283–302. Reprinted in Diebold and Rudebusch (1999).

Diebold, F. X., and Lopez, J. (1995). "Modeling Volatility Dynamics." In Kevin Hoover (ed.), *Macroeconometrics:*

Developments, Tensions and Prospects. Boston: Kluwer Academic Press, 427–472.

Diebold, F. X., and Rudebusch, G. D. (1996) . "Measuring Business Cycles: A Modern Perspective." *Review of Economics and Statistics,* 78, 67–77. Reprinted in Diebold and Rudebusch (1999).

Diebold, F. X., and Rudebusch, G. D. (1999). *Business Cycles: Durations, Dynamics, and Forecasting.* Princeton, N.J.: Princeton University Press.

Engle, R. F. (1982). "Autoregressive Conditional Heteroskedasticity with Estimates of the Variance of U.K. Inflation." *Econometrica,* 50, 987–1008.

Fildes, R., and Steckler, H. (2000). "The State of Macroeconomic Forecasting." Manuscript.

Granger, C. W. J. (1990). "Aggregation of Time Series Variables: A Survey." In T. Barker and M. H. Pesaran (eds.), *Disaggregation in Econometric Modelling.* London: Routledge.

Granger, C. W. J., and Newbold, P. (1986). *Forecasting Economic Time Series.* 2nd ed. Orlando, Fla.: Academic Press.

Granger, C. W. J., and Terasvirta, Y. (1993). *Modelling Nonlinear Economic Relationships.* Oxford: Oxford University Press.

Hamilton, J. D. (1989). "A New Approach to the Economic Analysis of Nonstationary Time Series and the Business Cycle." *Econometrica,* 57, 357–384.

McCullough, B. D., and Vinod, H. D. (1999). "The Numerical Reliability of Econometric Software."*Journal of Economic Literature,* 37, 633–665.

Newbold, P., Agiakloglou, C., and Miller J. P. (1994). "Adventures with ARIMA Software." *Internalional Journal of Forecasting,* 10, 573–581.

Pesaran, M. H., Pierse, R. G., and Kumar, M. S. (1989). "Econometric Analysis of Aggregation in the Context of Linear Prediction Models." *Econometrica,* 57, 861–888.

Slutsky, E. (1927). "The Summation of Random Causes as the Source of Cyclic Processes." *Economellica,* 5, 105–146.

Stock, J. H., and Watson, M. W. (2003). "Macroeconomic Forecasting in the Euro Area: Country-Specific versus Area-Wide Information." *European Economic Review,* 47, 1–18.

Taylor, S. (1996). *Modeling Financial Time Series.* 2nd ed. New York: Wiley.

Tong, H. (1990). *Non-linear Time Series.* Oxford: Clarendon Press.

Estimating Volatilities and Correlations

14

Learning Objectives

Candidates, after completing this reading, should be able to:

- Explain how various weighting schemes can be used in estimating volatility.
- Apply the exponentially weighted moving average (EWMA) model to estimate volatility.
- Describe the generalized autoregressive conditional heteroskedasticity (GARCH (p,q)) model for estimating volatility and its properties:
  - Calculate volatility using the GARCH (1,1) model
  - Explain mean reversion and how it is captured in the GARCH (1,1) model

- Explain the weights in the EWMA and GARCH (1,1) models.
- Explain how GARCH models perform in volatility forecasting.
- Describe the volatility term structure and the impact of volatility changes.
- Describe how correlations and covariances are calculated, and explain the consistency condition for covariances.

Excerpt is Chapter 23 of Options, Futures, and Other Derivatives, *Ninth Edition, by John C. Hull.*

In this chapter we explain how historical data can be used to produce estimates of the current and future levels of volatilities and correlations. The chapter is relevant both to the calculation of value-at-risk using the model-building approach and to the valuation of derivatives. When calculating value-at-risk, we are most interested in the current levels of volatilities and correlations because we are assessing possible changes in the value of a portfolio over a very short period of time. When valuing derivatives, forecasts of volatilities and correlations over the whole life of the derivative are usually required.

The chapter considers models with imposing names such as exponentially weighted moving average (EWMA), autoregressive conditional heteroscedasticity (ARCH), and generalized autoregressive conditional heteroscedasticity (GARCH). The distinctive feature of the models is that they recognize that volatilities and correlations are not constant. During some periods, a particular volatility or correlation may be relatively low, whereas during other periods it may be relatively high. The models attempt to keep track of the variations in the volatility or correlation through time.

ESTIMATING VOLATILITY

Define σ_n as the volatility of a market variable on day n, as estimated at the end of day $n - 1$. The square of the volatility, σ_n^2, on day n is the *variance rate.* Suppose that the value of the market variable at the end of day i is S_i. The variable u_i is defined as the continuously compounded return during day i (between the end of day $i - 1$ and the end of day i):

$$u_i = \ln \frac{S_i}{S_{i-1}}$$

An unbiased estimate of the variance rate per day, σ_n^2, using the most recent m observations on the u_i is

$$\sigma_n^2 = \frac{1}{m - 1} \sum_{i=1}^{m} (u_{n-i} - \bar{u})^2 \qquad \textbf{(14.1)}$$

where $\bar{u}$ is the mean of the u_is:

$$\bar{u} = \frac{1}{m} \sum_{i=1}^{m} u_{n-i}$$

For the purposes of monitoring daily volatility, the formula in Equation (14.1) is usually changed in a number of ways:

1. u_i is defined as the percentage change in the market variable between the end of day $i - 1$ and the end of day i, so that:

$$u_i = \frac{S_i - S_{i-1}}{S_{i-1}} \qquad \textbf{(14.2)}$$

2. $\bar{u}$ is assumed to be zero.[1]

3. $m - 1$ is replaced by m.[2]

These three changes make very little difference to the estimates that are calculated, but they allow us to simplify the formula for the variance rate to

$$\sigma_n^2 = \frac{1}{m} \sum_{i=1}^{m} u_{n-i}^2 \qquad \textbf{(14.3)}$$

where u_i is given by Equation (14.2).

Weighting Schemes

Equation (14.3) gives equal weight to $u_{n-1}^2, u_{n-2}^2, \ldots, u_{n-m}^2$. Our objective is to estimate the current level of volatility, σ_n. It therefore makes sense to give more weight to recent data. A model that does this is

$$\sigma_n^2 = \sum_{i=1}^{m} \alpha_i u_{n-i}^2 \qquad \textbf{(14.4)}$$

The variable α_i is the amount of weight given to the observation i days ago. The α's are positive. If we choose them so that $\alpha_i < \alpha_j$ when $i > j$, less weight is given to older observations. The weights must sum to unity, so that

$$\sum_{i=1}^{m} \alpha_i = 1$$

An extension of the idea in Equation (14.4) is to assume that there is a long-run average variance rate and that this should be given some weight. This leads to the model that takes the form

$$\sigma_n^2 = \gamma V_L + \sum_{i=1}^{m} \alpha_i u_{n-i}^2 \qquad \textbf{(14.5)}$$

---

[1] This assumption usually has very little effect on estimates of the variance because the expected change in a variable in one day is very small when compared with the standard deviation of changes.

[2] Replacing $m - 1$ by m moves us from an unbiased estimate of the variance to a maximum likelihood estimate. Maximum likelihood estimates are discussed later in the chapter.

where V_L is the long-run variance rate and γ is the weight assigned to V_L. Since the weights must sum to unity, we have

$$\gamma + \sum_{i=1}^{m} \alpha_i = 1$$

This is known as an ARCH(m) model. It was first suggested by Engle.[3] The estimate of the variance is based on a long-run average variance and m observations. The older an observation, the less weight it is given. Defining $\omega = \gamma V_L$, the model in Equation (14.5) can be written

$$\sigma_n^2 = \omega + \sum_{i=1}^{m} \alpha_i u_{n-i}^2 \qquad \textbf{(14.6)}$$

In the next two sections we discuss two important approaches to monitoring volatility using the ideas in Equations (14.4) and (14.5).

THE EXPONENTIALLY WEIGHTED MOVING AVERAGE MODEL

The exponentially weighted moving average (EWMA) model is a particular case of the model in Equation (14.4) where the weights α_i decrease exponentially as we move back through time. Specifically, $\alpha_{i+1} = \lambda \alpha_i$, where λ is a constant between 0 and 1.

It turns out that this weighting scheme leads to a particularly simple formula for updating volatility estimates. The formula is

$$\sigma_n^2 = \lambda \sigma_{n-1}^2 + (1 - \lambda) u_{n-1}^2 \qquad \textbf{(14.7)}$$

The estimate, σ_n, of the volatility of a variable for day n (made at the end of day $n - 1$) is calculated from σ_{n-1} (the estimate that was made at the end of day $n - 2$ of the volatility for day $n - 1$) and u_{n-1} (the most recent daily percentage change in the variable).

To understand why Equation (14.7) corresponds to weights that decrease exponentially, we substitute for σ_{n-1}^2 to get

$$\sigma_n^2 = \lambda [\lambda \sigma_{n-2}^2 + (1 - \lambda) u_{n-2}^2] + (1 - \lambda) u_{n-1}^2$$

---

[3] See R. Engle "Autoregressive Conditional Heteroscedasticity with Estimates of the Variance of UK Inflation," *Econometrica,* 50 (1982): 987–1008.

or

$$\sigma_n^2 = (1 - \lambda)(u_{n-1}^2 + \lambda u_{n-2}^2) + \lambda^2 \sigma_{n-2}^2$$

Substituting in a similar way for σ_{n-2}^2 gives

$$\sigma_n^2 = (1 - \lambda)(u_{n-1}^2 + \lambda u_{n-2}^2 + \lambda^2 u_{n-3}^2) + \lambda^3 \sigma_{n-3}^2$$

Continuing in this way gives

$$\sigma_n^2 = (1 - \lambda) \sum_{i=1}^{m} \lambda^{i-1} u_{n-i}^2 + \lambda^m \sigma_{n-m}^2$$

For large m, the term $\lambda^m \sigma_{n-m}^2$ is sufficiently small to be ignored, so that Equation (14.7) is the same as Equation (14.4) with $\alpha_i = (1 - \lambda)\lambda^{i-1}$. The weights for the u_i decline at rate λ as we move back through time. Each weight is λ times the previous weight.

Example 14.1

Suppose that λ is 0.90, the volatility estimated for a market variable for day $n - 1$ is 1% per day, and during day $n - 1$ the market variable increased by 2%. This means that $\sigma_{n-1}^2 = 0.01^2 = 0.0001$ and $u_{n-1}^2 = 0.02^2 = 0.0004$. Equation (14.7) gives

$$\sigma_n^2 = 0.9 \times 0.0001 + 0.1 \times 0.0004 = 0.00013$$

The estimate of the volatility, σ_n, for day n is therefore $\sqrt{0.00013}$, or 1.14%, per day. Note that the expected value of u_{n-1}^2 is σ_{n-1}^2, or 0.0001. In this example, the realized value of u_{n-1}^2 is greater than the expected value, and as a result our volatility estimate increases. If the realized value of u_{n-1}^2 had been less than its expected value, our estimate of the volatility would have decreased.

The EWMA approach has the attractive feature that relatively little data need be stored. At any given time, only the current estimate of the variance rate and the most recent observation on the value of the market variable need be remembered. When a new observation on the market variable is obtained, a new daily percentage change is calculated and Equation (14.7) is used to update the estimate of the variance rate. The old estimate of the variance rate and the old value of the market variable can then be discarded.

The EWMA approach is designed to track changes in the volatility. Suppose there is a big move in the market variable on day $n - 1$, so that u_{n-1}^2 is large. From Equation (14.7) this causes the estimate of the current volatility to move upward. The value of λ governs how responsive the estimate of the daily volatility is to the most recent daily percentage change. A low value of λ leads to a great deal of weight being given to the u_{n-1}^2 when σ_n is calculated. In this case, the estimates produced for the volatility on successive days are themselves highly volatile. A high value of λ (i.e., a value close to 1.0) produces estimates of the daily volatility that respond relatively slowly to new information provided by the daily percentage change.

The RiskMetrics database, which was originally created by JPMorgan and made publicly available in 1994, used the EWMA model with $\lambda = 0.94$ for updating daily volatility estimates. This is because the company found that, across a range of different market variables, this value of λ gives forecasts of the variance rate that come closest to the realized variance rate.[4] The realized variance rate on a particular day was calculated as an equally weighted average of the u_i^2 on the subsequent 25 days.

THE GARCH(1, 1) MODEL

We now move on to discuss what is known as the GARCH(1, 1) model, proposed by Bollerslev in 1986.[5] The difference between the GARCH(1, 1) model and the EWMA model is analogous to the difference between Equation (14.4) and Equation (14.5). In GARCH(1, 1), σ_n^2 is calculated from a long-run average variance rate, V_L, as well as from σ_{n-1} and u_{n-1}. The equation for GARCH(1, 1) is

$$\sigma_n^2 = \gamma V_L + \alpha u_{n-1}^2 + \beta \sigma_{n-1}^2 \qquad \text{(14.8)}$$

where γ is the weight assigned to V_L, α is the weight assigned to u_{n-1}^2, and β is the weight assigned to σ_{n-1}^2. Since the weights must sum to unity, it follows that

$$\gamma + \alpha + \beta = 1$$

The EWMA model is a particular case of GARCH(1, 1) where $\gamma = 0$, $\alpha = 1 - \lambda$, and $\beta = \lambda$.

The "(1, 1)" in GARCH(1, 1) indicates that σ_n^2 is based on the most recent observation of u^2 and the most recent estimate of the variance rate. The more general GARCH(p, q)

model calculates σ_n^2 from the most recent p observations on u^2 and the most recent q estimates of the variance rate.[6] GARCH(1, 1) is by far the most popular of the GARCH models.

Setting $\omega = \gamma V_L$, the GARCH(1, 1) model can also be written

$$\sigma_n^2 = \omega + \alpha u_{n-1}^2 + \beta \sigma_{n-1}^2 \qquad \text{(14.9)}$$

This is the form of the model that is usually used for the purposes of estimating the parameters. Once ω, α, and β have been estimated, we can calculate γ as $1 - \alpha - \beta$. The long-term variance V_L can then be calculated as ω/γ. For a stable GARCH(1, 1) process we require $\alpha + \beta < 1$. Otherwise the weight applied to the long-term variance is negative.

Example 14.2

Suppose that a GARCH(1, 1) model is estimated from daily data as

$$\sigma_n^2 = 0.000002 + 0.13 u_{n-1}^2 + 0.86 \sigma_{n-1}^2$$

This corresponds to $\alpha = 0.13$, $\beta = 0.86$, and $\omega = 0.000002$. Because $\gamma = 1 - \alpha - \beta$, it follows that $\gamma = 0.01$. Because $\omega = \gamma V_L$, it follows that $V_L = 0.0002$. In other words, the long-run average variance per day implied by the model is 0.0002. This corresponds to a volatility of $\sqrt{0.0002} = 0.014$, or 1.4%, per day.

Suppose that the estimate of the volatility on day $n - 1$ is 1.6% per day, so that $\sigma_{n-1}^2 = 0.016^2 = 0.000256$, and that on day $n - 1$ the market variable decreased by 1%, so that $u_{n-1}^2 = 0.01^2 = 0.0001$. Then

$$\sigma_n^2 = 0.000002 + 0.13 \times 0.0001 + 0.86 \times 0.000256$$
$$= 0.00023516$$

The new estimate of the volatility is therefore $\sqrt{0.00023516} = 0.0153$, or 1.53%, per day.

---

[4] See JPMorgan, *RiskMetrics Monitor*, Fourth Quarter, 1995. We will explain an alternative (maximum likelihood) approach to estimating parameters later in the chapter.

[5] See T. Bollerslev, "Generalized Autoregressive Conditional Heteroscedasticity," *Journal of Econometrics*, 31 (1986): 307-27.

[6] Other GARCH models have been proposed that incorporate asymmetric news. These models are designed so that σ_n depends on the sign of u_{n-1}. Arguably, the models are more appropriate for equities than GARCH(1, 1). The volatility of an equity's price tends to be inversely related to the price so that a negative u_{n-1} should have a bigger effect on σ_n than the same positive u_{n-1}. For a discussion of models for handling asymmetric news, see D. Nelson, "Conditional Heteroscedasticity and Asset Returns: A New Approach," *Econometrica*, 59 (1990): 347-70; R. F. Engle and V. Ng, "Measuring and Testing the Impact of News on Volatility," *Journal of Finance*, 48 (1993): 1749-78.

The Weights

Substituting for σ_{n-1}^2 in Equation (14.9) gives

$$\sigma_n^2 = \omega + \alpha u_{n-1}^2 + \beta(\omega + \alpha u_{n-2}^2 + \beta\sigma_{n-2}^2)$$

or

$$\sigma_n^2 = \omega + \beta\omega + \alpha u_{n-1}^2 + \alpha\beta u_{n-2}^2 + \beta^2\sigma_{n-2}^2$$

Substituting for σ_{n-2}^2 gives

$$\sigma_n^2 = \omega + \beta\omega + \beta^2\omega + \alpha u_{n-1}^2 + \alpha\beta u_{n-2}^2 + \alpha\beta^2 u_{n-3}^2 + \beta^3\sigma_{n-3}^2$$

Continuing in this way, we see that the weight applied to u_{n-i}^2 is $\alpha\beta^{i-1}$. The weights decline exponentially at rate β. The parameter β can be interpreted as a "decay rate". It is similar to λ in the EWMA model. It defines the relative importance of the observations on the u's in determining the current variance rate. For example, if $\beta = 0.9$, then u_{n-2}^2 is only 90% as important as u_{n-1}^2; u_{n-3}^2 is 81% as important as u_{n-1}^2; and so on. The GARCH(1, 1) model is similar to the EWMA model except that, in addition to assigning weights that decline exponentially to past u^2, it also assigns some weight to the long-run average volatility.

Mean Reversion

The GARCH (1, 1) model recognizes that over time the variance tends to get pulled back to a long-run average level of V_L. The amount of weight assigned to V_L is $\gamma = 1 - \alpha - \beta$. The GARCH(1,1) is equivalent to a model where the variance V follows the stochastic process

$$dV = a(V_L - V)dt + \xi V \, dz$$

where time is measured in days, $a = 1 - \alpha - \beta$, and $\xi = \alpha\sqrt{2}$. This is a mean-reverting model. The variance has a drift that pulls it back to V_L at rate a. When $V > V_L$, the variance has a negative drift; when $V < V_L$, it has a positive drift. Superimposed on the drift is a volatility ξ.

CHOOSING BETWEEN THE MODELS

In practice, variance rates do tend to be mean reverting. The GARCH(1, 1) model incorporates mean reversion, whereas the EWMA model does not. GARCH(1, 1) is therefore theoretically more appealing than the EWMA model.

In the next section, we will discuss how best-fit parameters ω, α, and β in GARCH(1, 1) can be estimated. When the parameter ω is zero, the GARCH(1, 1) reduces to EWMA. In circumstances where the best-fit value of ω turns out to be negative, the GARCH(1, 1) model is not stable and it makes sense to switch to the EWMA model.

MAXIMUM LIKELIHOOD METHODS

It is now appropriate to discuss how the parameters in the models we have been considering are estimated from historical data. The approach used is known as the *maximum likelihood method.* It involves choosing values for the parameters that maximize the chance (or likelihood) of the data occurring.

To illustrate the method, we start with a very simple example. Suppose that we sample 10 stocks at random on a certain day and find that the price of one of them declined on that day and the prices of the other nine either remained the same or increased. What is the best estimate of the probability of a stock's price declining on the day? The natural answer is 0.1. Let us see if this is what the maximum likelihood method gives.

Suppose that the probability of a price decline is p. The probability that one particular stock declines in price and the other nine do not is $p(1 - p)^9$. Using the maximum likelihood approach, the best estimate of p is the one that maximizes $p(1 - p)^9$. Differentiating this expression with respect to p and setting the result equal to zero, we find that $p = 0.1$ maximizes the expression. This shows that the maximum likelihood estimate of p is 0.1, as expected.

Estimating a Constant Variance

Our next example of maximum likelihood methods considers the problem of estimating the variance of a variable X from m observations on X when the underlying distribution is normal with zero mean. Assume that the observations are $u_1, u_2, \ldots, u_m$. Denote the variance by v. The likelihood of u_i being observed is defined as the probability density function for X when $X = u_i$. This is

$$\frac{1}{\sqrt{2\pi v}}\exp\left(\frac{-u_i^2}{2v}\right)$$

The likelihood of m observations occurring in the order in which they are observed is

$$\prod_{i=1}^{m}\left[\frac{1}{\sqrt{2\pi v}}\exp\left(\frac{-u_i^2}{2v}\right)\right] \quad \text{(14.10)}$$

Using the maximum likelihood method, the best estimate of v is the value that maximizes this expression.

Maximizing an expression is equivalent to maximizing the logarithm of the expression. Taking logarithms of the expression in Equation (14.10) and ignoring constant multiplicative factors, it can be seen that we wish to maximize

$$\sum_{i=1}^{m}\left[-\ln(\upsilon)-\frac{u_i^2}{\upsilon}\right] \qquad \textbf{(14.11)}$$

or

$$-m\ln(\upsilon)-\sum_{i=1}^{m}\frac{u_i^2}{\upsilon}$$

Differentiating this expression with respect to υ and setting the resulting equation to zero, we see that the maximum likelihood estimator of υ is[7]

$$\frac{1}{m}\sum_{i=1}^{m}u_i^2$$

Estimating EWMA or GARCH(1, 1) Parameters

We now consider how the maximum likelihood method can be used to estimate the parameters when EWMA,

GARCH(1,1), or some other volatility updating scheme is used. Define $\upsilon_i = \sigma_i^2$ as the variance estimated for day i. Assume that the probability distribution of u_i conditional on the variance is normal. A similar analysis to the one just given shows the best parameters are the ones that maximize

$$\prod_{i=1}^{m}\left[\frac{1}{\sqrt{2\pi\upsilon_i}}\exp\left(\frac{-u_i^2}{2\upsilon_i}\right)\right]$$

Taking logarithms, we see that this is equivalent to maximizing

$$\sum_{i=1}^{m}\left[-\ln(\upsilon_i)-\frac{u_i^2}{\upsilon_i}\right] \qquad \textbf{(14.12)}$$

This is the same as the expression in Equation (14.11), except that υ is replaced by υ_i. It is necessary to search iteratively to find the parameters in the model that maximize the expression in Equation (14.12).

The spreadsheet in Table 14-1 indicates how the calculations could be organized for the GARCH(1,1) model. The table analyzes data on the S&P 500 between July 18, 2005, and August 13, 2010.[8] The first column in the table

---

[7] This confirms the point made in footnote 2.

[8] The data and calculations can be found at www.rotman.utoronto.ca/~hull/OFOD/GarchExample.

TABLE 14-1 Estimation of Parameters in GARCH(1, 1) Model for S&P 500 between July 18, 2005, and August 13, 2010

Date	Day i	S_i	u_i	$\upsilon_i = \sigma_i^2$	$-\ln(\upsilon_i) - u_i^2/\upsilon_i$
18-Jul-2005	1	1221.13			
19-Jul-2005	2	1229.35	0.006731		
20-Jul-2005	3	1235.20	0.004759	0.00004531	9.5022
21-Jul-2005	4	1227.04	−0.006606	0.00004447	9.0393
22-Jul-2005	5	1233.68	0.005411	0.00004546	9.3545
25-Jul-2005	6	1229.03	−0.003769	0.00004517	9.6906
⋮	⋮	⋮	⋮	⋮	⋮
11-Aug-2010	1277	1089.47	−0.028179	0.00011834	2.3322
12-Aug-2010	1278	1083.61	−0.005379	0.00017527	8.4841
13-Aug-2010	1279	1079.25	−0.004024	0.00016327	8.6209
					10,228.2349

Trial estimates of GARCH parameters
$\omega = 0.0000013465$ $\alpha = 0.083394$ $\beta = 0.910116$

records the date. The second column counts the days. The third column shows the S&P 500, S_i, at the end of day i. The fourth column shows the proportional change in the S&P 500 between the end of day $i - 1$ and the end of day i. This is $u_i = (S_i - S_{i-1})/S_{i-1}$. The fifth column shows the estimate of the variance rate, $v_i = \sigma_i^2$, for day i made at the end of day $i - 1$. On day 3, we start things off by setting the variance equal to u_2^2. On subsequent days, Equation (14.9) is used. The sixth column tabulates the likelihood measure, $-\ln(v_i) - u_i^2/v_i$. The values in the fifth and sixth columns are based on the current trial estimates of ω, α, and β. We are interested in choosing ω, α, and β to maximize the sum of the numbers in the sixth column. This involves an iterative search procedure.[9]

In our example, the optimal values of the parameters turn out to be

$$\omega = 0.0000013465, \quad \alpha = 0.083394, \quad \beta = 0.910116$$

and the maximum value of the function in Equation (14.12) is 10,228.2349. The numbers shown in Table 14-1 were calculated on the final iteration of the search for the optimal ω, α, and β.

The long-term variance rate, V_L, in our example is

$$\frac{\omega}{1 - \alpha - \beta} = \frac{0.0000013465}{0.006490} = 0.0002075$$

The long-term volatility is $\sqrt{0.0002075}$, or 1.4404%, per day.

Figures 14.1 and 14.2 show the S&P 500 index and its GARCH(1, 1) volatility during the 5-year period covered by the data. Most of the time, the volatility was less than 2% per day, but volatilities as high as 5% per day were experienced during the credit crisis. (Very high volatilities are also indicated by the VIX index.)

An alternative approach to estimating parameters in GARCH(1, 1), which is sometimes more robust, is known as *variance targeting*.[10] This involves setting the long-run average variance rate, V_L, equal to the sample variance calculated from the data (or to some other value that is

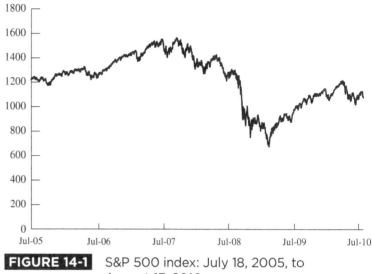

[9] As discussed later, a general purpose algorithm such as Solver in Microsoft's Excel can be used. Alternatively, a special purpose algorithm, such as Levenberg–Marquardt, can be used. See, e.g., W. H. Press, B. P. Flannery, S. A. Teukolsky, and W. T. Vetterling. *Numerical Recipes in C: The Art of Scientific Computing*, Cambridge University Press, 1988.

[10] See R. Engle and J. Mezrich, "GARCH for Groups," *Risk*, August 1996: 36–40.

FIGURE 14-1 S&P 500 index: July 18, 2005, to August 13, 2010.

FIGURE 14-2 Daily volatility of S&P 500 index: July 18, 2005, to August 13, 2010.

believed to be reasonable). The value of ω then equals $V_L(1 - \alpha - \beta)$ and only two parameters have to be estimated. For the data in Table 14-1, the sample variance is 0.0002412, which gives a daily volatility of 1.5531%. Setting V_L equal to the sample variance, the values of α and β that maximize the objective function in Equation (14.12) are 0.08445 and 0.9101, respectively. The value of the objective function is 10,228.1941, only marginally below the value of 10,228.2349 obtained using the earlier procedure.

When the EWMA model is used, the estimation procedure is relatively simple. We set $\omega = 0$, $\alpha = 1 - \lambda$, and $\beta - \lambda$, and only one parameter has to be estimated. In the data in Table 14-1, the value of λ that maximizes the objective function in Equation (14.12) is 0.9374 and the value of the objective function is 10,192.5104.

For both GARCH(1, 1) and EWMA, we can use the Solver routine in Excel to search for the values of the parameters that maximize the likelihood function. The routine works well provided that the spreadsheet is structured so that the parameters being searched for have roughly equal values. For example, in GARCH(1, 1) we could let cells A1, A2, and A3 contain $\omega \times 10^5$, 10α, and β. We could then set B1 = A1/100,000, B2 = A2/10, and B3 = A3. We would use B1, B2, and B3 to calculate the likelihood function. We would ask Solver to calculate the values of A1, A2, and A3 that maximize the likelihood function. Occasionally Solver gives a local maximum, so testing a number of different starting values for parameters is a good idea.

How Good Is the Model?

The assumption underlying a GARCH model is that volatility changes with the passage of time. During some periods volatility is relatively high; during other periods it is relatively low. To put this another way, when u_i^2 is high, there is a tendency for u_{i+1}^2, u_{i+2}^2, ... to be high; when u_i^2 is low, there is a tendency for u_{i+1}^2, u_{i+2}^2, ... to be low. We can test how true this is by examining the autocorrelation structure of the u_i^2.

Let us assume the u_i^2 do exhibit autocorrelation. If a GARCH model is working well, it should remove the autocorrelation. We can test whether it has done so by considering the autocorrelation structure for the variables u_i^2/σ_i^2. If these show very little autocorrelation, our model for σ_i has succeeded in explaining autocorrelations in the u_i^2.

Table 14-2 shows results for the S&P 500 data used above. The first column shows the lags considered when the autocorrelation is calculated. The second shows autocorrelations for u_i^2; the third shows autocorrelations for u_i^2/σ_i^2.[11] The table shows that the autocorrelations are positive for u_i^2 for all lags between 1 and 15. In the case of u_i^2/σ_i^2, some of the autocorrelations are positive and some are negative. They are all much smaller in magnitude than the autocorrelations for u_i^2.

TABLE 14-2 Autocorrelations before and after the Use of a GARCH Model for S&P 500 Data

Time Lag	Autocorrelation for u_i^2	Autocorrelation for u_i^2/σ_i^2
1	0.183	−0.063
2	0.385	−0.004
3	0.160	−0.007
4	0.301	0.022
5	0.339	0.014
6	0.308	−0.011
7	0.329	0.026
8	0.207	0.038
9	0.324	0.041
10	0.269	0.083
11	0.431	−0.007
12	0.286	0.006
13	0.224	0.001
14	0.121	0.017
15	0.222	−0.031

The GARCH model appears to have done a good job in explaining the data. For a more scientific test, we can use what is known as the Ljung–Box statistic.[12] If a certain series has m observations the Ljung–Box statistic is

$$m \sum_{k=1}^{K} w_k \eta_k^2$$

where η_k is the autocorrelation for a lag of k, K is the number of lags considered, and

$$w_k \frac{m+2}{m-k}$$

For $K = 15$, zero autocorrelation can be rejected with 95% confidence when the Ljung–Box statistic is greater than 25.

---

[11] For a series x_i, the autocorrelation with a lag of k is the coefficient of correlation between x_i and x_{i+k}.

[12] See G. M. Ljung and G. E. P. Box, "On a Measure of Lack of Fit in Time Series Models," *Biometrica*, 65 (1978): 297–303.

From Table 14-2, the Ljung–Box statistic for the u_i^2 series is about 1,566. This is strong evidence of autocorrelation. For the u_i^2/σ_i^2 series, the Ljung–Box statistic is 21.7, suggesting that the autocorrelation has been largely removed by the GARCH model.

USING GARCH(1, 1) TO FORECAST FUTURE VOLATILITY

The variance rate estimated at the end of day $n - 1$ for day n, when GARCH(1, 1) is used, is

$$\sigma_n^2 = (1 - \alpha - \beta)V_L + \alpha u_{n-1}^2 + \beta \sigma_{n-1}^2$$

so that

$$\sigma_n^2 - V_L = \alpha(u_{n-1}^2 - V_L) + \beta(\sigma_{n-1}^2 - V_L)$$

On day $n + t$ in the future,

$$\sigma_{n+t}^2 - V_L = \alpha(u_{n+t-1}^2 - V_L) + \beta(\sigma_{n+t-1}^2 - V_L)$$

The expected value of u_{n+t-1}^2 is σ_{n+t-1}^2. Hence,

$$E[\sigma_{n+t}^2 - V_L] = (\alpha + \beta)E[\sigma_{n+t-1}^2 - V_L]$$

where E denotes expected value. Using this equation repeatedly yields

$$E[\sigma_{n+t}^2 - V_L] = (\alpha + \beta)^t(\sigma_n^2 - V_L)$$

or

$$E[\sigma_{n+t}^2] = V_L + (\alpha + \beta)^t(\sigma_n^2 - V_L) \qquad \textbf{(14.13)}$$

This equation forecasts the volatility on day $n + t$ using the information available at the end of day $n - 1$. In the EWMA model, $\alpha + \beta = 1$ and Equation (14.13) shows that the expected future variance rate equals the current variance rate. When $\alpha + \beta < 1$, the final term in the equation becomes progressively smaller as t increases. Figure 14-3 shows the expected path followed by the variance rate for situations where the current variance rate is different from V_L. As mentioned earlier, the variance rate exhibits mean reversion with a reversion level of V_L and a reversion rate of $1 - \alpha - \beta$. Our forecast of the future variance rate tends towards V_L as we look further and further ahead. This analysis emphasizes the point that we must have $\alpha + \beta < 1$ for a stable

GARCH(1, 1) process. When $\alpha + \beta > 1$, the weight given to the long-term average variance is negative and the process is "mean fleeing" rather than "mean reverting".

For the S&P 500 data considered earlier, $\alpha + \beta = 0.9935$ and $V_L = 0.0002075$. Suppose that the estimate of the current variance rate per day is 0.0003. (This corresponds to a volatility of 1.732% per day.) In 10 days, the expected variance rate is

$$0.0002075 + 0.9935^{10}(0.0003 - 0.0002075) = 0.0002942$$

The expected volatility per day is 1.72%, still well above the long-term volatility of 1.44% per day. However, the expected variance rate in 500 days is

$$0.0002075 + 0.9935^{500}(0.0003 - 0.0002075) = 0.0002110$$

and the expected volatility per day is 1.45%, very close to the long-term volatility.

Volatility Term Structures

Suppose it is day n. Define:

$$V(t) = E(\sigma_{n+t}^2)$$

and

$$a = \ln \frac{1}{\alpha + \beta}$$

so that Equation (14.13) becomes

$$V(t) = V_L + e^{-at}[V(0) - V_L]$$

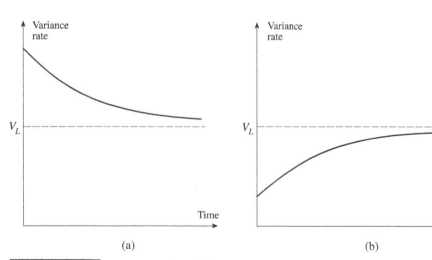

(a)	(b)

FIGURE 14-3 Expected path for the variance rate when (a) current variance rate is above long-term variance rate and (b) current variance rate is below long-term variance rate.

Here, $V(t)$ is an estimate of the instantaneous variance rate in t days. The average variance rate per day between today and time T is given by

$$\frac{1}{T}\int_0^T V(t)dt = V_L + \frac{1 - e^{-aT}}{aT}[V(0) - V_L]$$

The larger T is, the closer this is to V_L. Define $\sigma(T)$ as the volatility per annum that should be used to price a T-day option under GARCH(1, 1). Assuming 252 days per year, $\sigma(T)^2$ is 252 times the average variance rate per day, so that

$$\sigma(T)^2 = 252\left(V_L + \frac{1 - e^{-aT}}{aT}[V(0) - V_L]\right) \quad \textbf{(14.14)}$$

The market prices of different options on the same asset are often used to calculate a *volatility term structure*. This is the relationship between the implied volatilities of the options and their maturities. Equation (14.14) can be used to estimate a volatility term structure based on the GARCH(1, 1) model. The estimated volatility term structure is not usually the same as the implied volatility term structure. However, as we will show, it is often used to predict the way that the implied volatility term structure will respond to volatility changes.

When the current volatility is above the long-term volatility, the GARCH(1, 1) model estimates a downward-sloping volatility term structure. When the current volatility is below the long-term volatility, it estimates an upward-sloping volatility term structure. In the case of the S&P 500 data, $a = \ln(1/0.99351) = 0.006511$ and $V_L = 0.0002075$. Suppose that the current variance rate per day, $V(0)$, is estimated as 0.0003 per day. It follows from Equation (14.14) that

$$\sigma(T)^2 = 252\left(0.0002075 + \frac{1 - e^{-0.006511T}}{0.006511T}(0.0003 - 0.0002075)\right)$$

where T is measured in days. Table 14-3 shows the volatility per year for different values of T.

Impact of Volatility Changes

Equation (14.14) can be written

$$\sigma(T)^2 = 252\left[V_L + \frac{1 - e^{-aT}}{aT}\left(\frac{\sigma(0)^2}{252} - V_L\right)\right]$$

When $\sigma(0)$ changes by $\Delta\sigma(0)$, $\sigma(T)$ changes by approximately

$$\frac{1 - e^{-aT}}{aT}\frac{\sigma(0)}{\sigma(T)}\Delta\sigma(0) \quad \textbf{(14.15)}$$

TABLE 14-3 S&P 500 Volatility Term Structure Predicted from GARCH(1, 1)

Option life (days)	10	30	50	100	500
Option volatility (% per annum)	27.36	27.10	26.87	26.35	24.32

TABLE 14-4 Impact of 1% Change in the Instantaneous Volatility Predicted from GARCH(1, 1)

Option life (days)	10	30	50	100	500
Increase in volatility (%)	0.97	0.92	0.87	0.77	0.33

Table 14-4 shows the effect of a volatility change on options of varying maturities for the S&P 500 data considered above. We assume as before that $V(0) = 0.0003$, so that $\sigma(0) = \sqrt{252} \times \sqrt{0.003} = 27.50\%$. The table considers a 100-basis-point change in the instantaneous volatility from 27.50% per year to 28.50% per year. This means that $\Delta\sigma(0) = 0.01$, or 1%.

Many financial institutions use analyses such as this when determining the exposure of their books to volatility changes. Rather than consider an across-the-board increase of 1% in implied volatilities when calculating vega, they relate the size of the volatility increase that is considered to the maturity of the option. Based on Table 14-4, a 0.97% volatility increase would be considered for a 10-day option, a 0.92% increase for a 30-day option, a 0.87% increase for a 50-day option, and so on.

CORRELATIONS

The discussion so far has centered on the estimation and forecasting of volatility. Correlations also play a key role in the calculation of VaR. In this section, we show how correlation estimates can be updated in a similar way to volatility estimates.

The correlation between two variables X and Y can be defined as

$$\frac{\text{cov}(X, Y)}{\sigma_X \sigma_Y}$$

where σ_X and σ_Y are the standard deviations of X and Y and $\text{cov}(X, Y)$ is the covariance between X and Y. The covariance between X and Y is defined as

$$E[(X - \mu_X)(Y - \mu_Y)]$$

where μ_X and μ_Y are the means of X and Y, and E denotes the expected value. Although it is easier to develop intuition about the meaning of a correlation than it is for a covariance, it is covariances that are the fundamental variables of our analysis.[13]

Define x_i and y_i as the percentage changes in X and Y between the end of day $i - 1$ and the end of day i:

$$x_i = \frac{X_i - X_{i-1}}{X_{i-1}}, \qquad y_i = \frac{Y_i - Y_{i-1}}{Y_{i-1}}$$

where X_i and Y_i are the values of X and Y at the end of day i. We also define the following:

$\sigma_{x,n}$: Daily volatility of variable X, estimated for day n

$\sigma_{y,n}$: Daily volatility of variable Y, estimated for day n

cov_n : Estimate of covariance between daily changes in X and Y, calculated on day n.

The estimate of the correlation between X and Y on day n is

$$\frac{\text{cov}_n}{\sigma_{x,n}\sigma_{y,n}}$$

Using equal weighting and assuming that the means of x_i and y_i are zero, Equation (14.3) shows that the variance rates of X and Y can be estimated from the most recent m observations as

$$\sigma_{x,n}^2 = \frac{1}{m}\sum_{i=1}^{m} x_{n-i}^2, \qquad \sigma_{y,n}^2 = \frac{1}{m}\sum_{i=1}^{m} y_{n-i}^2$$

A similar estimate for the covariance between X and Y is

$$\text{cov}_n = \frac{1}{m}\sum_{i=1}^{m} x_{n-i}y_{n-i} \qquad \textbf{(14.16)}$$

One alternative for updating covariances is an EWMA model similar to Equation (14.7). The formula for updating the covariance estimate is then

$$\text{cov}_n = \lambda\,\text{cov}_{n-1} + (1 - \lambda)x_{n-1}y_{n-1}$$

A similar analysis to that presented for the EWMA volatility model shows that the weights given to observations on the $x_i y_i$ decline as we move back through time. The lower the value of λ, the greater the weight that is given to recent observations.

---

[13] An analogy here is that variance rates were the fundamental variables for the EWMA and GARCH procedures in the first part of this chapter, even though volatilities are easier to understand.

Example 14.3

Suppose that $\lambda = 0.95$ and that the estimate of the correlation between two variables X and Y on day $n - 1$ is 0.6. Suppose further that the estimate of the volatilities for the X and Y on day $n - 1$ are 1% and 2%, respectively. From the relationship between correlation and covariance, the estimate of the covariance between the X and Y on day $n - 1$ is

$$0.6 \times 0.01 \times 0.02 = 0.00012$$

Suppose that the percentage changes in X and Y on day $n - 1$ are 0.5% and 2.5%, respectively. The variance and covariance for day n would be updated as follows:

$$\sigma_{x,n}^2 = 0.95 \times 0.01^2 + 0.05 \times 0.005^2 = 0.00009625$$

$$\sigma_{y,n}^2 = 0.95 \times 0.02^2 + 0.05 \times 0.025^2 = 0.00041125$$

$$\text{cov}_n = 0.95 \times 0.00012 + 0.05 \times 0.005 \times 0.025$$
$$= 0.00012025$$

The new volatility of X is $\sqrt{0.00009625} = 0.981\%$ and the new volatility of Y is $\sqrt{0.00041125} = 2.028\%$. The new coefficient of correlation between X and Y is

$$\frac{0.00012025}{0.00981 \times 0.02028} = 0.6044$$

GARCH models can also be used for updating covariance estimates and forecasting the future level of covariances. For example, the GARCH(1, 1) model for updating a covariance is

$$\text{cov}_n = \omega + \alpha x_{n-1} y_{n-1} + \beta\text{cov}_{n-1}$$

and the long-term average covariance is $\omega/(1 - \alpha - \beta)$. Formulas similar to those in Equations (14.13) and (14.14) can be developed for forecasting future covariances and calculating the average covariance during the life of an option.[14]

Consistency Condition for Covariances

Once all the variances and covariances have been calculated, a variance–covariance matrix can be constructed. When $i \neq j$, the (i, j)th element of this matrix shows the

---

[14] The ideas in this chapter can be extended to multivariate GARCH models, where an entire variance–covariance matrix is updated in a consistent way. For a discussion of alternative approaches, see R. Engle and J. Mezrich, "GARCH for Groups," *Risk*, August 1996: 36–40.

covariance between variable i and variable j. When $i = j$, it shows the variance of variable i.

Not all variance–covariance matrices are internally consistent. The condition for an $N \times N$ variance–covariance matrix Ω to be internally consistent is

$$\omega^T \Omega \omega \geq 0 \qquad \textbf{(14.17)}$$

for all $N \times 1$ vectors ω, where ω^T is the transpose of ω. A matrix that satisfies this property is known as *positive-semidefinite*.

To understand why the condition in Equation (14.17) must hold, suppose that ω^T is $[\omega_1, \omega_2, \ldots, \omega_n]$. The expression $\omega^T \Omega \omega$ is the variance of $\omega_1 x_1 + \omega_2 x_2 + \ldots + \omega_n x_n$, where x_i is the value of variable i. As such, it cannot be negative.

To ensure that a positive-semidefinite matrix is produced, variances and covariances should be calculated consistently. For example, if variances are calculated by giving equal weight to the last m data items, the same should be done for covariances. If variances are updated using an EWMA model with $\lambda = 0.94$, the same should be done for covariances.

An example of a variance–covariance matrix that is not internally consistent is

$$\begin{bmatrix} 1 & 0 & 0.9 \\ 0 & 1 & 0.9 \\ 0.9 & 0.9 & 1 \end{bmatrix}$$

The variance of each variable is 1.0, and so the covariances are also coefficients of correlation. The first variable is highly correlated with the third variable and the second variable is highly correlated with the third variable. However, there is no correlation at all between the first and second variables. This seems strange. When ω is set equal to $(1, 1, -1)$, the condition in Equation (14.17) is not satisfied, proving that the matrix is not positive-semidefinite.[15]

APPLICATION OF EWMA TO FOUR-INDEX EXAMPLE

A portfolio on September 25, 2008, consisted of a $4 million investment in the Dow Jones Industrial Average, a

---

[15] It can be shown that the condition for a 3×3 matrix of correlations to be internally consistent is

$$\rho_{12}^2 + \rho_{13}^2 + \rho_{23}^2 - 2\rho_{12}\rho_{13}\rho_{23} \leq 1$$

where ρ_{ij} is the coefficient of correlation between variables i and j.

$3 million investment in the FTSE 100, a $1 million investment in the CAC 40, and a $2 million investment in the Nikkei 225. Daily returns were collected over 500 days ending on September 25, 2008. Data and all calculations presented here can be found at: www.rotman.utoronto.ca/~hull/OFOD/VaRExample.

The correlation matrix that would be calculated on September 25, 2008, by giving equal weight to the last 500 returns is shown in Table 14-5. The FTSE 100 and CAC 40 are very highly correlated. The Dow Jones Industrial Average is moderately highly correlated with both the FTSE 100 and the CAC 40. The correlation of the Nikkei 225 with other indices is less high.

The covariance matrix for the equal-weight case is shown in Table 14-6. This matrix gives the variance of the portfolio losses ($000s) as 8,761.833. The standard deviation is the square root of this, or 93.60. The one-day 99% VaR in $000s is therefore $2.33 \times 93.60 = 217.757$. This is $217,757, which compares with $253,385, calculated using the historical simulation approach.

Instead of calculating variances and covariances by giving equal weight to all observed returns, we now use the exponentially weighted moving average method with $\lambda = 0.94$. This gives the variance–covariance matrix in

TABLE 14-5   Correlation Matrix

On September 25, 2008, calculated by giving equal weight to the last 500 daily returns: variable 1 is DJIA; variable 2 is FTSE 100; variable 3 is CAC 40; variable 4 is Nikkei 225.

$$\begin{bmatrix} 1 & 0.489 & 0.496 & -0.062 \\ 0.489 & 1 & 0.918 & 0.201 \\ 0.496 & 0.918 & 1 & 0.211 \\ -0.062 & 0.201 & 0.211 & 1 \end{bmatrix}$$

TABLE 14-6   Covariance Matrix

On September 25, 2008, calculated by giving equal weight to the last 500 daily returns: variable 1 is DJIA; variable 2 is FTSE 100; variable 3 is CAC 40; variable 4 is Nikkei 225.

$$\begin{bmatrix} 0.0001227 & 0.0000768 & 0.0000767 & -0.0000095 \\ 0.0000768 & 0.0002010 & 0.0001817 & 0.0000394 \\ 0.0000767 & 0.0001817 & 0.0001950 & 0.0000407 \\ -0.0000095 & 0.0000394 & 0.0000407 & 0.0001909 \end{bmatrix}$$

TABLE 14-7 Covariance Matrix

On September 25, 2008, calculated using the EWMA method with λ = 0.94: variable 1 is DJIA; variable 2 is FTSE 100; variable 3 is CAC 40; variable 4 is Nikkei 225.

$$\begin{bmatrix} 0.0004801 & 0.0004303 & 0.0004257 & -0.0000396 \\ 0.0004303 & 0.0010314 & 0.0009630 & 0.0002095 \\ 0.0004257 & 0.0009630 & 0.0009535 & 0.0001681 \\ -0.0000396 & 0.0002095 & 0.0001681 & 0.0002541 \end{bmatrix}$$

TABLE 14-8 Volatilities (% per day) Using Equal Weighting and EWMA

	DJIA	FTSE 100	CAC 40	Nikkei 225
Equal weighting:	1.11	1.42	1.40	1.38
EWMA:	2.19	3.21	3.09	1.59

TABLE 14-9 Correlation Matrix

On September 25, 2008, calculated using the EWMA method: variable 1 is DJIA; variable 2 is FTSE 100; variable 3 is CAC 40; variable 4 is Nikkei 225.

$$\begin{bmatrix} 1 & 0.611 & 0.629 & -0.113 \\ 0.611 & 1 & 0.971 & 0.409 \\ 0.629 & 0.971 & 1 & 0.342 \\ -0.113 & 0.409 & 0.342 & 1 \end{bmatrix}$$

Table 14-7.[16] The variance of portfolio losses ($000s) is 40,995.765. The standard deviation is the square root of this, or 202.474. The one-day 99% VaR is therefore

$$2.33 \times 202.474 = 471.025$$

This is $471,025, over twice as high as the value given when returns are equally weighted. Tables 14-8 and 14-9 show the reasons. The standard deviation of a portfolio consisting of long positions in securities increases with the standard deviations of security returns and also with the correlations between security returns. Table 14-8 shows that the estimated daily standard deviations are much higher when EWMA is used than when data are equally

weighted. This is because volatilities were much higher during the period immediately preceding September 25, 2008, than during the rest of the 500 days covered by the data. Comparing Table 14-9 with Table 14-5, we see that correlations had also increased.[17]

SUMMARY

Most popular option pricing models, such as Black–Scholes–Merton, assume that the volatility of the underlying asset is constant. This assumption is far from perfect. In practice, the volatility of an asset, like the asset's price, is a stochastic variable. Unlike the asset price, it is not directly observable. This chapter has discussed procedures for attempting to keep track of the current level of volatility.

We define u_i as the percentage change in a market variable between the end of day $i - 1$ and the end of day i. The variance rate of the market variable (that is, the square of its volatility) is calculated as a weighted average of the u_i^2. The key feature of the procedures that have been discussed here is that they do not give equal weight to the observations on the u_i^2. The more recent an observation, the greater the weight assigned to it. In the EWMA and the GARCH(1, 1) models, the weights assigned to observations decrease exponentially as the observations become older. The GARCH(1, 1) model differs from the EWMA model in that some weight is also assigned to the long-run average variance rate. It has a structure that enables forecasts of the future level of variance rate to be produced relatively easily.

Maximum likelihood methods are usually used to estimate parameters from historical data in the EWMA, GARCH(1, 1), and similar models. These methods involve using an iterative procedure to determine the parameter values that maximize the chance or likelihood that the historical data will occur. Once its parameters have been determined, a GARCH(1, 1) model can be judged by how well it removes autocorrelation from the u_i^2.

For every model that is developed to track variances, there is a corresponding model that can be developed to track covariances. The procedures described here can therefore be used to update the complete variance–covariance matrix used in value-at-risk calculations.

---

[16] In the EWMA calculations, the variance was initially set equal to the population variance. This is an alternative to setting it equal to the first squared return as in Table 14-1. The two approaches give similar final variances, and the final variance is all we are interested in.

---

[17] This is an example of the phenomenon that correlations tend to increase in adverse market conditions.

Further Reading

Bollerslev, T. "Generalized Autoregressive Conditional Heteroscedasticity," *Journal of Econometrics*, 31 (1986): 307–27.

Cumby, R., S. Figlewski, and J. Hasbrook. "Forecasting Volatilities and Correlations with EGARCH Models," *Journal of Derivatives*, 1, 2 (Winter 1993): 51–63.

Engle, R. F. "Autoregressive Conditional Heteroscedasticity with Estimates of the Variance of UK Inflation," *Econometrica* 50 (1982): 987–1008.

Engle R. F., and J. Mezrich. "Grappling with GARCH," *Risk*, September 1995: 112–117.

Engle, R. F., and J. Mezrich, "GARCH for Groups," *Risk*, August 1996: 36–40.

Engle, R. F., and V. Ng, "Measuring and Testing the Impact of News on Volatility," *Journal of Finance*, 48 (1993): 1749–78.

Noh, J., R. F. Engle, and A. Kane. "Forecasting Volatility and Option Prices of the S&P 500 Index," *Journal of Derivatives*, 2 (1994): 17–30.

Simulation Methods

Learning Objectives

Candidates, after completing this reading, should be able to:

- Describe the basic steps to conduct a Monte Carlo simulation.
- Describe ways to reduce Monte Carlo sampling error.
- Explain how to use antithetic variate technique to reduce Monte Carlo sampling error.
- Explain how to use control variates to reduce Monte Carlo sampling error and when it is effective.
- Describe the benefits of reusing sets of random number draws across Monte Carlo experiments and how to reuse them.

- Describe the bootstrapping method and its advantage over Monte Carlo simulation.
- Describe the pseudo-random number generation method and how a good simulation design alleviates the effects the choice of the seed has on the properties of the generated series.
- Describe situations where the bootstrapping method is ineffective.
- Describe disadvantages of the simulation approach to financial problem solving.

Excerpt is Chapter 13 of Introductory Econometrics for Finance, *Third Edition by Chris Brooks.*

MOTIVATIONS

There are numerous situations, in finance and in econometrics, where the researcher has essentially no idea what is going to happen! To offer one illustration, in the context of complex financial risk measurement models for portfolios containing large numbers of assets whose movements are dependent on one another, it is not always clear what will be the effect of changing circumstances. For example, following full European Monetary Union (EMU) and the replacement of member currencies with the euro, it is widely believed that European financial markets have become more integrated, leading the correlation between movements in their equity markets to rise. What would be the effect on the properties of a portfolio containing equities of several European countries if correlations between the markets rose to 99%? Clearly, it is probably not possible to be able to answer such a questions using actual historical data alone, since the event (a correlation of 99%) has not yet happened.

The practice of econometrics is made difficult by the behaviour of series and inter-relationships between them that render model assumptions at best questionable. For example, the existence of fat tails, structural breaks and bi-directional causality between dependent and independent variables, etc. will make the process of parameter estimation and inference less reliable. Real data is messy, and no one really knows all of the features that lurk inside it. Clearly, it is important for researchers to have an idea of what the effects of such phenomena will be for model estimation and inference.

By contrast, simulation is the econometrician's chance to behave like a 'real scientist', conducting experiments under controlled conditions. A simulations experiment enables the econometrician to determine what the effect of changing one factor or aspect of a problem will be, while leaving all other aspects unchanged. Thus, simulations offer the possibility of complete flexibility. Simulation may be defined as an approach to modelling that seeks to mimic a functioning system as it evolves. The simulations model will express in mathematical equations the assumed form of operation of the system. In econometrics, simulation is particularly useful when models are very complex or sample sizes are small.

MONTE CARLO SIMULATIONS

Simulations studies are usually used to investigate the properties and behaviour of various statistics of interest. The technique is often used in econometrics when the properties of a particular estimation method are not known. For example, it may be known from asymptotic theory how a particular test behaves with an infinite sample size, but how will the test behave if only fifty observations are available? Will the test still have the desirable properties of being correctly sized and having high power? In other words, if the null hypothesis is correct, will the test lead to rejection of the null 5% of the time if a 5% rejection region is used? And if the null is incorrect, will it be rejected a high proportion of the time?

Examples from econometrics of where simulation may be useful include:

- Quantifying the simultaneous equations bias induced by treating an endogenous variable as exogenous
- Determining the appropriate critical values for a Dickey–Fuller test
- Determining what effect heteroscedasticity has upon the size and power of a test for autocorrelation.

Simulations are also often extremely useful tools in finance, in situations such as:

- The pricing of exotic options, where an analytical pricing formula is unavailable
- Determining the effect on financial markets of substantial changes in the macroeconomic environment
- 'Stress-testing' risk management models to determine whether they generate capital requirements sufficient to cover losses in all situations.

In all of these instances, the basic way that such a study would be conducted (with additional steps and modifications where necessary) is shown in Box 15-1.

A brief explanation of each of these steps is in order. The first stage involves *specifying the model* that will be used to generate the data. This may be a pure time series model or a structural model. Pure time series models are usually simpler to implement, as a full structural model would also require the researcher to specify a data generating process for the explanatory variables as well. Assuming that a time series model is deemed appropriate, the next choice to be made is of the *probability distribution* specified for the errors. Usually, standard normal draws are used, although any other empirically plausible distribution (such as a Student's t) could also be used.

The second stage involves estimation of the parameter of interest in the study. The parameter of interest might be, for example, the value of a coefficient in a regression, or the value of an option at its expiry date. It could instead be the value of a portfolio under a particular set of scenarios governing the way that the prices of the component assets move over time.

The quantity N is known as the number of replications, and this should be as large as is feasible. The central idea behind Monte Carlo is that of random sampling from a given distribution. Therefore, if the number of replications is set too small, the results will be sensitive to 'odd' combinations of random number draws. It is also worth noting that asymptotic arguments apply in Monte Carlo studies as well as ill other areas of econometrics. That is, the results of a simulation study will be equal to their analytical counterparts (assuming that the latter exist) asymptotically.

VARIANCE REDUCTION TECHNIQUES

Suppose that the value of the parameter of interest for replication i is denoted x_i. If the average value of this parameter is calculated for a set of, say, $N = 1,000$ replications, and another researcher conducts an otherwise identical study with different sets of random draws, a different average value of x is almost certain to result. This situation is akin to the problem of selecting only a sample of observations from a given population in standard regression analysis. The sampling variation in a Monte Carlo study is measured by the standard error estimate, denoted S_x

$$S_x = \sqrt{\frac{\text{var}(x)}{N}} \quad \text{(15.1)}$$

where var(x) is the variance of the estimates of the quantity of interest over the N replications. It can be seen from this equation that to reduce the Monte Carlo standard error by a factor of 10, the number of replications must be increased by a factor of 100. Consequently, in order to achieve acceptable accuracy, the number of replications may have to be set at an infeasibly high level. An alternative way to reduce Monte Carlo sampling error is to use a variance reduction technique. There are many variance reduction techniques available. Two of the intuitively simplest and most widely used methods are the method of *antithetic variates* and the method of *control variates*. Both of these techniques will now be described.

Antithetic Variates

One reason that a lot of replications are typically required of a Monte Carlo study is that it may take many, many repeated sets of sampling before the entire probability space is adequately covered. By their very nature, the values of the random draws are random, and so after a given number of replications, it may be the case that not the whole range of possible outcomes has actually occurred.[1] What is really required is for successive replications to cover different parts of the probability space—that is, for the random draws from different replications to generate outcomes that span the entire spectrum of possibilities. This may take a long time to achieve naturally.

The antithetic variate technique involves taking the complement of a set of random numbers and running a

---

[1] Obviously, for a continuous random variable, there will be an infinite number of possible values. In this context, the problem is simply that if the probability space is split into arbitrarily small intervals, some of those intervals will not have been adequately covered by the random draws that were actually selected.

parallel simulation on those. For example, if the driving stochastic force is a set of $TN(0, 1)$ draws, denoted u_t, for each replication, an additional replication with errors given by $-u_t$ is also used. It can be shown that the Monte Carlo standard error is reduced when antithetic variates are used. For a simple illustration of this, suppose that the average value of the parameter of interest across two sets of Monte Carlo replications is given by

$$\bar{x} = (x_1 + x_2)/2 \qquad \textbf{(15.2)}$$

where x_1 and x_2 are the average parameter values for replications sets 1 and 2, respectively. The variance of $\bar{x}$ will be given by

$$\text{var}(\bar{x}) = \frac{1}{4}(\text{var}(x_1) + \text{var}(x_2) + 2\text{cov}(x_1, x_2)) \qquad \textbf{(15.3)}$$

If no antithetic variates are used, the two sets of Monte Carlo replications will be independent, so that their covariance will be zero, i.e.

$$\text{var}(\bar{x}) = \frac{1}{4}(\text{var}(x_1) + \text{var}(x_2)) \qquad \textbf{(15.4)}$$

However, the use of antithetic variates would lead the covariance in Equation (15.3) to be negative, and therefore the Monte Carlo sampling error to be reduced.

It may at first appear that the reduction in Monte Carlo sampling variation from using antithetic variates will be huge since, by definition, $\text{corr}(u_t, -u_t) = \text{cov}(u_t, -u_t) = -1$. However, it is important to remember that the relevant covariance is between the simulated quantity of interest for the standard replications and those using the antithetic variates. But the perfect negative covariance is between the random draws (i.e. the error terms) and their antithetic variates. For example, in the context of option pricing (discussed below), the production of a price for the underlying security (and therefore for the option) constitutes a non-linear transformation of u_t. Therefore the covariances between the terminal prices of the underlying assets based on the draws and based on the antithetic variates will be negative, but not -1.

Several other variance reduction techniques that operate using similar principles are available, including stratified sampling, moment-matching and low-discrepancy sequencing. The latter are also known as *quasi-random sequences* of draws. These involve the selection of a specific sequence of representative samples from a given probability distribution. Successive samples are selected so that the unselected gaps left in the probability distribution are filled by subsequent replications. The result is a set of random draws that are appropriately distributed across all of the outcomes of interest. The use of low-discrepancy sequences leads the Monte Carlo standard errors to be reduced in direct proportion to the number of replications rather than in proportion to the square root of the number of replications. Thus, for example, to reduce the Monte Carlo standard error by a factor of 10, the number of replications would have to be increased by a factor of 100 for standard Monte Carlo random sampling, but only 10 for low-discrepancy sequencing. Further details of low-discrepancy techniques are beyond the scope of this text, but can be seen in Boyle (1977) or Press *et al.* (1992). The former offers a detailed and relevant example in the context of options pricing.

Control Variates

The application of control variates involves employing a variable similar to that used in the simulation, but whose properties are known prior to the simulation. Denote the variable whose properties are known by y, and that whose properties are under simulation by x. The simulation is conducted on x and also on y, with the same sets of random number draws being employed in both cases. Denoting the simulation estimates of x and y by $\hat{x}$ and $\hat{y}$, respectively, a new estimate of x can be derived from

$$x^* = y + (\hat{x} - \hat{y}) \qquad \textbf{(15.5)}$$

Again, it can be shown that the Monte Carlo sampling error of this quantity, x^*, will be lower than that of x provided that a certain condition holds. The control variates help to reduce the Monte Carlo variation owing to particular sets of random draws by using the same draws on a related problem whose solution is known. It is expected that the effects of sampling error for the problem under study and the known problem will be similar, and hence can be reduced by calibrating the Monte Carlo results using the analytic ones.

It is worth noting that control variates succeed in reducing the Monte Carlo sampling error only if the control and simulation problems are very closely related. As the correlation between the values of the control statistic and the statistic of interest is reduced, the variance reduction is weakened. Consider again Equation (15.5), and take the variance of both sides

$$\text{var}(x^*) = \text{var}(y + (\hat{x} - \hat{y})) \qquad \textbf{(15.6)}$$

var(y) = 0 since y is a quantity which is known analytically and is therefore not subject to sampling variation, so Equation (15.6) can be written

$$\text{var}(x^*) = \text{var}(y + (\hat{x} - \hat{y})) \qquad \textbf{(15.7)}$$

The condition that must hold for the Monte Carlo sampling variance to be lower with control variates than without is that var(x^*) is less than var($\hat{x}$). Taken from Equation (15.7), this condition can also be expressed as

$$\text{var}(\hat{y}) - 2\text{cov}(\hat{x}, \hat{y}) < 0$$

or

$$\text{cov}(\hat{x}, \hat{y}) > \frac{1}{2}\text{var}(\hat{y})$$

Divide both sides of this inequality by the products of the standard deviations, i.e. by (var($\hat{x}$), var($\hat{y}$))$^{1/2}$, to obtain the correlation on the LHS

$$\text{corr}(\hat{x}, \hat{y}) > \frac{1}{2}\sqrt{\frac{\text{var}(\hat{y})}{\text{var}(\hat{x})}}$$

To offer an illustration of the use of control variates, a researcher may be interested in pricing an arithmetic Asian option using simulation. Recall that an arithmetic Asian option is one whose payoff depends on the arithmetic average value of the underlying asset over the lifetime of the averaging; at the time of writing, an analytical (closed-form) model is not yet available for pricing such options. In this context, a control variate price could be obtained by finding the price via simulation of a similar derivative whose value is known analytically—e.g. a vanilla European option. Thus, the Asian and vanilla options would be priced using simulation, as shown below, with the simulated price given by P_A and P^*_{BS}, respectively. The price of the vanilla option, P_{BS} is also calculated using an analytical formula, such as Black–Scholes. The new estimate of the Asian option price, P^*_A, would then be given by

$$P^*_A = (P_A - P_{BS}) + P^*_{BS} \qquad \textbf{(15.8)}$$

Random Number Re-Usage across Experiments

Although of course it would not be sensible to re-use sets of random number draws within a Monte Carlo experiment, using the same sets of draws across experiments can greatly reduce the variability of the difference in the estimates across those experiments. For example, it may be of interest to examine the power of the Dickey–Fuller test for samples of size 100 observations and for different values of ϕ. Thus, for each experiment involving a different value of ϕ, the same set of standard normal random numbers could be used to reduce the sampling variation across experiments. However, the accuracy of the actual estimates in each case will not be increased, of course.

Another possibility involves taking long series of draws and then slicing them up into several smaller sets to be used in different experiments. For example, Monte Carlo simulation may be used to price several options of different times to maturity, but which are identical in all other respects. Thus, if six-month, three-month and one-month horizons were of interest, sufficient random draws to cover six months would be made. Then the six-months' worth of draws could be used to construct two replications of a three-month horizon, and six replications for the one-month horizon. Again, the variability of the simulated option prices across maturities would be reduced, although the accuracies of the prices themselves would not be increased for a given number of replications.

Random number re-usage is unlikely to save computational time, for making the random draws usually takes a very small proportion of the overall time taken to conduct the whole experiment.

BOOTSTRAPPING

Bootstrapping is related to simulation, but with one crucial difference. With simulation, the data are constructed completely artificially. Bootstrapping, on the other hand, is used to obtain a description of the properties of empirical estimators by using the sample data points themselves, and it involves sampling repeatedly with replacement from the actual data. Many econometricians were initially highly sceptical of the usefulness of the technique, which appears at first sight to be some kind of magic trick—creating useful additional information from a given sample. Indeed, Davison and Hinkley (1997, p. 3), state that the term 'bootstrap' in this context comes from an analogy with the fictional character Baron Munchhausen, who got out from the bottom of a lake by pulling himself up by his bootstraps.

Suppose a sample of data, $\mathbf{y} = y_1, y_2, \ldots, y_T$ are available and it is desired to estimate some parameter θ. An approximation to the statistical properties of $\hat{\theta}_T$ can be obtained by studying a sample of bootstrap estimators. This is done by taking N samples of size T with replacement from $\mathbf{y}$ and re-calculating $\hat{\theta}$ with each new sample. A series of $\hat{\theta}$ estimates is then obtained, and their distribution can be considered.

The advantage of bootstrapping over the use of analytical results is that it allows the researcher to make inferences without making strong distributional assumptions, since the distribution employed will be that of the actual data. Instead of imposing a shape on the sampling distribution of the $\hat{\theta}$ value, bootstrapping involves empirically estimating the sampling distribution by looking at the variation of the statistic within-sample.

A set of new samples is drawn with replacement from the sample and the test statistic of interest calculated from each of these. Effectively, this involves sampling from the sample, i.e. treating the sample as a population from which samples can be drawn. Call the test statistics calculated from the new samples $\hat{\theta}^*$. The samples are likely to be quite different from each other and from the original $\hat{\theta}$ value, since some observations may be sample several times and others not all. Thus a distribution of values of $\hat{\theta}^*$ is obtained, from which standard errors or some other statistics of interest can be calculated.

Along with advances in computational speed and power, the number of bootstrap applications in finance and in econometrics have increased rapidly in previous years. For example, in econometrics, the bootstrap has been used in the context of unit root testing. Scheinkman and LeBaron (1989) also suggest that the bootstrap can be used as a 'shuffle diagnostic', where as usual the original data are sampled with replacement to form new data series. Successive applications of this procedure should generate a collection of data sets with the same distributional properties, on average, as the original data. But any kind of dependence in the original series (e.g. linear or non-linear autocorrelation) will, by definition, have been removed. Applications of econometric tests to the shuffled series can then be used as a benchmark with which to compare the results on the actual data or to construct standard error estimates or confidence intervals.

In finance, an application of bootstrapping in the context of risk management is discussed below. Another important recent proposed use of the bootstrap is as a method for detecting data snooping (data mining) in the context of tests of the profitability of technical trading rules. Data snooping occurs when the same set of data is used

to construct trading rules and also to test them. In such cases, if a sufficient number of trading rules are examined, some of them are bound, purely by chance alone, to generate statistically significant positive returns. Intra-generational data snooping is said to occur when, over a long period of time, technical trading rules that 'worked' in the past continue to be examined, while the ones that did not fade away. Researchers are then made aware of only the rules that worked, and not the other, perhaps thousands, of rules that failed.

Data snooping biases are apparent in other aspects of estimation and testing in finance. Lo and MacKinlay (1990) find that tests of financial asset pricing models (CAPM) may yield misleading inferences when properties of the data are used to construct the test statistics. These properties relate to the construction of portfolios based on some empirically motivated characteristic of the stock, such as market capitalisation, rather than a theoretically motivated characteristic, such as dividend yield.

Sullivan, Timmermann and White (1990) and White (2000) propose the use of a bootstrap to test for data snooping. The technique works by placing the rule under study in the context of a 'universe' of broadly similar trading rules. This gives some empirical content to the notion that a variety of rules may have been examined before the final rule is selected. The bootstrap is applied to each trading rule, by sampling with replacement from the time series of observed returns for that rule. The null hypothesis is that there does not exist a superior technical trading rule. Sullivan, Timmermann and White show how a p-value of the 'reality check' bootstrap-based test can be constructed, which evaluates the significance of the returns (or excess returns) to the rule after allowing for the fact that the whole universe of rules may have been examined.

An Example of Bootstrapping in a Regression Context

Consider a standard regression model

$$y = X\beta + u \qquad (15.9)$$

The regression model can be bootstrapped in two ways.

Re-Sample the Data

This procedure involves taking the data, and sampling the entire rows corresponding to observation i together. The steps would then be as shown in Box 15-2.

BOX 15-2 Re-Sampling the Data

1. Generate a sample of size T from the original data by sampling with replacement from the whole rows taken together (that is, if observation 32 is selected, take y_{32} and all values of the explanatory variables for observation 32).

2. Calculate $\hat{\beta}^*$, the coefficient matrix for this bootstrap sample.

3. Go back to stage 1 and generate another sample of size T. Repeat these stages a total of N times. A set of N coefficient vectors, $\hat{\beta}^*$, will thus be obtained and in general they will all be different, so that a distribution of estimates for each coefficient will result.

A methodological problem with this approach is that it entails sampling from the regressors, and yet under the CLRM, these are supposed to be fixed in repeated samples, which would imply that they do not have a sampling distribution. Thus, resampling from the data corresponding to the explanatory variables is not in the spirit of the CLRM.

As an alternative, the only random influence in the regression is the errors, u, so why not just bootstrap from those?

Re-Sampling from the Residuals

This procedure is 'theoretically pure' although harder to understand and to implement. The steps are shown in Box 15-3.

BOX 15-3 Re-Sampling from the Residuals

1. Estimate the model on the actual data, obtain the fitted values $\hat{y}$, and calculate the residuals, $\hat{u}$

2. Take a sample of size T with replacement from these residuals (and call these $\hat{u}^*$), and generate a bootstrapped-dependent variable by adding the fitted values to the bootstrapped residuals

$$y^* = \hat{y} + \hat{u}^* \qquad (15.10)$$

3. Then regress this new dependent variable on the original X data to get a bootstrapped coefficient vector, $\hat{\beta}^*$

4. Go back to stage 2, and repeat a total of N times.

Situations Where the Bootstrap Will Be Ineffective

There are at least two situations where the bootstrap, as described above, will not work well.

Outliers in the Data

If there are *outliers* in the data, the conclusions of the bootstrap may be affected. In particular, the results for a given replication may depend critically on whether the outliers appear (and how often) in the bootstrapped sample.

Non-Independent Data

Use of the bootstrap implicitly assumes that the data are *independent of one another*. This would obviously not hold if, for example, there were autocorrelation in the data. A potential solution to this problem is to use a 'moving block bootstrap'. Such a method allows for the dependence in the series by sampling whole blocks of observations at a time. These, and many other issues relating to the theory and practical usage of the bootstrap are given in Davison and Hinkley (1997); see also Efron (1979, 1982).

It is also worth noting that variance reduction techniques are also available under the bootstrap, and these work in a very similar way to those described above in the context of pure simulation.

RANDOM NUMBER GENERATION

Most econometrics computer packages include a random number generator. The simplest class of numbers to generate are from a uniform (0, 1) distribution. A uniform (0, 1) distribution is one where only values between zero and one are drawn, and each value within the interval has an equal chance of being selected. Uniform draws can be either discrete or continuous. An example of a discrete uniform number generator would be a die or a roulette wheel. Computers generate continuous uniform random number draws.

Numbers that are a continuous uniform (0, 1) can be generated according to the following recursion

$$y_{i+1} = (ay_i + c) \text{ modulo } m, i = 0, 1, \ldots, T \qquad (15.11)$$

then

$$R_{i+1} = y_{i+1}/m \text{ for } i = 0, 1, \ldots, T \qquad (15.12)$$

for T random draws, where y_0 is the seed (the initial value of y), a is a multiplier and c is an increment. All three of these are simply constants. The 'modulo operator' simply functions as a clock, returning to one after reaching m.

Any simulation study involving a recursion, such as that described by Equation (15.11) to generate the random draws, will require the user to specify an initial value, y_0, to get the process started. The choice of this value will, undesirably, affect the properties of the generated series. This effect will be strongest for $y_1, y_2, \ldots$, but will gradually die away. For example, if a set of random draws is used to construct a time series that follows a GARCH process, early observations on this series will behave less like the GARCH process required than subsequent data points. Consequently, a good simulation design will allow for this phenomenon by generating more data than are required and then dropping the first few observations. For example, if 1,000 observations are required, 1,200 observations might be generated, with observations 1 to 200 subsequently deleted and 201 to 1,200 used to conduct the analysis.

These computer-generated random number draws are known as *pseudo-random numbers*, since they are in fact not random at all, but entirely deterministic, since they have been derived from an exact formula! By carefully choosing the values of the user-adjustable parameters, it is possible to get the pseudo-random number generator to meet all the statistical properties of true random numbers. Eventually, the random number sequences will start to repeat, but this should take a long time to happen. See Press *et al.* (1992) for more details and Fortran code, or Greene (2002) for an example.

The U(0, 1) draws can be transformed into draws from any desired distribution—for example a normal or a Student's t. Usually, econometric software packages with simulations facilities would do this automatically.

DISADVANTAGES OF THE SIMULATION APPROACH TO ECONOMETRIC OR FINANCIAL PROBLEM SOLVING

• *It might be computationally expensive*

That is, the number of replications required to generate precise solutions may be very large, depending upon the nature of the task at hand. If each replication is relatively complex in terms of estimation issues, the problem might be computationally infeasible, such that it could take days, weeks or even years to run the experiment. Although CPU time is becoming ever cheaper as faster computers are brought to market, the technicality of the problems studied seems to accelerate just as quickly!

• *The results might not be precise*

Even if the number of replications is made very large, the simulation experiments will not give a precise answer to the problem if some unrealistic assumptions have been made of the data generating process. For example, in the context of option pricing, the option valuations obtained from a simulation will not be accurate if the data generating process assumed normally distributed errors while the actual underlying returns series is fat-tailed.

• *The results are often hard to replicate*

Unless the experiment has been set up so that the sequence of random draws is known and can be reconstructed, which is rarely done in practice, the results of a Monte Carlo study will be somewhat specific to the given investigation. In that case, a repeat of the experiment would involve different sets of random draws and therefore would be likely to yield different results, particularly if the number of replications is small.

• *Simulation results are experiment-specific*

The need to specify the data generating process using a single set of equations or a single equation implies that the results could apply to only that exact type of data. Any conclusions reached may or may not hold for other data generating processes. To give one illustration, examining the power of a statistical test would, by definition, involve determining how frequently a wrong null hypothesis is rejected. In the context of DF tests, for example, the power of the test as determined by a Monte Carlo study would be given by the percentage of times that the null of a unit root is rejected. Suppose that the following data generating process is used for such a simulation experiment

$$y_t = 0.99y_{t-1} + u_t, \qquad u_t \sim N(0,1) \qquad \textbf{(15.13)}$$

Clearly, the null of a unit root would be wrong in this case, as is necessary to examine the power of the test. However, for modest sample sizes, the null is likely to be rejected quite infrequently. It would not be appropriate to conclude from such an experiment that the DF test is generally not powerful, since in this case the null ($\phi = 1$) is not very wrong! This is a general problem with many Monte Carlo studies. The solution is to run simulations using as many different and relevant data generating processes as feasible. Finally, it should be obvious that the Monte Carlo data generating process should match the real-world problem of interest as far as possible.

To conclude, simulation is an extremely useful tool that can be applied to an enormous variety of problems. The technique has grown in popularity over the past decade, and continues to do so. However, like all tools, it is dangerous in the wrong hands. It is very easy to jump into a simulation experiment without thinking about whether such an approach is valid or not.

AN EXAMPLE OF MONTE CARLO SIMULATION IN ECONOMETRICS: DERIVING A SET OF CRITICAL VALUES FOR A DICKEY–FULLER TEST

Recall, that the equation for a Dickey–Fuller (DF) test applied to some series y_t is the regression

$$y_t = \phi y_{t-1} + u_t \qquad \textbf{(15.14)}$$

so that the test is one of $H_0: \phi = 1$ against $H_1: \phi < 1$. The relevant test statistic is given by

$$\tau = \frac{\hat{\phi} - 1}{SE(\hat{\phi})} \qquad \textbf{(15.15)}$$

Under the null hypothesis of a unit root, the test statistic does not follow a standard distribution, and therefore a simulation would be required to obtain the relevant critical values. Obviously, these critical values are well documented, but it is of interest to see how one could generate them. A very similar approach could then potentially be adopted for situations where there has been less research and where the results are relatively less well known.

AN EXAMPLE OF HOW TO SIMULATE THE PRICE OF A FINANCIAL OPTION

A simple example of how to use a Monte Carlo study for obtaining a price for a financial option is shown below. Although the option used for illustration here is just a plain vanilla European call option which could be valued analytically using the standard Black–Scholes (1973) formula, again, the method is sufficiently general that only relatively minor modifications would be required to value more complex options. Boyle (1977) gives an excellent and highly readable introduction to the pricing of financial options using Monte Carlo. The steps involved are shown in Box 15-4.

BOX 15-4 Simulating the Price of an Asian Option

1. *Specify a data generating process for the underlying asset.* A random walk with drift model is usually assumed. Specify also the assumed size of the drift component and the assumed size of the volatility parameter. Specify also a strike price K, and a time to maturity, T.

2. Draw a series of length T, the required number of observations for the life of the option, from a normal distribution. This will be the *error series*, so that $\varepsilon_t \sim N(0, 1)$.

3. Form a series of observations of length T on the *underlying asset.*

4. *Observe the price of the underlying asset at maturity observation T.* For a call option, if the value of the underlying asset on maturity date, $P_T \leq K$, the option expires worthless for this replication. If the value of the underlying asset on maturity date, $P_T > K$, the option expires in the money, and has value on that date equal to $P_T - K$, which should be discounted back to the present day using the risk-free rate. Use of the risk-free rate relies upon risk-neutrality arguments (see Duffie, 1996).

5. Repeat steps 1 to 4 a total of N times, and take the average value of the option over the N replications. This average will be the *price of the option.*

Simulating the Price of a Financial Option Using a Fat-Tailed Underlying Process

A fairly limiting and unrealistic assumption in the above methodology for pricing options is that the underlying asset returns are normally distributed, whereas in practice, it is well known that asset returns are fat-tailed. There are several ways to remove this assumption. First, one could employ draws from a fat-tailed distribution, such as a Student's *t*, in step 2 above. Another method, which would generate a distribution of returns with fat tails, would be to assume that the errors and therefore the returns follow a GARCH process. To generate draws from a GARCH process, do the steps shown in Box 15-5.

Simulating the Price of an Asian Option

An Asian option is one whose payoff depends upon the average value of the underlying asset over the averaging horizon specified in the contract. Most Asian options contracts specify that arithmetic rather than geometric averaging should be employed. Unfortunately, the arithmetic average of a unit root process with a drift is not well defined. Additionally, even if the asset prices are assumed to be log-normally distributed, the arithmetic average of them will not be. Consequently, a closed-form analytical expression for the value of an Asian option has yet to be developed. Thus, the pricing of Asian options represents a natural application for simulations methods. Determining the value of an Asian option is achieved in almost exactly the same way as for a vanilla call or put. The simulation is conducted identically, and the only difference occurs in the very last step where the value of the payoff at the date of expiry is determined.

BOX 15-5 Generating Draws from a GARCH Process

1. Draw a series of length T, the required number of observations for the life of the option, from a normal distribution. This will be the error series, so that $\varepsilon_t \sim N(0, 1)$.

2. Recall that one way of expressing a GARCH model is

$$r_t = \mu + u_t \qquad u_t = \varepsilon_t \sigma_t \qquad \varepsilon_t \sim N(0, 1) \qquad \textbf{(15.16)}$$

$$\sigma_t^2 = \alpha_0 + \alpha_1 u_{t-1}^2 + \beta \sigma_{t-1}^2 \qquad \textbf{(15.17)}$$

A series of ε_t, have been constructed and it is necessary to specify initialising values y_1 and σ_1^2 and plausible parameter values for α_0, α_1, β. Assume that y_1 and σ_1^2 are set to μ and one, respectively, and the parameters are given by $\alpha_0 = 0.01$, $\alpha_1 = 0.15$, $\beta = 0.80$. The equations above can then be used to generate the model for r_t as described above.

SAMPLE EXAM QUESTIONS—QUANTITATIVE ANALYSIS

1. For a sample of the past 30 monthly stock returns for McCreary, Inc., the mean return is 4% and the sample standard deviation is 20%. Since the population variance is unknown, the standard error of the sample is estimated to be:

$$S_x = \frac{20\%}{\sqrt{30}} = 3.65\%$$

The related t-table values are ($t_{i,j}$ denotes the $(100-j)^{th}$ percentile of t-distribution value with i degrees of freedom):

$t_{29,2.5}$	2.045
$t_{29,5.0}$	1.699
$t_{30,2.5}$	2.042
$t_{29,5.0}$	1.697

What is the 95% confidence interval for the mean monthly return?

A. [−3.453%, 11.453%]

B. [−2.201%, 10.201%]

C. [−2.194%, 10.194%]

D. [−3.464%, 11.464%]

2. Suppose that a quiz consists of 20 true-false questions. A student has not studied for the exam and just randomly guesses the answers. How would you find the probability that the student will get 8 or fewer answers correct?

A. Find the probability that $X = 8$ in a binomial distribution with $n = 20$ and $p = 0.5$.

B. Find the area between 0 and 8 in a uniform distribution that goes from 0 to 20.

C. Find the probability that $X = 8$ for a normal distribution with mean of 10 and standard deviation of 5.

D. Find the cumulative probability for 8 in a binomial distribution with $n = 20$ and $p = 0.5$.

3. Assume that a random variable follows a normal distribution with a mean of 80 and a standard deviation of 24. What percentage of this distribution is not between 32 and 116?

A. 4.56%

B. 8.96%

C. 13.36%

D. 18.15%

4. An insurance company estimates that 40% of policyholders who have only an auto policy will renew next year, and 60% of policyholders who have only a homeowner policy will renew next year. The company estimates that 80% of policyholders who have both an auto and a homeowner policy will renew at least one of those policies next year. Company records show that 65% of policyholders have an auto policy, 50% of policyholders have a homeowner policy, and 15% of policyholders have both an auto and a homeowner policy. Using the company's estimates, what is the percentage of policyholders that will renew at least one policy next year?

    A. 20%

    B. 29%

    C. 41%

    D. 53%

5. The following graphs show the cumulative distribution function (CDF) of four different random variables. The dotted vertical line indicates the mean of the distribution. Assuming each random variable can only be values between −10 and 10, which distribution has the highest variance?

A.

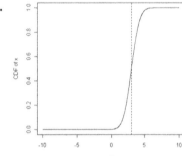

B.

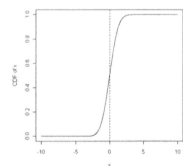

C.

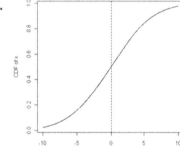

D.

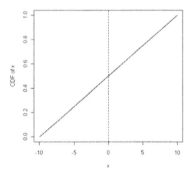

6. You are running a Monte Carlo simulation to price a portfolio of options. When generating random numbers for use in the simulation:

   A. The stratified sampling method eliminates extreme observations.

   B. A truly random number generator would avoid clustered observations.

   C. A congruential pseudorandom number generator creates sequences converging to a constant value.

   D. The Latin hypercube sampling method ensures that all strata are sufficiently well-represented.

7. A risk manager is calculating the VaR of a fund with a data set of 25 weekly returns. The mean and standard deviation of weekly returns are 7% and 10%, respectively. Assuming that weekly returns are independent and identically distributed, what is the standard deviation of the mean of the weekly returns?

   A. 0.4%

   B. 0.7%

   C. 2.0%

   D. 10.0%

8. The recent performance of Prudent Fund, with USD 50 million in assets, has been weak and the institutional sales group is recommending that it be merged with Aggressive Fund, a USD 200 million fund. The returns on Prudent Fund are normally distributed with a mean of 3% and a standard deviation of 7% and the returns on Aggressive Fund are normally distributed with a mean of 7% and a standard deviation of 15%. Senior management has asked you to estimate the likelihood that returns on the combined portfolio will exceed 26%. Assuming the returns on the two funds are independent, your estimate for the probability that the returns on the combined fund will exceed 26% is closest to:

   A. 1.0%

   B. 2.5%

   C. 5.0%

   D. 10.0%

9. Which of the following four statements on models for estimating volatility is INCORRECT?

   A. In the exponentially weighted moving average (EWMA) model, some positive weight is assigned to the long-run average variance.

   B. In the EWMA model, the weights assigned to observations decrease exponentially as the observations become older.

   C. In the GARCH (1, 1) model, a positive weight is estimated for the long-run average variance.

   D. In the GARCH (1, 1) model, the weights estimated for observations decrease exponentially as the observations become older.

10. Based on 21 daily returns of an asset, a risk manager estimates the standard deviation of the asset's daily returns to be 2%. Assuming that returns are normally distributed and that there are 260 trading days in a year, what is the appropriate Chi-square test statistic if the risk manager wants to test the null hypothesis that the true annual volatility is 25% at a 5% significance level?

    A. 25.80

    B. 33.28

    C. 34.94

    D. 54.74

SAMPLE EXAM ANSWERS AND EXPLANATIONS— QUANTITATIVE ANALYSIS

1. **Answer: D**

   Explanation: Here the t-reliability factor is used since the population variance is unknown. Since there are 30 observations, the degrees of freedom are $30 - 1 = 29$. The t-test is a two-tailed test. So the correct critical t-value is $t_{29,2.5} = 2.045$, thus the 95% confidence interval for the mean return is:

   $$[4\% - 2.045\left(\frac{20\%}{\sqrt{30}}\right), 4\% + 2.045\left(\frac{20\%}{\sqrt{30}}\right)] = [-3.464\%, 11.464\%]$$

2. **Answer: D**

   Explanation: A binomial distribution is a probability distribution, and it refers to the various probabilities associated with the number of correct answers out of the total sample.

   The correct approach is to find the cumulative probability for 8 in a binomial distribution with $N = 20$ and $p = 0.5$. The cumulative probability is to be calculated on the basis of a binomial distribution with number of questions (n) equaling 20 and probability of a single event occurring being 50% ($p = 0.5$).

3. **Answer: B**

   Explanation:

   Prob(mean $- 2^*\sigma < X <$ mean $+ 1.5^*\sigma$) = $(0.5 - 0.0228) + (0.5 - 0.0668) = 0.9104$

   Prob(mean $- 2^*\sigma > X$ or $X >$ mean $+ 1.5^*\sigma$) = $1 - $ Prob(mean $- 2^*\sigma < X <$ mean $+ 1.5^*\sigma$) = 0.0896

4. **Answer: D**

   Explanation: Let:

   A = event that a policyholder has an auto policy

   H = event that a policyholder has a homeowners policy

   Then, based on the information given:

   $$P(A \cap H) = 0.15$$

   $$P(A \cap H^c) = P(A) - P(A \cap H) = 0.65 - 0.15 = 0.5$$

   $$P(A^c \cap H) = P(H) - P(A \cap H) = 0.5 - 0.15 = 0.35$$

   Therefore, the proportion of policyholders that will renew at least one policy is shown below:

   $$0.4 \cdot P(A \cap H^c) + 0.6 \cdot P(A^c \cap H) + 0.8 \cdot P(A \cap H)$$

   $$= 0.4 \times 0.5 + 0.6 \times 0.35 + 0.8 \times 0.15 = 0.53$$

5. **Answer: D**

    Explanation: Variance is a measure of the mean deviation. In the above four graphs, it can be seen that (D) has the highest proportion of the distribution that deviates from the mean, and it also has a relatively higher density in both tails. Hence, "D" has the highest variance.

6. **Answer: D**

    Explanation: The stratified sampling method in random number generation divides the population into groups, called strata, with similar characteristics and then attempts to distribute the group of random numbers across all the strata. By doing so, the method tries to ensure that extreme observations will be incorporated into the sample. The Latin hypercube sampling method is an enhanced version of the basic stratified sampling method which reduces the number of times each particular random number is generated and therefore, ensures that all strata included in the population are sufficiently well-represented.

7. **Answer: C**

    Explanation: In order to calculate the standard deviation of the mean of weekly returns, we must divide the standard deviation of the weekly returns by the square root of the sample size. Therefore the correct answer is 10%/sqrt (25) = 2%.

8. **Answer: C**

    Explanation: Since these are independent normally distributed random variables, the combined expected mean return is:

    $$\mu = 0.2 * 3\% + 0.8 * 7\% = 6.2\%$$

    Combined volatility is:

    $$\sigma = \sqrt{0.2^2 0.07^2 + 0.8^2 0.15^2} = 0.121 = 12.1\%$$

    The appropriate Z-statistic is $Z = \dfrac{26\% - 6.2\%}{12.1\%} = 1.64$

    and therefore $P(Z>1.64) = 1 - .095 = .05 = 5\%$

9. **Answer: A**

    Explanation: The EWMA model does not involve the long-run average variance in updating volatility, in other words, the weight assigned to the long-run average variance is zero. Only the current estimate of the variance is used. The other statements are all correct.

10. **Answer: B**

    Explanation: The formula for the Chi-squared test statistic is:

    $$(n - 1)* \text{(sample variance/hypothesis variance)}$$

    annualized. Since we are given a daily standard deviation, we must first annualize it by multiplying it by the square root of the number of trading days. Therefore:

    $$\text{Sample volatility} = \text{sqrt (260) } 2\% = 32.25\%,$$
    $$\text{and the Chi-squared test statistic} = (21 - 1)* 0.3225^2/0.25^2 = 33.28$$

APPENDIX TABLE 1

Reference Table: Let Z be a standard normal random variable.

z	P(Z < z)	z	P(Z < z)	z	P(Z < z)	z	P(Z < z)	z	P(Z < z)	z	P(Z < z)
-3.00	0.0013	-2.50	0.0062	-2.00	0.0228	-1.50	0.0668	-1.00	0.1587	-0.50	0.3085
-2.99	0.0014	-2.49	0.0064	-1.99	0.0233	-1.49	0.0681	-0.99	0.1611	-0.49	0.3121
-2.98	0.0014	-2.48	0.0066	-1.98	0.0239	-1.48	0.0694	-0.98	0.1635	-0.48	0.3156
-2.97	0.0015	-2.47	0.0068	-1.97	0.0244	-1.47	0.0708	-0.97	0.1660	-0.47	0.3192
-2.96	0.0015	-2.46	0.0069	-1.96	0.0250	-1.46	0.0721	-0.96	0.1685	-0.46	0.3228
-2.95	0.0016	-2.45	0.0071	-1.95	0.0256	-1.45	0.0735	-0.95	0.1711	-0.45	0.3264
-2.94	0.0016	-2.44	0.0073	-1.94	0.0262	-1.44	0.0749	-0.94	0.1736	-0.44	0.3300
-2.93	0.0017	-2.43	0.0075	-1.93	0.0268	-1.43	0.0764	-0.93	0.1762	-0.43	0.3336
-2.92	0.0018	-2.42	0.0078	-1.92	0.0274	-1.42	0.0778	-0.92	0.1788	-0.42	0.3372
-2.91	0.0018	-2.41	0.0080	-1.91	0.0281	-1.41	0.0793	-0.91	0.1814	-0.41	0.3409
-2.90	0.0019	-2.40	0.0082	-1.90	0.0287	-1.40	0.0808	-0.90	0.1841	-0.40	0.3446
-2.89	0.0019	-2.39	0.0084	-1.89	0.0294	-1.39	0.0823	-0.89	0.1867	-0.39	0.3483
-2.88	0.0020	-2.38	0.0087	-1.88	0.0301	-1.38	0.0838	-0.88	0.1894	-0.38	0.3520
-2.87	0.0021	-2.37	0.0089	-1.87	0.0307	-1.37	0.0853	-0.87	0.1922	-0.37	0.3557
-2.86	0.0021	-2.36	0.0091	-1.86	0.0314	-1.36	0.0869	-0.86	0.1949	-0.36	0.3594
-2.85	0.0022	-2.35	0.0094	-1.85	0.0322	-1.35	0.0885	-0.85	0.1977	-0.35	0.3632
-2.84	0.0023	-2.34	0.0096	-1.84	0.0329	-1.34	0.0901	-0.84	0.2005	-0.34	0.3669
-2.83	0.0023	-2.33	0.0099	-1.83	0.0336	-1.33	0.0918	-0.83	0.2033	-0.33	0.3707
-2.82	0.0024	-2.32	0.0102	-1.82	0.0344	-1.32	0.0934	-0.82	0.2061	-0.32	0.3745
-2.81	0.0025	-2.31	0.0104	-1.81	0.0351	-1.31	0.0951	-0.81	0.2090	-0.31	0.3783
-2.80	0.0026	-2.30	0.0107	-1.80	0.0359	-1.30	0.0968	-0.80	0.2119	-0.30	0.3821
-2.79	0.0026	-2.29	0.0110	-1.79	0.0367	-1.29	0.0985	-0.79	0.2148	-0.29	0.3859
-2.78	0.0027	-2.28	0.0113	-1.78	0.0375	-1.28	0.1003	-0.78	0.2177	-0.28	0.3897
-2.77	0.0028	-2.27	0.0116	-1.77	0.0384	-1.27	0.1020	-0.77	0.2206	-0.27	0.3936
-2.76	0.0029	-2.26	0.0119	-1.76	0.0392	-1.26	0.1038	-0.76	0.2236	-0.26	0.3974
-2.75	0.0030	-2.25	0.0122	-1.75	0.0401	-1.25	0.1056	-0.75	0.2266	-0.25	0.4013
-2.74	0.0031	-2.24	0.0125	-1.74	0.0409	-1.24	0.1075	-0.74	0.2296	-0.24	0.4052
-2.73	0.0032	-2.23	0.0129	-1.73	0.0418	-1.23	0.1093	-0.73	0.2327	-0.23	0.4090
-2.72	0.0033	-2.22	0.0132	-1.72	0.0427	-1.22	0.1112	-0.72	0.2358	-0.22	0.4129
-2.71	0.0034	-2.21	0.0136	-1.71	0.0436	-1.21	0.1131	-0.71	0.2389	-0.21	0.4168
-2.70	0.0035	-2.20	0.0139	-1.70	0.0446	-1.20	0.1151	-0.70	0.2420	-0.20	0.4207
-2.69	0.0036	-2.19	0.0143	-1.69	0.0455	-1.19	0.1170	-0.69	0.2451	-0.19	0.4247
-2.68	0.0037	-2.18	0.0146	-1.68	0.0465	-1.18	0.1190	-0.68	0.2483	-0.18	0.4286
-2.67	0.0038	-2.17	0.0150	-1.67	0.0475	-1.17	0.1210	-0.67	0.2514	-0.17	0.4325
-2.66	0.0039	-2.16	0.0154	-1.66	0.0485	-1.16	0.1230	-0.66	0.2546	-0.16	0.4364
-2.65	0.0040	-2.15	0.0158	-1.65	0.0495	-1.15	0.1251	-0.65	0.2578	-0.15	0.4404
-2.64	0.0041	-2.14	0.0162	-1.64	0.0505	-1.14	0.1271	-0.64	0.2611	-0.14	0.4443
-2.63	0.0043	-2.13	0.0166	-1.63	0.0516	-1.13	0.1292	-0.63	0.2643	-0.13	0.4483
-2.62	0.0044	-2.12	0.0170	-1.62	0.0526	-1.12	0.1314	-0.62	0.2676	-0.12	0.4522
-2.61	0.0045	-2.11	0.0174	-1.61	0.0537	-1.11	0.1335	-0.61	0.2709	-0.11	0.4562
-2.60	0.0047	-2.10	0.0179	-1.60	0.0548	-1.10	0.1357	-0.60	0.2743	-0.10	0.4602
-2.59	0.0048	-2.09	0.0183	-1.59	0.0559	-1.09	0.1379	-0.59	0.2776	-0.09	0.4641
-2.58	0.0049	-2.08	0.0188	-1.58	0.0571	-1.08	0.1401	-0.58	0.2810	-0.08	0.4681
-2.57	0.0051	-2.07	0.0192	-1.57	0.0582	-1.07	0.1423	-0.57	0.2843	-0.07	0.4721
-2.56	0.0052	-2.06	0.0197	-1.56	0.0594	-1.06	0.1446	-0.56	0.2877	-0.06	0.4761
-2.55	0.0054	-2.05	0.0202	-1.55	0.0606	-1.05	0.1469	-0.55	0.2912	-0.05	0.4801
-2.54	0.0055	-2.04	0.0207	-1.54	0.0618	-1.04	0.1492	-0.54	0.2946	-0.04	0.4840
-2.53	0.0057	-2.03	0.0212	-1.53	0.0630	-1.03	0.1515	-0.53	0.2981	-0.03	0.4880
-2.52	0.0059	-2.02	0.0217	-1.52	0.0643	-1.02	0.1539	-0.52	0.3015	-0.02	0.4920
-2.51	0.0060	-2.01	0.0222	-1.51	0.0655	-1.01	0.1562	-0.51	0.3050	-0.01	0.4960

Index

mean squared error (MSE), 156–159
measures of fit, 90–92
    in multiple regression, 127–129
median, 12–14
Miller, Michael B., 3–67
mixture distribution, 42–44
mode, 12–14
model selection, 156
model specification, for multiple regression, 146–147
modulo operator, 220
moments, 21–23, 167
Monte Carlo simulation, 38–39, 214–217
    in econometrics, 221
    motivations, 214
moving average (MA) models, 178–182
    MA(1) process, 178–181
    MA(q) process, 181–182
Mozart effect, 122
multicollinearity, 131–133
multiple regression model
    confidence sets for, 145–146
    defined, 124
    measures of fit in, 127–129
    model specification for, 146–147
    OLS estimator in, 126–127
    omitted variable bias in, 146–147
    population multiple regression model, 124–125
    population regression line, 124
    testing single restrictions involving, 144–145
    tests of joint hypotheses, 140–144
multivariate copulas, 77
multivariate normal distributions, 73–74
mutually exclusive events, 7

95% confidence set, 145
normal distribution, 34–35
    generating random samples from, 73
    multivariate, 73–74
normal random variables, 38–39
normal white noise, 166
null hypothesis, 60–61, 103

OLS regression line, 88, 126
OLS residual, 126
omitted variable bias
    addressing by dividing data into groups, 122–124
    defined, 120–121
    first least squares assumption and, 121
    formula for, 121–122
    Mozart effect, 122
    in multiple regression, 146–147
    overview, 120
    in regression with single regressor, 121
On the Logic of Games of Chance, 14
"one at a time" method, 141
one-factor model, 74
one-sided hypotheses, 104–105

one-tailed values, 35, 61
ordinary least squares (OLS) estimator
    derivation of, 98
    distribution of, in multiple regression, 130
    explained, 87–90
    homoskedasticity and, 109–110
    in multiple regression, 126–127
    sampling distribution of, 95–97
    standard errors for, 138
    theoretical foundations of, 111–113
outliers, 94, 129, 219
out-of-sample 1-step-ahead prediction error variance, 157
overall regression F-statistic, 142–143

parameters, 85
parametric distributions, 30
parsimonious, 170
partial autocorrelation function, 164
partial effect, 124
perfect multicollinearity, 129–130, 131–132
Poisson, Simeon Denis, 33
Poisson distribution, 33–34
polynomial in the lag operator, 168
population, sample data and, 12–13
population mean, 102–103
population multiple regression model, 124–125
population regression, 164
population regression function, 85, 86, 124
population regression line, 85, 86, 124
portfolio variance, hedging and, 20–21
positive-semidefinite matrix, 72–73, 208
predicted value, 88, 126
    OLS estimator, residuals, and, 88
probabilities
    conditional, 8–9
    continuous random variables, 4–7
    discrete random variables, 4
    independent events, 7–8
    matrices, 8
    mutually exclusive events, 7
probability density functions (PDFs), 4–5, 13, 30
pseudo-random numbers, 220
p-value
    computing using F-statistic, 142
    null hypothesis testing and, 102, 103, 104
    for single coefficient, 138–139

quasirandom (low-discrepancy) sequences, 216

R^2, 147, 148
random number generation, 219–220
random number variable table, 233
random samples, generating, from normal distributions, 73
rational distributed lags, 170
rational polynomials, 170
realization, of time series, 162
regression, bootstrapping and, 218–219